Lipids, Health, and Behavior

Lipids, Health, and Behavior

Edited by Marc Hillbrand and Reuben T. Spitz

AMERICAN PSYCHOLOGICAL ASSOCIATION • WASHINGTON DC

Published by the
American Psychological Association
750 First Street, NE
Washington, DC 20002

Copies may be ordered from
APA Order Department
P.O. Box 92984
Washington, DC 20090-2984

In the United Kingdom and Europe, copies may be ordered from
American Psychological Association
3 Henrietta Street
Covent Garden
London WC2E 8LU
England

Typeset in Century by EPS Group Inc., Easton, MD

Printer: Braun-Brumfield, Inc., Ann Arbor, MI
Cover designer: Berg Design, Albany, NY
Technical/production editor: Valerie Montenegro

Library of Congress Cataloging-in-Publication Data
Lipids, health, and behavior / edited by Marc Hillbrand and Reuben T. Spitz.
   p.   cm.
   Includes bibliographical references and index.
   ISBN 1-55798-384-4 (pb : acid-free paper)
   1. Blood lipids—Psychological aspects.   2. Stress (Physiology)
3. Anxiety—Physiological aspects.   4. Neurochemistry.
I. Hillbrand, Marc.   II. Spitz, Reuben T.
QP99.3.L5L57   1996
612'.01577—dc20   96-41709
                                                                      CIP

British Library Cataloguing-in-Publication Data
A CIP record is available from the British Library.

Printed in the United States of America
First edition

To my parents, Kurt and Eva
M. H.

To my wife, Stephanie
R. T. S.

Contents

Contributors

David Benton, *Department of Psychology, University of Wales, Swansea, Wales*

Federico Calzi, *Laboratory of Enzymology, Istituto di Recerche Farmacologiche "Mario Negri," Milan, Italy*

Frank M. Corrigan, *Argyll and Bute Hospital, Lochgilphead, Argyll, Scotland*

Jacqueline M. Dekker, *Department of Epidemiology and Public Health, Wageningen Agricultural University, Wageningen, The Netherlands*

M. Babette Fontenot, *Comparative Medicine Clinical Research Center, Bowman Gray School of Medicine, Wake Forest University, Winston-Salem, NC*

Charles J. Glueck, *Cholesterol Center, Jewish Hospital, Cincinnati, OH*

Ronald F. Gray, *Argyll and Bute Hospital, Lochgilphead, Argyll, Scotland*

Chris Hayward, *Department of Psychiatry and Behavioral Sciences, Stanford University School of Medicine, Stanford, CA*

Marc Hillbrand, *Department of Psychology, Connecticut Valley Hospital, Whiting Forensic Division, Middletown, CT*

David F. Horrobin, *Scotia Pharmaceuticals, Guildford, England*

David R. Jacobs, Jr., *School of Public Health, University of Minnesota, Minneapolis*

Jay R. Kaplan, *Comparative Medicine Clinical Research Center, Bowman Gray School of Medicine, Wake Forest University, Winston-Salem, NC*

Mark Ketterer, *Department of Psychiatry, Henry Ford Health Sciences Center, Case Western Reserve University, Detroit, MI*

Robert Kunkel, *Cholesterol Center, Jewish Hospital of Cincinnati, OH*

John C. LaRosa, *Tulane University Medical Center, New Orleans, LA*

J. John Mann, *Department of Psychiatry, Columbia University College of Physicians and Surgeons, New York, NY*

Stephen B. Manuck, *Department of Psychology, University of Pittsburgh, PA*

Pamela E. Mason, *Neurosciences Research Center, Allegheny University of the Health Sciences, Pittsburgh, PA*

R. Preston Mason, *Neurosciences Research Center, Allegheny University of the Health Sciences, Pittsburgh, PA*

Matthew F. Muldoon, *Center for Clinical Pharmacology, University of Pittsburgh, PA*

Ray H. Rosenman, *San Francisco, CA*

Robert T. Rubin, *Neurosciences Research Center, Allegheny University of the Health Sciences, Pittsburgh, PA*

Mario Salmona, *Laboratory of Enzymology, Istituto di Recerche Farmacologiche "Mario Negri," Milan, Italy*

Evert G. Schouten, *Department of Epidemiology and Public Health, Wageningen Agricultural University, The Netherlands*

Albertine J. Schuit, *Department of Epidemiology and Public Health, Wageningen Agricultural University, Wageningen, The Netherlands*

Steven M. Schwartz, *Department of Psychiatry, Henry Ford Health Sciences Center, Case Western Reserve University, Detroit, MI*

Carol A. Shively, *Comparative Medicine Clinical Research Center, Bowman Gray School of Medicine, Wake Forest University, Winston-Salem, NC*

E. Roy Skinner, *Department of Molecular and Cell Biology, University of Aberdeen, Scotland*

Reuben T. Spitz, *Ferkauf Graduate School of Psychology and Department of Epidemiology and Social Medicine, Albert Einstein College of Medicine, Yeshiva University, Bronx, NY*

Catherine M. Stoney, *Department of Psychology, Ohio State University, Columbus, OH*

Amanda Strathdee, *Department of Molecular and Cell Biology, University of Aberdeen, Scotland*

Maria Teresa Tacconi, *Laboratory of Enzymology, Istituto di Recerche Farmacologiche "Mario Negri," Milan, Italy*

Murray Tieger, *Cholesterol Center, Jewish Hospital of Cincinnati, OH*

Thomas N. Tulenko, *Department of Physiology, Allegheny University of the Health Sciences, Philadelphia, PA*

Lorenz J. P. van Doornen, *Department of Psychophysiology, Vrije Universiteit, Amsterdam, The Netherlands*

Roy B. Verdery, *Arizona Center on Aging, University of Arizona, Tucson*

Sheila G. West, *Department of Psychiatry, University of North Carolina, Chapel Hill*

Foreword

My scientific career may be a paradigm for the lay view of cholesterol. Through much of my career, beginning in the early 1970s, I learned and taught that cholesterol was bad for health, the cause of epidemic coronary heart disease in developed countries. For example, as a clinic project officer and case manager in the Multiple Risk Factor Intervention Trial (Anonymous, 1981; Cutler, Neaton, Hulley, Kuller, & Stamler, 1985; The Multiple Risk Factor Intervention Trial Group, 1976), I personally exhorted members of the special intervention group to lower serum cholesterol through dietary change. I subsequently provided the evaluation design for the Minnesota Heart Health Program (Jacobs et al., 1986; Luepkev et al., 1994), assisting my colleagues in a community-based program to modify risk factors for coronary heart disease; prominently featured were dietary changes for serum cholesterol lowering. With considerable zeal, my colleagues and I worked to enable individuals and communities alike to reduce serum cholesterol.

My graduate training was in mathematical statistics; this may excuse me for not knowing the role of cholesterol and other lipids in the whole body economy. Nevertheless, in 1986–1988, I was amazed to observe (Iso, Jacobs, Wentworth, Neaton, & Cohen, 1989) that cholesterol was associated not only with increased levels of death attributed to hemorrhagic stroke but also to a variety of other nonatherosclerotic causes of death.

I was one of the organizers of an October 1990 conference concerning inverse associations of blood cholesterol with nonatherosclerotic disease (Jacobs et al., 1992). In this conference, the association of cholesterol with atherosclerotic heart disease came through loud and clear. However, the perplexing inverse associations of low cholesterol and various diseases persisted (Jacobs et al., 1992). Attempts by many to prove that the basis for the inverse associations was some form of confounding have proven unsatisfying. To me, the most convincing evidence of confounders are articles by Iribarren, Reed, Chen, Yano, and Dwyer (1995) and by Ettinger, Harris, Verdery, Tracy, and Kouba (1995), which suggest that decreasing cholesterol is associated with excess risk, whereas stably low cholesterol is not. On the other hand, I read and talked biology. Perhaps the most interesting leads are the strong coherence of the association of low cholesterol with hemorrhagic stroke (Konishi et al., 1993) and the observation that higher lipoprotein levels protect rats against mortality after an endotoxin challenge (Feingold et al., 1995). Proof of a biologic basis for the inverse associations is just as elusive as is proof of confounders. I conclude that I do not know that low cholesterol is causally associated with nonatherosclerotic diseases and equally do not know that the basis of the associations of low cholesterol with disease is some form of con-

This work was supported in part by National Institute on Aging Grant R01 AG12264-01A1.

founding. I consciously choose the negative tone of the preceding sentence: The answers to these questions do not seem to be readily forthcoming. Both the scientific and lay communities are learning as the picture unfolds.

However much the lay public might want definitive answers, science is in a rather typical place, working provisionally with facts, attempting to forge a prudent public policy, and, at the same time, trying to advance knowledge. Particularly on the heels of spectacular successes in clinical trials of cholesterol lowering using 3-hydroxy-3-methyl-glutaryl-coenzyme (HMG CoA) reductase inhibitors (Scandinavian Simvastatin Survival Study Group, 1994; Shepherd et al., 1995) and angiographic observations of regression and retarded progression of atherosclerosis (LaRosa, chapter 16, this volume), it seems that reduction of atherosclerotic heart disease is possible (at least for the time window of several years follow-up covered by these studies) through drastic cholesterol lowering in at-risk middle-aged men and women. These studies and a recent meta-analysis by Gould, Rossouw, Santanello, Heyse, and Furberg (1995) suggest that it is safe to reduce serum cholesterol by diet or by a "safe" drug. One recent observational study suggests that a given level of blood cholesterol may be more or less safe, depending on cultural conditions, and most likely on diet (Verschuren et al., 1995). This and many other studies pointing to health benefits of a diet high in whole plant products (e.g., fruits, vegetables, and whole grains; Steinmetz & Potter, 1991a, 1991b) lead to my personal proposal for prudent population and individual action. I suggest that most people should eat a diet high in whole plant products, at the same time reducing the amount of saturated fat in the diet. In older people (something like after age 50) with a predisposition to coronary heart disease, drug therapy may be advisable.

Given a coherent strategy to ameliorate the devastating effects of coronary heart disease, we may be able to cool the rhetoric (Hulley, Walsh, & Newman, 1992; Jacobs & Blackburn, 1993; LaRosa, chapter 16, this volume; Stamler et al., 1993); go beyond the known atherogenic effects of serum cholesterol; and get to work on understanding other potential disease or health effects of lipids in blood and cells.

I applaud the present book for doing just that, addressing various ways in which lipids in blood and cells may relate to health. An important caution at the outset is that epidemiologic results to date suggest excess risk as a function of low serum total cholesterol, but the only disease known to be related to serum total cholesterol is atherosclerosis. Nevertheless, cholesterol is one among many lipids, as pointed out in many chapters. Study of the relation of lipids in the blood on lipids elsewhere in the body remains in its infancy. We barely begin to understand cell membranes, as a case in point. Although the cholesterol:phospholipid ratio in cell membranes may be close to constant under a wide variety of circumstances, the membrane may still be responsive to dietary change. For example, Wood, Schroeder, Hogy, Rao, and Nemecz (1990) showed in mice that extreme alcohol intake causes a substantial shift in cholesterol distribution: away from the cytoplasmic bilayer and into the ectoplasmic bilayer of synaptic plasma membranes. Thus, diet probably affects phospholipid fatty acid composition and cholesterol distribution across the membrane bilayers. Are any cell functions modified by such changes?

In chapter 2 of this book, Rosenman hypothesizes that serum cholesterol increases in response to naturally occurring stressors that are perceived as severe. In keeping with this assertion is the finding by Hayward (chapter 4, this volume) that serum total cholesterol is generally associated with increased anxiety disorders. On the other hand, serum cholesterol decreases in proportion to the degree of insult during disease, particularly infection or trauma, mediated by cytokine release in immune response (Ettinger et al., 1995; Verdery, chapter 14, this volume). Could these two phenomena—decrease in blood cholesterol in an acute phase reaction and increase in blood cholesterol in perceived stress—be linked, the latter being the body's preparation for the former? Kaplan et al. (chapter 9, this volume) add to the evidence that a cholesterol-lowering diet leads to aggressive behavior in monkeys, perhaps as a function of reduced circulating serotonin. A linkage of serum cholesterol and circulating serotonin is suggested by Schuit, Dekker, and Schouten (chapter 15, this volume), noting that Steegmans et al. (1996) reported lower plasma serotonin levels in middle-aged men with persistently low serum cholesterol levels (≤ 4.5 mmol/L), compared with men with a cholesterol level between 6 and 7 mmol/L. One may speculate that low serum cholesterol may be a marker of famine or starvation, so that, as follows from Rosenman's theory (chapter 2, this volume), aggressive behavior might serve as an evolutionary advantage in the search for food.

A link between low serum cholesterol and disease is not the only lipid hypothesis explored in this book. Glueck, Kunkel, and Tieger (chapter 6, this volume) ameliorated depressive symptoms by reducing severe hypertriglyceridemia. They theorize that reduced triglyceride levels lead to increased cerebrovascular oxygenation, in turn, leading to reduced depressive symptoms. Benton (chapter 13, this volume) suggests that dietary fatty acids may affect cognitive function in rodents and humans. Horrobin (chapter 11, this volume) adds to the variety of concepts by which variation in membrane fatty acid and phospholipid metabolism may cause disease. He presents evidence that a genetically and environmentally influenced phospholipase abnormality resulting in deficient levels of arachodonic acid and docosahexaenoic acid may underlie schizophrenia and a variety of clinically distinct but biologically related disorders.

Tacconi, Calzi, and Salmona (chapter 12, this volume) state clearly that fat and other dietary constituents play a critical role, if not yet entirely understood, in development and, probably, maintenance of the brain and other neurologic function. Mason, Rubin, Mason, and Tulenko (chapter 8, this volume) present recent molecular biochemical and biophysical evidence of the importance of cholesterol in neuronal cell membrane function; modulation of neurotransmitters; and maintenance of ion channels, adrenergic, serotonergic, and opiate receptors, and width and structure of neuronal and other cell membrane bilayers. They suggest that perfect cell membrane cholesterol homeostasis does not always hold, that low density lipoprotein receptors are expressed on neural cells throughout the central nervous system, and that membrane lipid bilayer structure changes with aging in rats. It is possible that there is a physiologic need for increased levels of blood cholesterol in elderly humans.

This book does not resolve whether low serum total cholesterol is causally related to disease. It does raise myriad issues concerning lipids in the body economy, particularly in the brain. I suspect that there is a rich future in studying the biology of lipids in the body and in disease. The conclusion that serum cholesterol and other lipids in the blood play no other role in human disease than, under certain circumstances, to cause atherosclerosis seems to me naive and may impede scientific progress. Almost all remains to be discovered.

DAVID R. JACOBS, JR.

References

Anonymous. (1981). Forum: The Multiple Risk Factor Intervention Trial (MRFIT). The methods and impact of intervention over four years. *Preventive Medicine, 10,* 387–553.

Cutler, J. A., Neaton, J. D., Hulley, S. B., Kuller, L., Paul, O. & Stamler, J. (1985). Coronary heart disease and all-causes mortality in the Multiple Risk Factor Intervention Trial; Subgroup findings and comparisons with other trials. *Preventive Medicine, 14,* 293–311.

Ettinger, W. H., Harris, T., Verdery, R. B., Tracy, R., & Kouba, E. (1995). Evidence for inflammation as a cause of hypocholesterolemia in older people. *Journal of the American Geriatric Society, 43,* 264–266.

Feingold, K. R., Funk, J. L., Moser, A. H., Shigenaga, J. K., Rapp, J. H., & Grunfeld, C. (1995). Role for circulating lipoproteins in protection from endotoxin toxicity. *Infection and Immunity, 63,* 2041–2046.

Gould, A. L., Rossouw, J. E., Santanello, N. C., Heyse, J. F., & Furberg, C. D. (1995). Cholesterol reduction yields clinical benefit: A new look at old data. *Circulation, 91,* 2274–2282.

Hulley, S. B., Walsh, J. M. B., & Newman, T. B. (1992). Health policy on blood cholesterol. *Circulation, 86,* 1026–1029.

Iribarren, C., Reed, D. M., Chen, R., Yano, K., & Dwyer, J. H. (1995). Low serum cholesterol and mortality. Which is the cause and which is the effect? *Circulation, 92,* 2396–2403.

Iso, H., Jacobs, D. R., Wentworth, D., Neaton, J. D., & Cohen, J. D., for the MRFIT Research Group. (1989). Serum cholesterol levels and six-year mortality from stroke in 350,977 men screened for the Multiple Risk Factor Intervention Trial. *New England Journal of Medicine, 320,* 904–910.

Jacobs, D. R., & Blackburn, H. (1993). Models of effects of low blood cholesterol on the public health: Implications for practice and policy. *Circulation, 87,* 1033–1036.

Jacobs, D., Blackburn, H., Higgins, M., Reed, D., Iso, H., McMillan, G., Neaton, J., Nelson, J., Potter, J., Rifkind, B., Rossouw, J., Shekelle, R., & Yusuf, S. (1992). Report of the conference on low blood cholesterol: Mortality associations. *Circulation, 86,* 1046–1060.

Jacobs, D. R., Luepker, R. V., Mittelmark, M. B., Folsom, A. R., Pirie, P. L., Mascioli, S. R., Hannan, P. J., Pechacek, T. F., Bracht, N. F., Carlaw, R. W., Kline, F. G., Blackburn, H., for the Minnesota Heart Health Program Research Group. (1986). Community-wide prevention strategies: Evaluation design of the Minnesota Heart Health Program. *Journal of Chronic Diseases, 39,* 777–788.

Konishi, M., Iso, H., Komachi, Y., Iida, M., Shimamoto, T., Jacobs, D. R., Terao, A., Baba, S., & Ito, M. (1993). Associations of serum cholesterol, different types of stroke and stenosis distribution of cerebral arteries: The Akita Pathology Study. *Stroke, 24,* 954–964.

Leupker, R. V., Murray, D. M., Jacobs, D. R., Mittelmark, M. B., Bracht, N., Carlaw, R., Crow, R., Elmer, P., Finnegan, J., Folsom, A. R., Grimm, R., Hannan, P. J., Jeffery, R., Lando, H., McGovern, P., Mullis, R., Perry, C. L., Pechacek, T., Pirie, P., Sprafka, J. M., Weisbrod, R., & Blackburn, H. (1994). Community education for cardiovascular disease prevention: Risk factor changes in the Minnesota Heart Health Program. *American Journal of Public Health*, 1393.

Scandinavian Simvastatin Survival Study Group. (1994). Randomised trial of cholesterol lowering in 4444 patients with coronary heart disease: The Scandinavian Simvastatin Survival Study (4S). *The Lancet*, *344*, 1383–1389.

Shepherd, J., Cobbe, S. M., Ford, I., Isles, C. G., Lorimer, A. R., MacFarlane, P. W., McKillop, J. H., & Packard, C. J., for the West Scotland Coronary Prevention Study Group. (1995). Prevention of coronary heart disease with pravastatin in men with hypercholesterolemia. *New England Journal of Medicine*, *333*, 1301–1307.

Stamler, J., Stamler, R., Brown, V., Gotto, A. M., Greenland, P., Grundy, S., Hegsted, M., Luepker, R. V., Neaton, J. D., Steinberg, D., Stone, N., VanHorn, L., & Wissler, R. W. (1993). Serum cholesterol: Doing the right thing. *Circulation*, *88*, 1954–1960.

Steegmans, P. H., Fekkes, D., Hoes, A. W., Bak, A. A., van der Does, E., & Grobbee, D. E. (1996). Low serum cholesterol concentration and serotonin metabolism in men. *British Medical Journal*, *312*, 221.

Steinmetz, K. A., & Potter, J. D. (1991a). Vegetables, fruit, and cancer: I. Epidemiology. *Cancer Causes and Control*, *2*, 325–357.

Steinmetz, K. A., & Potter, J. D. (1991b). Vegetables, fruit, and cancer: II. Mechanisms. *Cancer Causes and Control*, *2*, 427–442.

The Multiple Risk Factor Intervention Trial Group. (1976). The Multiple Risk Factor Intervention Trial (MRFIT): A national study of primary prevention of coronary heart disease. *Journal of the American Medical Association*, *235*, 825–827.

Verschuren, W. M. M., Jacobs, D. R., Bloemberg, B. M. P., Keys, A., Kromhout, D., Menotti, A., Aravanis, C., Blackburn, H. W., Buizina, R., Dontas, A. S., Fidanza, F., Karvonen, M. J., Nedeljkovic, S., Nissinen, A., & Toshima, H. (1995). Serum total cholesterol and long-term coronary heart disease mortality in different cultures: Twenty-five-year follow-up of the Seven Countries Study. *Journal of the American Medical Association*, *274*, 131–136.

Wood, W. G., Schroeder, F., Hogy, L., Rao, A. M., & Nemecz, G. (1990). Asymmetric distribution of a fluorescent sterol in synaptic plasma membranes: Effects of chronic ethanol consumption. *Biochimica et Biophysica Acta*, *1025*, 243–246.

Preface

The purpose of this book is to examine the growing body of evidence linking various constituents of the organic molecular class termed *lipids* to a wide range of psychological processes. This area of study has grown considerably in the past decade, and numerous disciplines have investigated this biobehavioral relationship. This volume is an attempt to bring together for the first time a selection of these multidisciplinary studies into a coherent whole.

We are grateful to the following people who provided their expertise to this project: Michael T. Allen (University of Pittsburgh), Alyson Bond (Institute of Psychiatry, London), Fiona Coulter (Hartfield Clinic, Dumbarton, Scotland), Nicholas J. Delva (Queen's University, Kingston, Ontario, Canada), Robin Dibble (Englewood, CO), Howard A. Eder (Albert Einstein College of Medicine, Bronx, NY), David Freedman (Centers for Disease Control and Prevention, Atlanta, GA), Jeremiah F. Kelly (National Institute of Health and National Institute of Aging, Baltimore, MD), Victoria M. Lingswiler (Middletown, CT), Andrew B. Littman (Harvard University), George Mamalakis (University of Crete), Matthias Mueller (University of California, San Diego), Stephen Patterson (University of Pittsburgh), Katri Raikkonen (University of Helsinki, Helsinki, Finland), Joan Russo (University of Washington), Ann Ryman (Royal Edinburgh Hospital, Edinburgh, Scotland), Carol Shively (Bowman Gray College of Medicine), Patrick Sullivan (Princess Margaret Hospital, Christchurch, New Zealand), Charles Swencionis (Albert Einstein College of Medicine, Bronx, NY), Erkki Vartiainen (National Public Health Institute, Helsinki, Finland), Shari Waldstein (University of Maryland Baltimore County), and several anonymous reviewers.

Special thanks are extended to Hilliard G. Foster, Jr. (Whiting Forensic Division of Connecticut Valley Hospital, Middletown, CT), David R. Jacobs, Jr. (University of Minnesota), Richard R. Manning (Manning Foundation for Biobehavioral Research, Middletown, CT), John R. MacKinnon (Connecticut College), and Barbara G. Melamed (Yeshiva University).

MARC HILLBRAND
REUBEN T. SPITZ

1

Introduction

Marc Hillbrand and Reuben T. Spitz

The relationship between serum lipids—in particular, cholesterol level elevations—and cardiovascular disease (CVD) in humans is well known. It is also common knowledge that cholesterol is influenced by genetics, homeostatic factors, body weight, dietary intake of fatty foods and alcohol, and lifestyle habits such as exercise and smoking. Less well known, however, is the fact that even in combination, these factors account for less than half of the variability in lipids between and even within most individuals. This has led behavioral scientists to explore whether psychological factors account for a significant proportion of this unexplained variability.

Behavioral factors associated with levels of serum lipids in humans have been the focus of research and study for much of this century (Sletten, Nilsen, Young, & Anderson, 1964). As early as 1925, for example, an association between serum lipid levels and affective states was noted in schizophrenic patients (Brice, 1935). Patients with low cholesterol were found to be more repressed and withdrawn, with less evidence of initiative and motor activity, whereas those with high cholesterol were noted to have more energy, drive, and intense emotional reactions. Beginning in the 1950s, there was an increased understanding of the relationship among psychological stress, cholesterol levels, and CVD. The discovery that cholesterol played a role in the etiology of CVD and also was subject to psychogenic fluctuation prompted many psychological studies. For example, a study examining the impact of occupational stress on plasma cholesterol suggested that periodic stress may influence total serum levels. Friedman, Rosenman, and Carroll (1958) obtained dietary records and biweekly cholesterol levels from middle-aged male accountants during the first 5 months of the year, to examine the influence of the stressor tax deadlines on cholesterol. They found that the average plasma cholesterol level was 252 mg/dl during high-stress periods (tax time) and 210 mg/dl during periods of relative low stress. Dietary changes did not explain this significant difference. These studies illustrate three important attributes of serum lipids, namely, their association with personality characteristics and their variability over time and in response to stress.

The nearly 40 years of research that have followed have shown that acute stressors of many types, as well as severe and threatening chronic stress, are related to alterations in lipid concentrations (Niaura, Stoney,

& Herbert, 1992). In addition, various human and animal behaviors have been linked to low serum cholesterol. One of the most interesting of these relationships is the apparent connection between low cholesterol and violent deaths, a phenomenon addressed in many of the chapters that follow. Early primary prevention trials in CVD revealed that although cholesterol lowering through diet, exercise, or medication resulted in reduced mortality from CVD, there was no reduction in total (all-cause) mortality because of a corresponding increase in mortality resulting from suicides, homicides, and accidents. These results have led to an increased interest in discovering the relationships among lipids, health, and behavior.

The Controversy Over Lowering Cholesterol

For the past several years, there has been considerable controversy over recommendations promoting nationwide lowering of cholesterol levels. During the 1970s, many cholesterol-reduction programs were implemented, when a more definitive relationship was found between elevations of total cholesterol and CVD. As the results of these efforts were compiled, in the 1980s, there was an indication that although cholesterol-reduction programs in countries taking an aggressive approach (e.g., United States and Finland) showed a decrease in cardiac mortality, an increase in non-cardiac deaths compensated for the observed reduction (Kaplan, Manuck, & Shumaker, 1991; Ryman, 1994; Schuit, van Dijk, Dekker, Schouten, & Kok, 1993). Debate on the justification for populationwide reduction approaches emerged as cholesterol-lowering campaigns came under scrutiny. For example, Frank, Reed, Grove, and Benfante (1992) examined the results of the Honolulu Heart Project. The Honolulu Heart Project involved 7,478 Japanese American middle-aged men given a comprehensive medical examination between 1965 and 1968. At follow-up, in 1985, 1,648 of the men had died. A U-shaped curve of baseline cholesterol level by total mortality (hazard rate ratio) was revealed. Cardiovascular-disease–related total mortality was directly related to total serum cholesterol, whereas mortality due to hemorrhagic stroke, all cancer, benign liver disease, chronic obstructive lung disease, and unknown causes was inversely related to total serum cholesterol. A zone of minimum mortality for total cholesterol, lying approximately between 188 mg/dl and 225 mg/dl, with a mean of 218 mg/dl, was observed.

On the basis of the findings of this study, Frank et al. (1992) created a number of cholesterol-lowering models to determine the best approach for reduction efforts. These models used a populationwide reduction approach, as well as high-risk targeting strategies, which isolated subgroups having specific serum lipid levels. In terms of a populationwide approach, it is generally accepted that in response to current lipid-lowering efforts (i.e., through dietary restrictions, antilipidemic drugs, exercise, or a combination thereof), overall serum levels will most likely not exceed a 10% reduction (approximately 20–30 mg/dl). Although some people at high cholesterol levels would suffer less serious CVD after such a shift, Frank et al. contended that there would be a compensatory mortality increase as a result of further lowering the cholesterol of the larger number of persons with low-to-intermediate baseline cholesterol levels. This latter mortality increase is presumed to be due to noncardiac events. A high-risk policy, targeting only those with total cholesterol levels above 240 mg/dl, would reduce incidence of new coronary disease in this group over a subsequent 15-year period by less than 5%, compared with approximately 14% for a population-based strategy. A more aggressive approach, targeting individuals with cholesterol levels over 222 mg/dl, would treat almost twice as many people and would result in only a 7.5% subsequent decline in CVD. Frank et al. speculated that only at the level of an approximate 50-mg/dl reduction would true mortality advantages be realized. This was a reduction that was not considered feasible. In general, Frank et al. suggested that no populationwide or high-risk strategy to lower serum cholesterol would substantially improve overall mortality.

Further evidence to support this conclusion was presented by Muldoon et al. (1993), who examined the relationship between non-illness-related mortality (i.e., mortality caused by accidents, suicides, or homicides) and low or lowered cholesterol. Muldoon et al. found that compared with adults with normal or high total cholesterol levels, adults with very low cholesterol levels (<160 mg/dl) experience increased mortality from a variety of causes, including cancer and chronic respiratory and gastrointestinal diseases. This group also had a higher incidence of death from suicide, accident, and trauma.

These findings were based on the examination of three epidemiological data sources. One cohort involved 52,000 Swedish adults, in which the relative risk of non-illness-related mortality in the lowest quartile (<160 mg/dl) was found to be 2.8 times that of those in the highest quartile group (>200 mg/dl) (Lindberg, Rastam, Gullberg, & Eklund, 1992). Most of the excess risk was attributed to suicide, with a 4.2 times greater risk for those in the lowest cholesterol quartile. A second study involved 350,977 men screened for the Multiple Risk Factor Intervention Trial (Neaton et al., 1992). It was found that suicide and mortality were highest in those men with the lowest total cholesterol levels. In a third study, a pooled analysis of 18 prospective studies, involving a total of approximately 300,000 men and women monitored for 9 to 30 years, demonstrated that men with low serum levels (<160 mg/dl) had a risk of suicide or trauma death 1.4 times that of those in the normal clinical range (Jacobs et al. 1992). For women, the risk was slightly lower (1.26). These relationships merge, with positive correlations observed between total cholesterol and CVD, to create the U-shaped curve mentioned above, with mortality elevated at either end.

Other studies presented contrasting findings. For example, Wysowski and Gross (1990) examined the results of the Helsinki Heart Study and the Lipid Research Clinics Coronary Primary Prevention Trial (LRC–CPPT). In the LRC–CPPT (N = 3,806), there were 6 deaths due to accidents, 1 homicide, and 4 suicides among the 1,907 volunteers randomly assigned to the cholestyramine-treatment group and 2 deaths, 0 homicides, and 2 suicides among the 1,899 volunteers randomized to placebo. For the Helsinki Heart Study ($N = 4,081$), there were 4 deaths due to accidents, 1 homicide, and 4 suicides among the 2,046 participants randomized to gemfibrozil and 4 deaths due to accidents, 0 homicide, and 1 suicide among the 2,035 randomized to placebo. On the basis of these and other findings, Wysowski and Gross concluded that there was little evidence for an association between cholesterol lowering and accidents or violence. A more recent study by Vartianen, Puska, Pekkanen, Tuomilehto, and Enholm (1994), involving two cohorts of Finnish men ($n = 10,898$) and women ($n = 11,534$), also concluded that the risk of accidents, suicide, and other violent death was not related to total cholesterol levels.

The qualitative difference between *low* and *lowered* serum lipid levels was largely overlooked in the studies just discussed (Santiago & Dalen, 1994). For example, violent individuals have been shown to possess abnormally low total cholesterol, in comparison with the general population (Hillbrand, Spitz, & Foster, 1995; Virkkunen, 1979, 1983). These levels are an inherent characteristic of the individual rather than a product of cholesterol-reduction efforts. In certain populations (e.g., among chronic offenders), a predisposition toward low cholesterol is accompanied by a tendency to manifest psychopathology (Virkkunen, 1985). Low serum cholesterol levels were also found to be related to poorly internalized social norms, irresponsibility, and poor self-control (Jenkins, Haimes, Zyzanski, Rosenman, & Friedman, 1979). This suggests that in certain populations, low levels of serum cholesterol are associated with behavioral disturbances. As suggested by Engelberg (1992), the increased rates of suicide and other violent death observed in cholesterol-lowering trials could be explained by alterations in mood or behavior arising from a reduced expression of serotonin receptors on brain cell membranes. Further research is needed to examine the distinction between a priori low serum cholesterol and active lowering through involvement in a cholesterol-reduction program.

The controversy over cholesterol lowering is one of many in the study of lipids, health, and behavior. In this book, five main questions are explored. First, how do we fit lipids into our conceptual framework aimed at understanding human behavior? Second, what are the implications of these lipid–behavior links for our understanding and treatment of various forms of psychological disturbance? Third, is the association between lipids and behavior relevant to our understanding of central nervous system function, for instance, with respect to aggression and schizophrenia? Fourth, does dietary fat play a role in normal and abnormal neurodevelopment? Finally, is the link between low cholesterol and violent deaths real or a mere epiphenomenon or artifact, and what are the public health implications of resolving that polemic?

Before we summarize the chapters presented in this text, we offer a primer on lipids. Although many readers may be familiar with this information, some may not, and others may appreciate a refresher on these complex mechanisms.

Lipids: A Brief Biological Review

In spite of their reputation as contributors to atherosclerosis, lipids are essential to life. Lipids constitute a class of large organic molecules, which along with cholesterol, includes triglycerides; phospholipids; hormones (e.g., cortisol and estrogen); and some vitamins (e.g., A, D, and E). Fats, primarily represented as triglycerides, are stored in cells and serve as a source of cellular energy and for cell maintenance, growth, and repair. A major role of phospholipids and cholesterol is their joint participation in the formation of the cell membrane and its lipid barrier. The cell membrane completely envelopes cells throughout the body and is composed of lipids and proteins in approximately equal amounts. The basic structure of this membrane is the lipid barrier, or bilayer, composed almost entirely of phospholipid and cholesterol molecules. These molecules are organized so that hydrophilic (water-soluble) and hydrophobic (fat-soluble) ends arrange themselves into a continuous surface according to mutual attraction. Variation in the ratio of phospholipid:cholesterol content of this lipid barrier is believed to influence the fluidity of the membrane surface and passage of substances into and out of the cell interior. Much current theory involving lipid levels and behavior is based on speculation that changes in the lipid composition of this barrier may influence cellular neurochemistry.

The dietary intake of fats and cholesterol results in their passage from the intestine to the blood stream as large particles (*chylomicrons*) that are later degraded and taken up by the liver, also the primary site of cholesterol synthesis. The intake of dietary cholesterol inhibits the synthesis of cholesterol by the liver. Under normal circumstances, this homeostatic process results in a roughly constant ($\pm 5\% - 10\%$) amount of cholesterol in the adult human from day to day.

The liver produces 70%–80% of the cholesterol and triglycerides in the body. Dietary carbohydrates and protein are absorbed and later converted by the liver into triglycerides. These are then packaged with cholesterol as chylomicrons, which are normally rapidly eliminated under the influence of enzymes and sufficient aerobic exercise. Because cholesterol is insoluble in the blood, it travels through the bloodstream surrounded by a protein shell called *lipoprotein*. With the help of enzymes, the liver produces large lipoproteins, called *very low density lipoproteins* (VLDLs), that carry cholesterol, triglycerides, and proteins called *apolipoproteins*. The *density* of lipoproteins refers to the ratio of lipid to protein—a high ratio corresponds to low density. The apolipoproteins serve a double function, binding with the lipids to create the lipoprotein shell and facilitating the reabsorption of lipids at specific sites. The VLDLs travel through the bloodstream, releasing triglycerides that provide energy to the various tissues or end up being stored as fat. As they release triglycerides, VLDLs become cholesterol-rich *low density lipoproteins* (LDLs). Specialized LDL receptors throughout the body receive this lipid subfraction for the manufacture and repair of cell membranes and the synthesis of steroid hormones and bile acids. However, when receptor activity fails to meet serum concentrations of LDL, levels of the latter increase with an accompanying increase in potential for these lipids to attach to arterial walls and collect as plaque, possibly leading to heart attacks, strokes, or other CVDs. Whereas LDL cholesterol is believed to play a key role in maintaining the quantity of serum cholesterol, another class of lipoprotein, *high density lipoproteins* (HDLs), is believed to mediate the exchange of cholesterol and other lipids in the bloodstream. Possessing the highest ratio of protein: cholesterol content, HDLs have been implicated in the process of reverse cholesterol transport, whereby excess cholesterol is removed from the serum and transported to the liver for processing.

Overview of Chapters

This text is organized to lead the reader through much current thinking concerning the lipid and behavior association. Part One, "Lipids: Understanding the Biobehavioral Nexus," reviews various conceptual frameworks. Chapter 2, "Neurogenic and Behavioral Influences on Plasma Lipids," by Rosenman, provides a foundation for the understanding of concepts and mechanisms behind the relationship of lipids and behavior. An early leader in the establishment of lipids as an important focus for psychological study, Rosenman presents an extensive survey of the literature that has evolved over the past half-century. A plethora of laboratory and field experiments has been conducted with a wide range of populations, generating a body of empirical evidence indicating a role for psychogenic influences on serum lipid levels in humans and animals. Much of this evidence has resulted in a concern that such influences can enhance CVD risk. Chapter 3, "Lipids, Personality, and Stress: Mechanisms and Modulators," by Stoney and West, focuses specifically on psychological stress and serum lipid changes. A detailed discussion of potential biobehavioral pathways is presented, and a wide range of traditional (e.g., sympathetic arousal) and more recent (e.g., hemoconcentration) explanatory models are examined.

Part Two, "Lipids and Psychological Distress," reviews the role of lipids as they relate to three types of psychological disturbances, namely, depression, anxiety, and Type A (or coronary-prone) personality. In an investigation of the association of behavioral factors with CVD, Hayward, Taylor, Roth, King, and Agras (1989) discovered that individuals with affective disorders, specifically panic disorder, are prone to higher serum cholesterol levels, leading to speculation that this population may be at increased risk for CVD. In chapter 4, "Anxiety Disorders and Serum Lipids," Hayward reviews the small body of literature addressing this relationship and offers a critique of these findings and their methodology. In chapter 5, "Lipids and the Coronary-Prone Personality," van Doornen examines a number of personality characteristics, such as anger, hostility, and depression, related to lipid changes and the CVD process. One particular issue raised by van Doornen and Rosenman is whether specific personality or behavioral response styles influence lipid levels or whether lipid changes foster psychological distress. In chapter 6, "Pathophysiologic Relationships and Linkage Among Triglycerides, Hypocholesterolemia, and Depression," Glueck, Kunkel, and Tieger report that in patients with hypertriglyceridemia (≥500 mg/dl), lipid lowering results in an improvement of psychiatric status. Triglyceride elevations may diffusely impact cerebral functioning by increasing serum viscosity and decreasing brain oxygenation. Although Glueck et al. hypothesize that hypertriglyceridemia is a factor in clinical depression, in chapter 7, "Cholesterol Lowering and Emotional Distress: Current Status and Future Directions," Schwartz and Ketterer argue that hypocholesterolemia (<160 mg/dl), specifically as treatment induced, may promote comparable emotional distress. Although the mechanism postulated involves lowered serotonergic activity, the position remains the same: Significant alteration of lipid levels results in a significant change in psychological state.

As with all modern investigation into the roots of behavior, the role of neural processes is fundamental to any explanatory model. At the core of this text lie four chapters addressing current theory regarding the impact of lipid levels on neuronal cell integrity and functioning. Part Three, "Lipids and Brain Function," reviews existing knowledge as well as theoretical speculations on the role of lipids in central nervous system function. As an introduction to the involvement of lipids in neurophysiology, chapter 8, "Molecular Mechanisms Underlying the Effects of Cholesterol on Neuronal Cell Membrane Function and Drug–Membrane Interactions," Mason, Rubin, Mason, and Tulenko propose that cholesterol serves a critical function at the cellular level. As a major component of the neuronal plasma membrane, the level of serum cholesterol, maintained from both endogenous and exogenous sources, strongly influences transmission of key neurochemicals, most notably serotonin. Of particular interest in their position is a putative role for cholesterol in neuropsychopharmacology. From their perspective, cholesterol may not only influence all drugs dependent on cell membrane passage for effectiveness, but as cholesterol membrane content varies, possibly due to antilipidemic therapy or stress, drug action will also vary. Cell membrane lipid level change may provide a basis for understanding the continuum of pharmacological action ranging from lack of effect to toxicity.

In chapter 9, "The Cholesterol–Serotonin Hypothesis: Interrelationships Among Dietary Lipids, Central Serotonergic Activity, and Social Behavior in Monkeys," Kaplan and his colleagues describe a number of separate experiments that have demonstrated that dietary manipulation of cholesterol level produces distinct behavioral change in nonhuman primates. Most notably, an increase in aggressive behavior is observed when serum cholesterol level is decreased. Results of these studies have led Kaplan et al. to hypothesize a neurobiological basis for aggression. Lowered cholesterol fosters a decrease in serotonin, which in turn promotes an increase in aggression and impulsivity. Furthermore, they speculate that the experimental results with nonhuman primates have implications for the understanding of human evolution. In short, the inherent neurobiological need for cholesterol by early man generated behavioral change (increased aggression), allowing for acquisition of this key dietary element.

In chapter 10, "Plasma Lipoproteins and Apolipoproteins in Individuals Convicted of Violent Crimes," Gray et al. hypothesize that apolipoprotein metabolism is causally related to aggression. Results of their lipid level analysis indicated a highly significant difference between offenders and controls for two apolipoproteins important in cholesterol homeostasis. They conclude that these individuals with violent histories had a biologically determined predisposition for altered cholesterol levels, which in turn negatively influenced the ability of their cell membranes to retain normal functioning.

In the last of the four chapters devoted to lipids and brain function, chapter 11, "Schizophrenia and Membrane Lipids," Horrobin presents an argument for the role of lipids in schizophrenia. Through an investigation of cell membranes in schizophrenic patients, he has discovered a candidate gene of significantly greater prevalence in this population, as opposed to normal controls. Furthermore, the role of this gene in the onset of schizophrenia is believed to be mediated by cell membrane lipid constitution. Horrobin theorizes that this latter factor is susceptible to manipulation (e.g., nutrition, disease, and hormones), leading to the position that schizophrenia is a preventable disorder. Thus, the interaction of genes and environment in one of the most severe psychiatric disturbances may be explained in the context of serum-lipid-level alterations.

Despite the suggestions that a manipulation of lipid levels may affect significant change in individuals with psychiatric and behavioral disturbances, it is generally accepted that the fully developed human brain is far less subject to such change than the brain of neonates or very young children. Part Four, "Diet, Lipids, and Cognitive Processes," contains data from a variety of scientific disciplines on the impact of diet on cognitive functioning, as mediated by serum lipid levels. In chapter 12, "Brain Lipids and Diet," Tacconi, Calzi, and Salmona present a strong argument for an association between neurodevelopmental disorders and dietary lipid deficiency. As an in vivo influence, certain polyunsaturated fatty acids may be significant modulators of brain development at critical periods in early life. Isolation of these specific nutritional elements may allow for prevention of a wide range of intellectual and behavioral deficits, currently afflicting millions in the human population.

The relationship between lipid levels and cognitive functioning has rarely been examined empirically. As Benton discusses in chapter 13, "Dietary Fat and Cognitive Functioning," experiments with rodents have shown that measures of learning and memory are influenced by the fatty acid content of diets. In a review of various paradigms used to test this association, Benton concludes that cognitive performance in rodents is affected by level of polyunsaturated fatty acids in the diet. On the basis of these animal studies, he decided to examine a measure of cognitive functioning in humans variously termed *mental speed* or *reaction time*. Benton found that lower plasma cholesterol levels were associated with slower decision times in tests of mental speed. He concludes that as lipid levels can influence brain structure and subsequent performance on learning tasks in rodents, the same may be true in humans.

Of more substantial empirical basis is the role that lipid levels play in numerous issues of physical health. Part Five, "Public Health Perspectives," explores the implications for public health of the findings presented in previous chapters. Although hypercholesterolemia has been definitively related to a greater risk for coronary artery and cerebrovascular disease, Verdery argues in chapter 14, "Hypocholesterolemia, Hypolipoproteinemia, and Risk of Death," that the relationship between low cholesterol and mortality is strong enough to predict early death in patients with abnormally low serum cholesterol levels (<150 mg/dl). In addition, the wide range of conditions believed to be related to low cholesterol (e.g., cancer, infection, arthritis, alcohol abuse, and mood disorders) are not easily linked to a common physiological denominator. One hypothesis examined by Verdery is that decreased lipid production alters cytokine activity and immune function.

Solely on the basis of the widely disseminated findings of a relationship between serum lipid levels and atherosclerosis, public health programs (e.g., National Cholesterol Education Program) have focused on recommendations that all individuals take steps to lower, or actively maintain, a low serum cholesterol level. These recommendations have also prompted numerous investigations into the effects of such population-wide health policy. As discussed by Schuit, Dekker, and Schouten in chapter 15, "Low Serum Total Cholesterol and Mortality From Accidents and Suicide," cholesterol-reducing recommendations are of proven benefit for those with established CVD or at high risk. However, for the general population, all risks should be considered, not just CVD risk. In Schuit et al.'s longitudinal study, an increase in non-illness-related mortality (i.e., suicide and accidents) was demonstrated in patients with low cholesterol. As a counterpoint to those advocating caution, LaRosa argues in chapter 16, "Cholesterol Lowering, Low Cholesterol, and Noncardiovascular Disease," that the epidemiological reports supporting policy maintenance are quite strong, whereas evidence favoring change is at best inconsistent.

Part Six addresses concluding issues. Spitz and Hillbrand review public health issues in chapter 17 and explore directions for future research.

Conclusion

As is apparent from this review, lipids play a major role in a multitude of psychological and physical health issues. There is a pervasive interest in cholesterol, not only in the scientific community but also in the general public. Joseph Goldstein, who along with Michael S. Brown received a Nobel Prize in medicine for discovery of the LDL receptor pathway, recently pointed out that of the approximately 300,000 annual recorded inquiries to the publishers of the *Encyclopedia Britannica*, cholesterol has been among the top five subjects. The other four were Albert Einstein, Madonna, Michelangelo, and Jesus Christ. Although this unprecedented quest for biological information may not be fully satisfied by the chapters to follow, we hope at least to clarify a number of directions worthy of further investigation.

References

Brice, A. T. (1935). The blood fats in schizophrenia. *Journal of Nervous and Mental Disease, 81*, 613–632.

Engelberg, H. (1992). Low serum cholesterol and suicide. *Lancet, 339*, 727–729.

Frank, J. W., Reed, D. M., Grove, J. S., & Benfante, R. (1992). Will lowering population levels of serum cholesterol affect total mortality? Expectations from the Honolulu Heart Program. *Journal of Clinical Epidemiology, 45*, 333–346.

Friedman, M., Rosenman, R. H., & Carroll, V. (1958). Changes in serum cholesterol and blood clotting time in men subjected to variation of occupational stress. *Circulation, 17*, 852–861.

Hayward, C., Taylor, C. B., Roth, W. T., King, R., & Agras, S. (1989). Plasma lipid levels in patients with panic disorder or agoraphobia. *American Journal of Psychiatry, 146*, 917–919.

Hillbrand, M., Spitz, R. T., & Foster, H. G. (1995). Serum cholesterol and aggression in hospitalized male forensic patients. *Journal of Behavioral Medicine, 18*, 33–43.

Jacobs, D., Blackburn, H., Higgins, M., Reed, D., Iso, H., McMillan, G., Neaton, J., Nelson, J., Potter, J., Rifkind, B., Rossouw, J., Shekelle, R., & Yusef, S., for participants in the Conference on Low Cholesterol: Mortality Associations. (1992). Report of the Conference on Low Blood Cholesterol: Mortality Associations. *Circulation, 86*, 1046–1060.

Jenkins, C. D., Haimes, C. G., Zyzanski, S. J., Rosenman, R. H., & Friedman, M. (1979). Psychological traits and serum lipids: Part 1. Findings from the California Psychological Inventory. *Psychosomatic Medicine, 31*, 115–128.

Kaplan, J. R., Manuck, S. B., & Shumaker, S. (1991). Does cholesterol cause increases in depression, suicide, and accidents? In H. S. Friedman (Ed.), *Hostility, coping, and health* (pp. 117–123). Washington, DC: American Psychological Association.

Lindberg, G., Rastam, L., Gullberg, B., & Eklund, G. A. (1992). Low serum cholesterol concentration and short term mortality from injuries in men and women. *British Medical Journal, 305*, 277–279.

Muldoon, M. F., Rossouw, J. E., Manuck, S. B., Glueck, C. J., Kaplan, J. R., & Kaufmann, P. G. (1993). Low or lowered cholesterol and risk of death from suicide and trauma. *Metabolism, 42*, 45–56.

Neaton, J. D., Blackburn, H., Jacobs, D., Kuller, L., Lee, D. J., Sherwin, J., Shih, J., Stamler, J., Wentworth, D. (1992). Serum cholesterol level and mortality findings for men screened in the Multiple Risk Factor Intervention Trial. *Archives of Internal Medicine, 152*, 1490–1500.

Niaura, R., Stoney, C. M., & Herbert, P. N. (1992). Lipids in psychological research: The last decade. *Biological Psychology, 34*, 1–43.

Ryman, A. (1994). Cholesterol, violent death, and mental disorder. *British Medical Journal, 309*, 421–422.

Santiago, J. M., & Dalen, J. E. (1994). Cholesterol and violent behavior. *Archives of Internal Medicine, 154*, 1317–1321.

Schuit, A. J., van Dijk, L. C. M. J., Dekker, J. M., Schouten, E. G., & Kok, F. J. (1993). Inverse association between total serum cholesterol and 28-year cancer mortality in Dutch civil servants. *American Journal of Epidemiology, 137*, 966–976.

Sletten, I. W., Nilsen, J. A., Young, R. C., & Anderson, J. T. (1964). Blood lipids and behavior in mental hospitals. *Psychosomatic Medicine, 26*, 261–266.

Vartianen, E., Puska, P., Pekkanen, J., Tuomilehto, J., & Enholm, C. (1994). Serum cholesterol concentration and mortality from accidents, suicide, and other violent crimes. *British Medical Journal, 309*, 445–447.

Virkkunen, M. (1979). Serum cholesterol in antisocial personality. *Neuropsychobiology, 5,* 27–30.

Virkkunen, M. (1983). Serum cholesterol levels in homicidal offenders. *Biological Psychiatry, 10,* 65–69.

Virkkunen, M. (1985). Lipid Research Clinics Coronary Primary Prevention Trial Results. *Journal of the American Medical Association, 253,* 635.

Wysowski, D. K., & Gross, T. P. (1990). Deaths due to accidents and violence in two recent trials of cholesterol lowering drugs. *Archives of Internal Medicine, 150,* 2169–2172.

Part I

Lipids: Understanding the Biobehavioral Nexus

2

Neurogenic and Behavioral Influences on Plasma Lipids

Ray H. Rosenman

A population study (Keys, Mickelsen, Miller, Hayes, & Todd, 1951) led to an early belief that plasma cholesterol levels were stable in adults, aside from small age-related increases. However, the dominant role of genetic factors in regulation of individual cholesterol levels (Christian et al., 1987) decreases with age (Heller, de Faire, Pedersen, Dahlen, & McClearn, 1993). It therefore is not surprising that under standardized conditions, within-person weekly levels of plasma cholesterol vary by 20% or more in adults or that these levels have a significant 10%–20% day-to-day variability that cannot be ascribed to dietary changes (Bookstein, Gidding, Donovan, & Smith, 1990; Mogadam, Ahmed, Mensh, & Godwin, 1991).

There is considerable evidence to document a major role of the sympathetic nervous system in this variability. It also may play an important role in the rise of plasma total cholesterol that can transiently occur during emotional stress and in higher levels that are associated with certain personality and behavioral characteristics (Dimsdale & Herd, 1982; Dzau & Sacks, 1987; Howes, Krum, & Louis, 1987; Krone, Muller-Wieland, Nagele, Behnke, & Greten, 1985; Lundberg, Hedman, Melin, & Frankenhaeuser, 1989; O'Donnell et al., 1987; Rosenman & Friedman, 1974).

In this chapter, I therefore discuss relationships of plasma lipids with emotional stress and certain personality and behavioral characteristics and the role of the sympathetic nervous system in these relationships. I review also aspects of the association of low plasma total cholesterol levels with increased mortality from relevant noncardiac causes.

Relationships Between Emotional Stress and Plasma Lipids

An impetus for the recurring interest in a relationship of the sympathetic nervous system to plasma lipids may have come from two independent early studies (Hammarsten, Cathey, Redmond, & Wolf, 1957; Rosenman & Friedman, 1957). In one of them (Friedman, Rosenman, & Carroll, 1958), plasma cholesterol was determined biweekly during the first 5 months of the year in a group of middle-aged male accountants, who were purposefully selected for study because their well-known phasic variations of workload and tax deadlines allowed other times to serve as control periods. Their average cholesterol levels were found to be significantly higher during periods of occupational deadlines, but these were not always self-perceived as the times of personal maximum stress during the 5-month period of study. It was therefore of great interest that the highest within-person cholesterol levels coincided with peak periods of self-perceived stress in 91% of the participants. There was an average plasma cholesterol level of 252 mg/dl during maximum periods of self-perceived stress, compared with 210 mg/dl during minimum periods. Participants meticulously recorded their dietary intake during several relevant weekly periods. The observed cholesterol fluctuations could not be attributed to dietary intake.

In the other study (Hammarsten et al., 1957), significant increases of plasma cholesterol were strongly correlated with the emotionally stressful events that were recorded by the participants in life-event diaries. The same investigators later reported that variations of cholesterol levels of up to 19% occurred in ambulatory participants during self-perceived stressful life periods, compared with neutral ones (Cathey, Jones, Naughton, Hammarsten, & Wolf, 1962). They observed also that stressful personal interviews could induce significant increases of plasma cholesterol in patients who were studied under metabolic ward control of exercise and diet and that a 70-mg/dl or greater rise of plasma cholesterol could occur within 1 hr after such interviews (Wolf, McCabe, Yamamoto, Adsett, & Schottstaedt, 1962).

These findings appear to have stimulated other studies of stress–plasma lipid relationships in natural milieus. Among them, it was found that plasma cholesterol often significantly increased in medical students during important school examinations (Dreyfuss & Czaczkes, 1959; Grundy & Griffin, 1959a, 1959b; Thomas & Murphy, 1958; Wertlake, Wilcox, Haley, & Peterson, 1958). The rise of plasma cholesterol averaged about 10% in two groups of male students (Thomas & Murphy, 1958; Wertlake et al., 1958), with an average 20% increase occurring in a third cohort during the interval between a few hours before and 48 hr after a final examination (Dreyfuss & Czackes, 1959). An average increase of plasma cholesterol of 11% was observed in 57 male medical students and an average increase of 26.5% was observed in 50 female medical students in another study, with a rise of 90 mg/dl or more in 10% of these participants (Grundy & Griffin, 1959a). The average 25% increase that occurred during school examinations, compared with neutral control periods, in still another student sample, was associated with increased levels of low density lipoprotein (LDL) cholesterol (Grundy & Griffin, 1959b). Other investigators of ambulatory participants that kept similar life-event diaries found that plasma cholesterol rose 20%–25% during periods of job dissatisfaction and strong emotional upsets (Groen, Tijong, Kamminger, & Willebrands, 1962). Increased variability of plasma cholesterol levels was found also in patients with ischemic heart disease (Groover, Jernigan, & Martin, 1962).

Significant increases of plasma cholesterol were found during other milieu situations, with an average rise of 36% occurring in novice flyers on aerobatic maneuvers (Pinter, Tolir, Guyda, & Katsarkas, 1979); of 25% in physical therapy students during their studies (Francis, 1979); and of 11% in underwater demolition trainees during the first day of training with demolition weaponry and during periods of intensive training (Rahe, Rubin, Gunderson, & Arthur, 1971). Failing a stressful U.S. Navy training program (Campbell & Rahe, 1974; Rahe, Ryman, & Biersner, 1976) and poor performance on medical school examinations (Bloch & Brackenridge, 1972) were also associated with significant increases. In an interesting study of three men who were repeatedly sampled over a period of three months of stressful naval training, one man showed a significant rise in plasma cholesterol at times of self-perceived stressful events (Rahe, Rubin, & Arthur, 1974). A 15% increase occurred in participants who were constantly bombarded with battle noise during a 3-day sleepless vigil (Palmblad, Karlsson, Levi, & Lindberg, 1979). Moreover, significant increases occurred during the first week after a shift to night work in railway workers (Theorell & Akerstedt, 1976). Others found higher levels both in shift workers (De Backer, Kornitzer, Dromaix, Peeters, & Kittel, 1987; Thelle, Forde, Try, & Lehman, 1976) and after threat of unemployment (Mattiasson, Lindgarde, Nilsson, & Theorell, 1990).

Significant increases of plasma cholesterol may also occur shortly after exposure to common laboratory mental stressors (Muldoon et al., 1991, 1995; Spence et al., 1990; Stoney, Matthews, McDonald, & Johnson, 1988). A group of participants was repeatedly sampled and then subdivided on the basis of daily variability of plasma cholesterol into labile and nonlabile groups (Peterson, Wilcox, Haley, & Keith, 1960). When asked to interpret proverbs during delayed auditory feedback, the average plasma cholesterol of the labile group increased 24%. The average cholesterol levels were significantly higher in 150 young men at the U.S. Air Force Academy during their first week of training, after the first month of the first academic year, and during the first week of intense military training (Clarke et al., 1975).

A rise of plasma cholesterol that occurred at times of exposure to stress in some other natural and laboratory settings did not reach statistical significance. This was observed in participants who were given attention-demanding but monotonous tasks while being criticized for poor performance and distracted with noise and light flashes (Carlson, Levi, & Oro, 1972); in participants who were simultaneously exposed to physical discomfort and the noise of pistol shots (Horowitz & Bronte-Stewart, 1962); and during competitive military training in another group, in whom it was noted that baseline plasma cholesterol levels may already have been elevated because the study was done at the beginning of their training period (Arguellos, Martinez, Hoffman, Ortiz, & Chekhberdemian, 1972). Plasma cholesterol also was determined in employees who anticipated an impending work shutdown and who were followed for several years. Those who were reemployed within 1 month manifested a nonsignificant increase, whereas the remainder of the later reemployed showed a 10% fall during the next 8 months (Kasl, Cobb, & Brooks, 1968).

Some studies found no effect of certain stressors on plasma cholesterol levels. No increase occurred during race car driving (Taggart & Carruthers, 1971); during simulated failure of an atmospheric pressure chamber (Beischer, 1956); during three launches of Cape Kennedy moon rockets (Reynolds, 1974); while watching violent films (Carruthers & Taggart, 1973); or in association with life-change scores or discord in either middle-aged, male construction workers (Theorell, 1975) or a small group of patients with ischemic heart disease (Theorell, Lind, Froberg, Karlsson, & Levi, 1972). One study (Niaura et al., 1991) also found no rise in 20 accountants at tax times. However, the earlier study of accountants (Friedman et al., 1958) was of older men, who were owners and senior partners, with much greater responsibility in their firms. This study (Niaura et al., 1991) also found no rise in freshmen medical students during school examinations but differed from earlier cohorts in that over half of the 22 participants were women.

It is not known how long plasma cholesterol elevations may persist after removal of short-term stressors in either laboratory settings or natural milieus. There is evidence of persistent effects in some longitudinal studies (Mattiasson et al., 1990). However, although a program that focused on reducing stressful work environments and on improving individual stress management skills was associated with favorable effects on LDL to high density lipoprotein (HDL) cholesterol ratios, there was no change of plasma total cholesterol or triglyceride levels in the intervention group (Orth-Gomer, 1994).

A rise of plasma triglycerides and very low density lipoproteins was observed to occur in students during school examinations (Grundy & Griffin, 1959b) and during race car driving (Taggart & Carruthers, 1971); simulated occupational stress (Carlson et al., 1972); and public speaking (Taggart, Carruthers, & Somerville, 1973). Brief laboratory stressors generally provoke small but significant increases of plasma triglycerides (Brindley, McCann, Niaura, Stoney, & Suarez, 1993). The higher triglyceride levels in shift workers, as compared with day workers, were not ascribable to differences in age, body mass index, diet, energy or alcohol intake, educational level, leisure activities, or smoking (Jenkins, Hames, Zyzanski, Rosenman, & Friedman, 1969; Knutsson, 1989; Romon et al., 1992; Theorell & Akerstedt, 1976). Moreover, in a sample of working men who were tested on four occasions during a year of follow-up, triglyceride levels increased in those with negative life changes and decreased in those with positive life changes (Theorell & Emlund, 1993).

It is thus generally found that significant and even marked rise of plasma total and LDL cholesterol may occur during exposure to a wide variety of stressors in both natural and laboratory settings, at least transiently (Brindley et al., 1993; Dimsdale & Herd, 1982; Rosenman, 1993b). The rapidity of elevations during exposure to mental stressors in the laboratory setting indicates that they are not due to dietary effects. This is also true of greater elevations that occur in a variety of self-perceived stressful situations in naturalistic settings, which are documented in studies in which diet and other potentially confounding variables were well controlled.

It is generally found that a greater rise of plasma cholesterol occurs in response to naturally occurring stressors that are severe or individually perceived as such (Siegrist, Matschinger, Cremer, & Seidel, 1988). This is in keeping with the general belief that differential stress responses depend on the individual appraisal of external stressors and coping capability. Because vulnerable personalities and inept or inappropriate coping methods are far more relevant than the stress exposure per se for determining individual differences in stress perceptions and associated physiologic activity, it is not surprising to find variable plasma cholesterol responses to different types and severity of perceived stress. As also might be expected, emotional reactivity was significantly correlated positively with plasma LDL levels and negatively with HDL concentrations in a large study of employed healthy females (Melamed, 1994). It is not known whether the observed differences in responsiveness to emotional stress parallel differences in individual responsiveness to altered dietary lipid intakes (Hopkins, 1992; Katan, Beynen, De Vries, & Nobels, 1986).

In the next section, I describe studies to support the belief that the sympathetic nervous system mediates the plasma lipid responses to stress.

The Sympathetic Nervous System as Mediator of Effects of Emotional Stress on Plasma Lipids

An infusion of epinephrine elevates plasma cholesterol in rats (Kunihara & Oshima, 1983) and cynomolgus monkeys (Dimsdale, Herd, & Hartley, 1978), and an infusion of norepinephrine elevates both plasma cholesterol and triglyceride levels in rabbits (O'Donnell et al., 1988). A disparity of plasma epinephrine and norepinephrine levels during different stress responses in humans suggested that psychological stress primarily stimulates an adrenomedullary response, whereas exercise stimulates a larger noradrenergic response (Dimsdale & Moss, 1980). This may be misleading, both because catecholamines are increased in most stress responses (Dimsdale & Ziegler, 1991; Hjemdahl, 1990) and because their release is strongly influenced by many factors, including age, diet, energy intake, and measures of body size and fatness (Young et al., 1992).

Conclusions drawn from plasma norepinephrine levels may be particularly misleading. Circulating norepinephrine is a "spillover," derived from various sources, and its plasma levels do not reveal either regional patterns of sympathetic nervous system activity or sites of origin (Hjemdahl, 1990). For example, an increase in plasma is mainly derived from renal nerves during assumption of the upright posture (Esler, 1990), but from both renal and cardiac sources in hypertensive persons (Dimsdale & Ziegler, 1991; Hjemdahl, 1990). Moreover, the norepinephrine concentration in the vicinity of adrenergic receptors is much higher than is reflected by circulating levels (Esler, 1990; Hjemdahl, 1990). The effects of mental stress on stimulating noradrenergic activity in humans are well known (Hjemdahl, 1990), and the evidence primarily implicates sympathetic nervous system activity in the increase of plasma total and LDL cholesterol that can occur at times of perceived stress.

The sympathetic nervous system plays an important and well-known role in regulation of both normal and elevated blood pressures (Esler, 1990; Hjemdahl, 1990; Rosenman, 1989), with an increased central noradrenergic outflow and augmented muscle sympathetic activity particularly in borderline and young hypertensives (E. A. Anderson, Simkey, Lawton, & Mark, 1989; Floras & Hara, 1993). It is therefore relevant that plasma lipids and blood pressure are strongly correlated (Bonaa & Thelle, 1991) and that hypertension is positively associated with higher levels of plasma total and LDL cholesterol (Assmann & Schulte, 1987) and negatively associated with HDL cholesterol (Robinson et al., 1987). As might be expected, antihypertensives that alter noradrenergic activity may increase plasma total and LDL cholesterol levels (Lardinois & Neuman, 1988). Beta-adrenergic blockers that leave alpha-adrenergic activity unopposed thus tend to elevate plasma total and LDL cholesterol, whereas alpha-1 agonists and drugs that diminish noradrenergic activity tend to lower both (Deger, 1986; Kellaway, & Lubbe, 1986).

The autonomic nervous system has a central role in the regulation of the cardiovascular system, which is achieved principally through noradrenergic effects on the function of the heart and kidneys and on large arteries, arterioles, and veins, whereas parasympathetic vagal nerve regulation of the heart rate plays a subsidiary role. As expected, because the sympathetic nervous system regulates body salt and water balance (Esler, 1990), both diuretics and dietary sodium restriction stimulate noradrenergic activity, with associated significant elevation of plasma total and LDL cholesterol levels (E. A. Anderson et al., 1989; Egan, Weder, Petrin, & Hofman, 1991; Kjeldsen et al., 1988; Luft et al., 1979; Ruppert et al., 1991; Weidmann et al., 1983). The evidence strongly suggests a major role of the sympathetic nervous system in the elevated plasma lipids (Egan et al., 1991; Ruppert et al., 1991). Moreover, the rise of plasma cholesterol that is associated with sodium depletion occurs in both normotensives and hypertensives (Egan et al., 1991; Fliser et al., 1993; Fliser, Nowak, & Ritz, 1991; Ruppert et al., 1991).

Acute mental stress can rapidly cause a decrease of plasma volume, which is induced by increased noradrenergic activity, and the hemoconcentration is at least partly responsible for an associated passive rise of plasma cholesterol (Muldoon et al., 1995; Patterson, Gottdiener, Hecht, Vargot, & Krantz, 1993; Stoney et al., 1988). A decreased blood volume due to dependent pooling probably also contributes to the rapid increase of plasma cholesterol that can occur after changing from a supine to erect posture (Hagan, Upton, Avakian, & Grundy, 1986; Tan, Wilmhurst, Gleason, & Soeldner, 1973). Assumption of the upright posture also markedly stimulates sympathetic nervous system activity (Esler, 1990) and can double urinary norepinephrine output, which is derived mainly from renal nerves (Dimsdale & Ziegler, 1991). Increased noradrenergic activity may have a contributing role aside from peripheral vascular effects, because the postural rise of plasma cholesterol may be better correlated with the rise in plasma norepinephrine than with the rise in hematocrit (Howes et al., 1987; Howes, Krum, & Louis, 1988; Stoker & Wynn, 1966).

Moreover, short-term stressors can elevate plasma cholesterol without affecting hematocrit levels (Stoney et al., 1988), for example, after cold water immersion (Kuhl, Beck, Gershberg, Street, & Ralli, 1955). An important role of the sympathetic nervous system, even in short-term fluctuation of plasma lipids, is also suggested by the variable plasma cholesterol response to different stressors by different individuals during emotional arousal. Also, the increase of plasma cholesterol in many studies is greater than can be explained only by hemoconcentration (Egan et al., 1991; Fliser et al., 1993; Ruppert et al., 1991).

It thus seems likely that hemoconcentration can account for only a fraction of the rise of plasma cholesterol that may occur during perceived emotional stress. It also seems possible that higher plasma cholesterol levels observed in natural life settings may partly be related to sympathetic nervous system activity, aside from noradrenergic effects on plasma volume. In support of this is the finding that healthy persons who respond to laboratory stressors with greater increases of catecholamines also have higher plasma cholesterol and triglyceride levels (Jorgensen, Nash, Lasser, Hymovitz, & Langer, 1988; Muldoon et al., 1991). Type A behavior is associated with both enhanced noradrenergic activity (Rosenman & Friedman, 1974; Williams, Suarez, Kuhn, Zimmerman, & Schanberg, 1990), and higher plasma cholesterol levels (Friedman & Rosenman, 1959; Rosenman & Friedman, 1961). Type A persons also often exhibit heightened cardiovascular reactivity to laboratory stressors (Rosenman, 1990), and their higher plasma cholesterol levels are associated with heightened sympathetic nervous system responses (Suarez, Williams, Kuhn, Zimmerman, & Schanberg, 1991). The association of higher plasma cholesterol levels with greater emotional reactivity in healthy employed women is believed to indicate that the propensity to experience sustained emotional arousal, rather than reported life stress, is the factor that is associated with chronic plasma cholesterol elevations (Melamed, 1994).

A rise of plasma triglycerides in association with perceived stress is also ascribed to enhanced noradrenergic activity (Taggart & Carruthers, 1971; Theorell & Akerstedt, 1976) that increases mobilization of fatty acids from adipose tissue (Jenkins et al., 1969). Many studies found that a marked rise of free fatty acids occurs during emotional arousal (Carruthers & Taggart, 1973; Dimsdale & Herd, 1982; Gottschalk, Stone, Glaser, & Iacono, 1969; Taggart & Carruthers, 1971; Taggart et al., 1973), in association with the rise of plasma triglyceride levels (Palmblad et al., 1979; Taggart et al., 1973).

A considerable literature on the effects of emotional stress on plasma lipids in animals has accumulated since an early finding that certain types of stress raise plasma cholesterol levels in squirrel monkeys (Lang, 1967). However, a review of these findings is beyond the present scope.

Various hypotheses are proposed, to explain the mechanism by which increased noradrenergic activity can elevate plasma cholesterol (Brindley et al., 1993). Noradrenergic stimulation may increase plasma cholesterol by suppressing LDL cholesterol receptors that are partly under sympathetic nervous system control (Krone et al., 1985), in keeping with findings that strongly implicate sympathetic neural excitation and increased central noradrenergic outflow in the elevation of plasma cholesterol, which occurs in both animals and humans under emotionally stressful conditions (Jorgensen et al., 1988; Lundberg et al., 1989).

Some of the effects of noradrenergic activity on plasma cholesterol may be mediated by insulin (Brindley et al., 1993). Thus, short-term dietary sodium restriction stimulates sympathetic neural activity and raises plasma levels of both insulin and cholesterol in normotensives, whether they are salt sensitive or resistant (Ruppert et al., 1991). There is an expected inverse relationship between plasma HDL cholesterol and insulin levels (Dean, Jones, Hutchinson, Peters, & Henderson, 1991; Stalder, Pometta, & Suenram, 1982).

The *metabolic* syndrome is defined as a combination of hypertension and abnormalities of glucose and lipid metabolism, which include elevated LDL and lowered HDL cholesterol levels. It is sometimes termed *abdominal* (Cigolini et al., 1995) or *insulin-resistance* syndrome (Howard, Schneiderman, Falkner, Haffner, & Laws, 1993), because it is often combined with abdominal obesity, insulin resistance, and compensatory hyperinsulinemia. An association of visceral obesity with multiple central endocrine disturbances may suggest a *hypothalamic arousal* syndrome, such as occurs after certain stress reactions in primates (Bjorntorp, 1995). The most aggregative factor in the syndrome may be obesity rather than hyperinsulinemia (Cigolini et al., 1995). However, the important role of the sympathetic nervous system in hypertension is associated with insulin resistance independent of obesity (Julius & Jamerson, 1994). Also, insulin administration induces a centrally mediated increase in norepinephrine (Howard et al., 1993).

Moreover, insulin mediates sympathetic nervous system stimulation in response to dietary intake and enhances noradrenergic activity in the obese, and excess weight and hyperinsulinemia are known risk factors for hypertension (Troisi et al., 1991). Body mass index is associated with insulin resistance and increased insulin levels and may contribute to a rise of blood pressure through effects on renal sodium reabsorption and noradrenergic stimulation of peripheral arterioles (Troisi et al., 1991). Impaired glucose tolerance thus strongly correlates with hypertension in both sexes (Kristiansson, Sigfusson, Sigvaldason, & Thorgeirsson, 1995), and the important neurogenic factor in hypertension may itself be the cause of insulin resistance in hypertensives (Julius & Jamerson, 1994). Increased activity in pressor systems that also affect glucose and lipid metabolism may thus account for the hyperinsulinemia, decreased sensitivity to insulin, and lower levels of plasma HDL cholesterol that are commonly found in hypertensives, particularly in those who have a low sodium sensitivity (Lind, Lithell, Gustafsson, Pollare, & Ljunghall, 1992).

Howard et al. (1993) found dyslipidemia to be the most consistent trait of the insulin-resistance syndrome. They also noted that psychological stressors stimulate increases in cortisol and catecholamines and that a resulting reduced sensitivity to insulin and hyperinsulinemia centrally stimulate noradrenergic activity, independent of effects on blood sugar. Although the complex mechanisms by which emotional stress affects plasma lipid levels are not fully clarified, there is considerable evidence to involve the sympathetic nervous system and insulin mediation.

Relationships Between Plasma Cholesterol Levels and Non-Cardiac-Related Mortality

Many epidemiologic and cholesterol-lowering studies have found an increased mortality from various non-cardiac-related causes at low plasma cholesterol levels (International Collaborative Group, 1992; Martin, Hulley, Browner, Kuller, & Wentworth, 1986; Morris et al., 1983; Petersson, Trell, & Hood, 1984). The excess mortality may include an increased risk of hemorrhagic stroke and cancer, as well as death from non-illness-related causes, such as suicide, accidents, and violence (Muldoon & Manuck, 1992). The failure to confirm this in some studies (Iribarren, Reed, Burchfiel, & Dwyer, 1995; Isles, Hole, Gillis, Hawthorne, & Lever, 1989; Kromhout, Bosschieter, Drijver, & Coulander, 1988) may be due to low power to examine these relationships in some and to the lack of participants with significantly low plasma cholesterol levels in others (Jacobs, Muldoon, & Rastam, 1995).

On the other hand, there are many consistent findings. Ischemic heart disease mortality in 50–59-year-old men declined 60% from 1950 to 1970 in the Framingham Heart Study (Sytkowski, Kannel, & D'Agostino, 1990). Although about half of this was ascribed to reduction of risk factors (Sytkowski, Kannel, & D'Agostino, 1991), the 10-year cumulative ischemic heart disease mortality rate was 43% less in the 1970 cohort than in the 1950 cohort. During this interval, its prevalence increased among those free of baseline disease, and its incidence was not significantly lower. A comparison (Seltzer, 1990) with its 30-year follow-up (K. Anderson, Castelli, & Levy, 1987) also showed that overall mortality was almost identical in the two cohorts, due to an increase of non-cardiac-related deaths. Moreover, falling cholesterol levels were related to mortality rates in both sexes. Thus, during a 14-year period, participants whose cholesterol levels fell 14 mg/dl had an 11% higher mortality rate than those whose levels remained constant or increased (K. Anderson et al., 1987). Non-cardiac-related mortality was also significantly related inversely to plasma cholesterol levels during a 3-year follow-up in the European Hypertension Study (Staessen et al., 1990).

An inverse relationship between plasma cholesterol and non-cardiac-related mortality is also observed in cholesterol-lowering intervention trials, in which a lack of effects on overall mortality is ascribed to an increase from non-cardiac-related causes (Canner et al., 1986; Committee of Principal Investigators, 1980; Hjermann, Holme, & Leren, 1986). Thus, there was an increase of such mortality in primary prevention trials such as the World Health Organization's clofibrate study (Committee of Principal Investigators, 1980); the Lipid Research Clinics Coronary Primary Prevention Trial (Lipid Research Clinics Investigators, 1984, 1992), of men given both diet and cholestyramine; and the Helsinki Heart Study, of men given both diet and gemfibrozil (Frick et al., 1987). Indeed, several meta-analyses (Muldoon, Manuck, & Matthews, 1990; Peto, Yusuf, & Collins, 1991; Roussow, Lewis, & Rifkind, 1990) found that a common denominator of lowering plasma cholesterol was a significant increase of non-cardiac-related deaths and that this was observed too consistently to be explained by chance or statistical quirks (Oliver, 1990).

Although one meta-analysis found the increase in such mortality to extend to secondary prevention trials (Ravnskov, 1992), it has particularly been observed in epidemiologic studies and primary prevention programs (Holme, 1990; Roussow, Canner, & Hulley, 1991; Santiago & Dalen, 1994). The excess mortality was found to be associated with lowering plasma cholesterol either by drugs or diet (Muldoon et al., 1990) but appears to be mainly observed in single-factor cholesterol-lowering trials that used drug treatments (Davey Smith & Pekkanen, 1992).

Davis and Havlik (1977) noted the small probability of finding proof of the belief that diet intervention could effectively lower plasma cholesterol and thereby reduce primary ischemic heart disease mortality (LaRosa et al., 1990). Thus, only slight fall of plasma cholesterol occurred on stringent diets in the Lipid Research Clinics (Lipid Research Clinics Investigators, 1992; Lipid Research Clinics Program, 1984); Helsinki (Frick et al., 1987); and North Karelia (Puska et al., 1989) studies, with little evidence that less than severe dietary changes can lower plasma cholesterol to levels that might prevent ischemic heart disease (McCormick & Skrabanek, 1988; Muldoon et al., 1990; Ramsay, Yeo, & Jackson, 1991). Cholesterol-lowering drugs are far more effective than diet for lowering plasma cholesterol, and the excess of non-cardiac-related deaths in drug studies is as significant as the decrease of ischemic heart disease mortality (Yusuf, Wittles, & Friedman, 1988a, 1988b). The relatively smaller excess of non-cardiac-related mortality in single-factor cholesterol-lowering-diet studies may plausibly be due to the failure of such diets to significantly lower plasma cholesterol levels (Neil et al., 1995; Rosenman, 1993a).

The excess non-cardiac-related mortality associated with low plasma cholesterol levels in epidemiologic and cholesterol-lowering studies may include higher risk of hemorrhagic stroke, cancer, and non-illness-related causes (Muldoon & Manuck, 1992). Hemorrhagic stroke was related to low plasma cholesterol in long-term follow-up in the Multiple Risk Factor Intervention Trial (MRFIT; Iso, Jacobs, Wentworth, Neaton, & Cohen, 1989; Neaton et al., 1992). One systematic review of randomized cholesterol-lowering trials concluded that the only cause of death attributable to low plasma cholesterol was hemorrhagic stroke (Law, Thompson, & Wald, 1994).

However, there is considerable evidence that the inverse association between plasma cholesterol and non-cardiac-related mortality includes an increased cancer mortality (Beaglehole, Foulkes, Prior, & Eyles, 1980), which is found during follow-up in many prospective and intervention studies (Carlson & Rosenhamer, 1988; Feinleib, 1981; Frick et al., 1987; Hjermann et al., 1986). The Framingham Study found an excess risk of cancer mortality at low cholesterol levels in older participants. In its 30-year follow-up (K. Anderson et al., 1987), after exclusion of those with intake cancer, plasma cholesterol was inversely related to cancer mortality in men under age 60. An inverse cholesterol–cancer mortality relationship was also observed during the 3-year follow-up in the European Hypertension Study (Staessen et al., 1990). Moreover, an inverse relationship, mainly for gastrointestinal cancer mortality in men, was found in a 28-year follow-up among 1,476 male and 1,469 female, 40–65-year-old, Dutch civil service workers and spouses who participated in a general health survey in 1953–1954 (Schuitt, Van Dijk, Dekker, Schouten, & Kok, 1993). Other findings also have particularly implicated colon cancer (Cowan et al., 1990; Kagan, McGee, Yano, Rhoads, & Nomura, 1981; Kozarevic et al., 1981; Stemmerman, Chyou, Kagan, Nomura, & Yano, 1991). However, a recent follow-up in the Honolulu Heart Program did not find a relationship between cancer mortality and total plasma cholesterol levels in the absence of factors such as smoking and high alcohol consumption (Iribarren et al., 1995).

Although the inverse relationship is more often found in older men (Feinleib, 1981, 1982), it is also observed at younger ages (Garcia-Palmieri et al., 1978) and occurs in primary cholesterol-lowering prevention trials, rather than in secondary prevention trials (Muldoon & Manuck, 1992). Although there was an increase of cancer mortality in older men given a cholesterol-lowering diet in a primary prevention trial in a domiciliary home (Dayton, Pearce, Hashimoto, Dixon, & Tomiyasu, 1969), the low plasma cholesterol–cancer association is not generally observed in dietary trials (Kritchevsky, 1992). However, this may be due to an inability of less-than-severe cholesterol-lowering diets to lower plasma cholesterol below threshold levels (Davis & Havlik, 1977; Neil et al., 1995; Rosenman, 1993a).

The relationship of low plasma cholesterol to cancer and other non-cardiac-related mortality has variously been ascribed to confounding variables (Jacobs et al., 1992), such as smoking, high alcohol intake, and untreated hypertension (Iribarren et al., 1995). It also has been denigrated (Cade, Barker, Margetts, & Morris, 1988) on the basis that low levels may only be markers for preclinical cancer and other undiagnosed serious illness that is nevertheless present at intake into studies (Lewis & Tikkanen, 1884; Rose & Shipley, 1980; Sherwin et al., 1987; Stamler, 1987). Although this might explain some of the association, the consistency of findings cannot be simply dismissed (Feinleib, 1981, 1982; Jacobs et al., 1992). The latter belief is well supported by long-term follow-up in persons screened for the MRFIT, among whom there was a persistent inverse relationship between total plasma cholesterol and cancer mortality (Neaton et al., 1992).

The inverse plasma cholesterol–cancer relationship persisted in the Framingham Study after exclusion of those with intake cancer and early deaths (K. Anderson et al., 1987). Also, after adjustment for alcohol intake and smoking in the study of the Dutch civil service worker cohort, the inverse association between plasma cholesterol and cancer mortality persisted over the entire 28 years of follow-up (Schuit, Van Dijk, et al., 1993). It seems likely that the relationship cannot simply be ascribed to low cholesterol levels caused by certain types of malignancies (Markel & Brook, 1994) or undetected preclinical cancer (Salmond, Beaglehole, & Prior, 1985), although the low levels may in fact be markers for the later disease.

A recent extensive review of the literature (Markel & Brook, 1994) noted that the low plasma cholesterol association with cancer is found in many prospective and retrospective studies and other sporadic reports. There is dual evidence, because participants with low cholesterol levels develop cancer more frequently, and on the other hand, patients with cancer show a higher prevalence of hypocholesteremia, although less consistently in females than in males.

The increased mortality that occurs in association with low or lowered plasma cholesterol also includes causes that are unrelated to illness (Neaton et al., 1992). The mortality outcomes in randomized primary prevention trials of cholesterol-lowering measures thus showed an excess of deaths from accident, violence, trauma, and suicide among treated men (Muldoon et al., 1993). The increase in non-illness-related mortality in the eight largest single-intervention, randomized trials was greater than the reduction of cardiac mortality and was observed in both dietary and drug studies.

Although it was noted (Paul & Hennekens, 1991) that the increase of such deaths in the Helsinki Businessmen Study (Strandberg et al., 1991) cannot be disregarded, the findings are ascribed to chance (Paul & Hennekens, 1992). However, a similar experience was also found in many other cholesterol-lowering trials (Lindberg, Rastam, Gullberg, & Eklund, 1992; Miettinen, Turpeinen, Karvonen, Elosuo, & Paavilainen, 1972; Pekkanen, 1993), including the large Helsinki (Frick et al., 1987) and Lipid Research Clinics (Lipid Research Clinics Investigators, 1984, 1992) trials. The consistency of findings at high levels of statistical significance (Newman, Browner, & Hulley, 1992) in cholesterol-lowering primary prevention trials (Muldoon et al., 1990, 1993) supports this unique but valid relationship, despite a contrary analysis (Cummings & Psaty, 1994a) that may be due to some differences in the population base (Cummings & Psaty, 1994b; Muldoon, 1994). Moreover, although ascribed mainly to drug effects (Modest, 1992), the excess mortality may not entirely be restricted to drug-treatment trials (Muldoon et al., 1993; Strandberg, 1992).

An accumulating body of evidence thus suggests that lowering plasma cholesterol to relatively low levels increases the risk of death from violent causes (Muldoon et al., 1993). Although the data cannot prove this, low levels do appear to be associated with increased mortality from accidents and violence during follow-up in epidemiologic studies (Jacobs et al., 1992), including the long-term follow-up in men screened in the MRFIT (Neaton et al., 1992). Moreover, the inverse relationship is also supported by other studies. For example, plasma cholesterol levels were significantly lower in a large number of participants hospitalized for parasuicide, compared with a paired cohort admitted for other reasons (Gallerini et al., 1988).

Relationships Among Plasma Cholesterol, Emotions, and Behaviors

The apparent inverse association between plasma cholesterol and mortality from suicide and violence stimulated many new areas of study, including the possible relationships of plasma cholesterol to mental disorders (Ryman, 1994). Plasma cholesterol was found to be related to cognitive efficiency in one study of 270 male and female students, in whom low levels were associated with slower movement and decision-making times (Benton, 1995). Low plasma cholesterol levels below 160 mg/dl were also more frequent in 203 patients hospitalized because of affective disorders, in comparison with 1,595 persons who were self-referred in an urban supermarket screening (Glueck et al., 1994). Moreover, the patients with affective disorders also had significantly lower total and LDL cholesterol levels, compared with NHANES II population data, and the findings were not ascribable to medications.

Various studies have linked plasma cholesterol with aggression in humans, although no relationships were found in the Whitehall Study of United Kingdom civil servants (Gottschalk et al., 1969; Knutsson, 1989) or the Edinburgh Artery Study of middle-aged men (Fowkes et al., 1992). Aggressiveness was found to be associated with higher cholesterol levels both in adult men (Harlan, Oberman, Mitchell, & Graybiel, 1967; Sletten, Nilsen, Young, & Anderson, 1964) and college students (Sloane, Davidson, Holland, & Payne, 1962). However, it differed from pathologic types of aggression and was associated with competitiveness in the men (Harlan et al., 1967; Sletten et al., 1964) and with competitiveness and restlessness in the students (Sloane et al., 1962).

In contrast, lowering plasma cholesterol in community samples was associated with an increased aggression-related mortality due to violence (Kaplan, Manuck, & Shumaker, 1992). Low cholesterol levels in men have been associated with low scores on adherence to social norms (Jenkins et al., 1969) and with pathologic aggressive behavior. They were thus correlated with aggressive conduct disorders and habitual violent tendencies (Virkkunen, 1979; Virkkunen & Penttinen, 1984) and with violence in men when under the influence of alcohol (Virkkunen, 1983). One retrospective analysis found that 106 male patients in a maximum security forensic hospital for violent psychiatric behavior had lower cholesterol levels than in a general population (Hillbrand, Spitz, & Foster, 1995). The levels were below 200 mg/dl in the 66% of patients who had engaged in more frequent aggressive behavior, although these patients did not show differences in verbal versus physical aggression or exhibit the greater severity of aggression that was previously found in an earlier study of similar patients (Hillbrand & Foster, 1993).

The association of low plasma cholesterol with antisocial personality was not observed in all studies (Stewart & Stewart, 1981) but is strongly supported (Jacobs et al., 1995) by the findings in a large cohort that was randomly drawn and enriched with participants who had psychiatric diagnoses. This was a cross-sectional study (Freedman et al., 1995) of several psychologic characteristics and plasma cholesterol levels in 3,490 men who were 31–45 years old and had served in the U.S. Army with the rank of sergeant or lower between 1965 and 1971. After adjustments for education, smoking, weight, medications, and other possible confounding variables, the mean plasma total cholesterol was significantly higher among 697 men with generalized anxiety disorder and lower among 325 men with antisocial personality disorders. The findings, of course, do not establish causal relationships.

Various mechanisms have been hypothesized to explain aggressive and violent behaviors that are associated with low or lowered plasma cholesterol levels. Aggressive behavior has been considered to be caused by elevated plasma triglycerides, but the converse sequence, operating through sympathetic nervous system activity, is a more reasonable explanation (Sugden, 1992). It also was suggested that antilipidemic drug treatment induces emotional distress that is associated with depression in males (Ketterer, Brymer, Rhoads, Kraft, & Goldberg, 1994), and it has been postulated that lowering plasma cholesterol may cause negative mood changes and thereby increase the probability of negative responding (Kaplan et al., 1992). Lower cholesterol levels were associated with depression in several studies (Rahe et al., 1971; Sletten et al., 1964; Sloane, Habib, Eveson, & Payne, 1961; van Doornen, 1980; Voldet, Scheidegger, & Garbone, 1959). However, no relationship with major depression was found in the follow-up of a large random sample of U.S. Army personnel (Freedman et al., 1995).

A possible relationship between plasma cholesterol and aggression is under ongoing investigation in animals. Shively, Knox, Sherwin, Walsh, and Wilson (1993) reviewed some aspects of the influence of psychosocial factors on lipid metabolism in cynomolgus monkeys. Females with low social status are subordinates in the important social status hierarchy and are behaviorally and physiologically different than dominant females. The females with low social status are the objects of more aggression, are more socially isolated, and are stressed, as judged by their cortisol hypersecretion in response to an ACTH challenge. Also, they have lower plasma HDL cholesterol levels. However, social disruption did not raise plasma cholesterol levels in monkeys (Kaplan et al., 1993).

Juvenile cynomolgus monkeys of both sexes that consumed a low-cholesterol diet were more aggressive and less affiliative and had lower cerebrospinal fluid levels of 5-hydroxyindolacetic acid than did their high-cholesterol-diet counterparts, suggesting that dietary lipids can influence brain neurochemistry and behavior. Adults randomized to a low-fat–low-cholesterol diet also were more aggressive than those fed a high-fat–high-cholesterol diet (Kaplan, Manuck, & Shively, 1991). Lowering dietary cholesterol intake in cynomolgus monkeys may thus be associated with reduced central serotonergic activity and increased aggressive behavior

(Kaplan et al., 1991, 1994; Muldoon, Kaplan, Manuck, & Mann, 1992). Male macaques with low central 5-hydroxytryptamine responsivity also exhibited increased aggression in both social and nonsocial settings (Kyes, Botchin, Kaplan, Manuck, & Mann, 1995). It is thus postulated (Kaplan et al., 1994) either that low cholesterol intake may exacerbate aggression or that a high-fat–high-cholesterol diet may suppress antagonistic behavior that might occur on the lower dietary fat and cholesterol intake that is more normal for such animals. Further discussion of animal studies is beyond the present scope, but it is significant that a low-cholesterol diet appears to cause increased aggression and that low central 5-hydroxytryptamine activity is also associated with a tendency toward aggressive behavior, in support of the data that link reduced central serotonergic activity with aggression in both humans and nonhuman primates (Kyes et al., 1995) and with violence and suicidal behavior in humans (Kaplan et al., 1994).

Increased attention is thus being given to serotonin, the neurotransmitter that appears to play a role in plasma cholesterol–behavior relationships (Adler, 1993). Central serotonergic mechanisms are strongly implicated in aggressive responding (Brown, Botsis, & van Praag, 1994) and hypothesized to mediate the link between cholesterol levels and aggression in humans (Virkkunen, Horrobin, Jenkins, & Manku, 1987). Low cholesterol levels may alter brain serotonin levels and disinhibit aggressive behavior (Gray et al., 1993) and thereby relate to depression, suicide, and violent death (Coccaro & Astill, 1990). It is relevant that obesity in humans is associated with lower cerebrospinal fluid concentrations of serotonin metabolites, which may link low central serotonin levels with peripheral metabolic and other abnormalities (Bjorntorp, 1995). Some of these mechanisms are explored in greater depth elsewhere in this book.

Plasma cholesterol levels also have been correlated with other personality, behavioral, and psychological variables (Jenkins et al., 1969), and some that are associated with low cholesterol levels, such as depression, may be related to suicide and violent death (Morgan, Palinkas, Barrett-Connor, & Wingard, 1993). Higher cholesterol levels were associated with extraversion (Sloane et al., 1961); with competitiveness and aggressiveness in adult men (Harlan et al., 1967; Sletten et al., 1964); and with aggressiveness, competitiveness, and restlessness in college students (Sloane et al., 1962). Higher levels were also associated with higher drive and restless impatience in one adult male sample (Jenkins, Rosenman, & Friedman, 1966), and with greater adherence to social norms and restless impatience, competitiveness, social activity, and active drive in other male samples (Jenkins et al., 1969; Sloane et al., 1961).

Many of these behaviors characterize persons with the Type A behavior pattern (Rosenman, 1990), in whom cholesterol levels tend to be higher than in Type B persons (Friedman & Rosenman, 1959; Kornitzer, Dramaix, de Backer, & Thilly, 1977; Rosenman & Friedman, 1961; Weidner, Sexton, McClelland, Connor, & Matarazzo, 1987). However, only small differences are found in random samples in which the respective behavior patterns are more simplistically assessed (Rosenman et al., 1975).

Plasma cholesterol was correlated with anger dimensions in one study (Rahe et al., 1971) and with adjudged Type A behavioral hostility in males (Jenkins et al., 1966) in the Western Collaborative Group Study (Rosenman et al., 1975). Young Type A persons of both sexes had elevated cholesterol levels in the Oregon family study (Weidner et al., 1987). Although correlations with hostility alone were found only in males in this cohort, the highest levels were found in those who scored high on both Type A behavior and hostility. Both Type A behavior and hostility were also correlated with plasma cholesterol in both sexes in another study (Lundberg et al., 1989). Fasting plasma triglyceride also tends to be higher in Type A males (Friedman, Rosenman, & Byers, 1964) and was correlated with hostile behaviors in males in the Edinburgh Artery Study (Fowkes et al., 1992). However, plasma cholesterol was not related to hostility in the Edinburgh Artery Study or in a study of adolescents (Siegel, 1984) or other samples (Shekelle, Gale, Ostfeld, & Paul, 1983). Moreover, no predictive relationship was found between plasma cholesterol and hostility in the follow-up of a large random sample of military personnel (Freedman et al., 1995).

Expressive hostility was found to be associated with increased total and LDL cholesterol in both sexes but was not related to hostile emotions in another study (Dujovne & Houston, 1991). Although young healthy males did not have a worsening of emotions on a cholesterol-lowering diet (Weidner, Connor, Hollis, & Connor, 1992), this was assessed by a simple self-report of symptoms. Moreover, the diet had only small effects on lowering cholesterol levels.

The somewhat confusing results in this area may be partly due to varied methodology and partly due to major difficulties of definition of hostility–anger dimensions. Those who attempt to relate dimensions of anger, hostility, or aggression may operationally define different constructs by using a confusing array of dissimilar methods in their studies, often interchangeably and without appropriate differentiation (Megargee, 1985). This results in considerable ambiguity and inconsistency in how these constructs overlap or are defined, separated, or measured (Rosenman, 1991).

Plasma cholesterol levels also have been related to feelings of depression (Rahe et al., 1971; Sletten et al., 1964; Sloane et al., 1961; van Doornen, 1980; Voldet, Scheidegger, & Garbone, 1959), and higher levels were found in depressed psychiatric patients in some (Sloane et al., 1961; Voldet et al., 1959) but not all studies (Freedman et al., 1995). However, in persons without mental illness, higher cholesterol levels appear to be associated with outgoing sociability, and lower levels appear to be associated with shyness and an antisocial personality (Harlan et al., 1967; Kornitzer et al., 1977). Moreover, the patients in a state psychiatric hospital who had behaviors resembling those living in the community and who manifested greater drive, energy, and emotional reactions had higher cholesterol levels, whereas the lowest levels were found in those who had regressed and withdrawn from active life (Sletten et al., 1964). Furthermore, Type A persons tend to be highly involved in life activities (Rosenman, 1990) and to exhibit higher plasma total cholesterol levels (Lundberg et al., 1989; Rosenman & Friedman, 1974) than Type B persons. Even after controlling for many potentially confounding variables, low plasma total cholesterol levels characterize older, depressed men (Morgan et al., 1993). In their commentary, Jacobs et al. (1995) noted that cross-sectional studies (Fowkes et al., 1992; Lindberg, Larsson, & Setterlind, 1994; Morgan et al., 1993) and studies comparing psychiatric patients with controls (Glueck et al., 1994; Virkkunen, 1979) generally agree in observing a linkage between low plasma cholesterol levels and depression and violent behavior, despite lack of ideal control for confounding factors. However, the correlations between plasma cholesterol and depressive mood are confined to males in cross-sectional studies (Freedman et al., 1995; Lindberg et al., 1994; Morgan et al., 1993).

The higher plasma cholesterol levels associated with "activation" (Jenkins et al., 1969) are in keeping with findings of long-term prisoners who, regardless of their social isolation and various emotional and other stresses, are withdrawn from a usual active life and its time pressures. Long-term prison inmates in the United States were thus found to have low cholesterol levels, despite high-fat diets (Hatch, Reisell, Poon-King, Canellas, & Lees, 1966; Sprague, 1966). Among 274 participants who had committed offenses in Finland, those who had antisocial personality features also had lower cholesterol levels than in a control group with other personality disorders (Virkkunen, 1979; Virkkunen & Penttinen, 1984).

Anxiety may play an important role in lipid responses to perceived stress, probably operating through the sympathetic nervous system (Hjemdahl, 1990). Thus, a rise of plasma total and LDL cholesterol occurred in students during anticipation of examinations, in the absence of dietary changes (O'Donnell et al., 1987; van Doornen & Orlebeke, 1982). A 36% average elevation of plasma cholesterol occurred during anticipation of immersion in cold water (Peterson et al., 1960), and an over 25% elevation occurred in anticipation of surgery (Peterson, Keith, & Wilcox, 1962; Sane & Kukreti, 1978). The increased plasma cholesterol in young cadets at the U.S. Air Force Academy was correlated with perceived stress and was adjudged to reflect the need for a sustained increase in physical or mental performance (Clarke et al., 1975). A role of anxiety in this response also is suggested by the rise that occurred during other anticipatory stress (O'Donnell et al., 1987; Peterson et al., 1960; Sane & Kukreti, 1978; van Doornen & Orlebeke, 1982). This was specifically found in frogmen during periods of anxiety that occurred while in underwater demolition team training (Rahe, Rubin, Arthur, & Clark, 1968).

A relationship with anxiety also is suggested by findings that the higher cholesterol levels in medical students at times of important school exams (Dreyfuss & Czackes, 1959; Grundy & Griffin, 1959a, 1959b; Thomas & Murphy, 1958; Wertlake et al., 1958) are more likely to occur during initial than later weeks of school (Thomas & Murphy, 1958) and, similarly, during early phases of training periods in other samples (Clarke et al., 1975; Francis, 1979; Rahe et al., 1968, 1971). This is in keeping with the rise that can occur in association with poor performance in school (Bloch & Brackenridge, 1972; Rahe et al., 1974) and with failed training programs (Campbell & Rahe, 1974; Rahe et al., 1976), stressful interviews (Wolf et al., 1962), stressful life events (Cathey et al., 1962; Hammarsten et al., 1957; Pinter et al., 1979; Rahe et al., 1974), emotional upsets (Groen et al., 1962), work shutdown (Kasl et al., 1968), major work deadlines (Rosenman & Friedman 1957), and laboratory stress tests (Muldoon et al., 1991; Peterson et al., 1960; Stoney et al., 1988).

Anxiety may also underlie the observed higher cholesterol levels associated with anger and hostility dimensions in some studies (Jenkins et al., 1966; Lundberg et al., 1989; Rahe et al., 1971; Rosenman et al., 1975; Weidner et al., 1987) and with the inappropriate competitiveness that appears to be the fundamental component of the Type A behavior pattern (Rosenman, 1990). This is also suggested by the correlation of plasma cholesterol with neuroticism and emotional instability (van Doornen, 1980). Moreover, among males under study for coronary disease, higher cholesterol levels were found in those who were taking tranquilizers for their anxiety (Chapman et al., 1966). It is therefore highly significant that the large cross-sectional study of random men, age 31–45 years, who had formerly served in the U.S. Army with the rank of sergeant or lower, found a significantly higher adjusted mean plasma cholesterol level among those with a generalized anxiety disorder, which was ascribed to increased sympathoadrenal activity (Freedman et al., 1995). It is also of interest that the rise of fatty acids that occurs during acute stressor situations (Dimsdale & Herd, 1982), including stress interviews, exposure to laboratory stressors, and watching erotic or suspenseful films, is associated with feelings of fear and anxiety (Gottschalk et al., 1969).

The problems inherent to defining, assessing, and separating personality and behavioral traits, to determine their independent relationship to plasma cholesterol levels, become more difficult in view of mixed findings. For example, plasma cholesterol levels were correlated with both anxiety and depression in young, obese persons (Segers & Mertens, 1976). In a recent study of adults, the highest cholesterol levels in men were found in those who repress negative emotions, and the lowest cholesterol levels were found in those with little anxiety, but the converse was found in women (Niaura, Herbert, McMahon, & Sommerville, 1992). Moreover, the elevation of plasma cholesterol in U.S. Navy underwater demolition trainees during the early phase of their training was correlated positively with feelings of depression, anger, fear, and lethargy and negatively with motivation, arousal, and happiness (Rahe et al., 1971). However, an association of achievement motivation and elevation of plasma cholesterol was found in another study of male students (van Doornen & Orlebeke, 1982). Furthermore, relationships between psychological factors and plasma lipids may weaken or even change over time. For example, an elevation of plasma cholesterol that was associated with extraversion at the beginning of a physical fitness program was not found at its end (Ismail & Young, 1977). In a longitudinal study of 20 young, male U.S. Navy Underwater Demolition Team trainees, who were repeatedly sampled over a 2-month period, there were statistically significant negative correlations between the trainees' measures of motivation, arousal, and happiness and their plasma cholesterol levels and positive correlations between their moods and feelings of anger, fear, depression, and lethargy and cholesterol levels (Rahe et al., 1971). Although correlations were consistent, the level of relationships varied over time, and the investigators were apparently unable to separate the individual emotions.

This chapter is not an exhaustive review either of relationships between plasma lipids and emotional stress or psychological variables or of causal mechanisms underlying them. Some studies were not included because they were of low power to test stated objectives or were not well defined or controlled. Various cited studies may also be critiqued for less than ideal control of baseline or follow-up lipid measurements or of definition and assessment of psychological variables, as noted by others (Dimsdale & Herd, 1982; Muldoon et al., 1995). Many of the additional studies can be found in another review of lipids in psychological research (Niaura, Stoney, & Herbert, 1992). However, this field has many difficult assessment problems, and the stated results of published studies cannot always be accepted at face value.

Summary

Plasma lipids have been widely studied in response to diverse stressors in both laboratory and natural settings. Experimental behavioral stress elicits short-term increases that can also occur with perceived emotional stress in natural milieus. Variable responses may be due to differential appraisal of external stressors, coping ability, and anxiety, with a greater rise of plasma cholesterol occurring in response to severe stress or when perceived as such. Noradrenergic stimulation may increase plasma cholesterol in response to emotional stress by suppressing susceptible LDL receptors and through complex interrelationships with other hormones, possibly mediated by insulin.

Plasma cholesterol is correlated also with certain personality–behavioral variables. Noradrenergic activity may explain higher cholesterol levels that are associated with behavioral activation and lower levels that are associated with relative withdrawal from active life participation. Individuals with high levels of neuroendocrine reactivity to stressors are thus more likely to have higher resting plasma cholesterol levels.

Epidemiologic studies and primary cholesterol-lowering trials find that an excess mortality occurs at relatively low plasma cholesterol levels from causes that include violence, accidents, and suicide. There is considerable evidence to associate low plasma cholesterol levels with an aggression-related mortality due to violent behaviors. Central serotonergic and noradrenergic mechanisms play a role in relationships between plasma cholesterol and psychological variables, and lowering plasma cholesterol may be associated with a reduced central serotonergic activity, which mediates the link between plasma cholesterol levels and aggressive responding and between low plasma cholesterol and increased mortality from violent causes. There is increasing evidence that psychological factors may contribute to the regulation of plasma lipid and lipoprotein levels.

References

Adler, T. (1993, April). Researchers sing low cholesterol blues. *APA Monitor*, pp. 14–15.

Anderson, E. A., Simkey, C. A., Lawton, W. J., & Mark, A. L. (1989). Elevated sympathetic nerve activity in borderline hypertensive humans. *Hypertension, 14*, 177–183.

Anderson, K., Castelli, W. P., & Levy, D. (1987). Cholesterol and mortality: 30 years of follow-up from the Framingham Study. *Journal of the American Medical Association, 257*, 2176–2180.

Arguellos, A., Martinez, M., Hoffman, C., Ortiz, G., & Chekhberdemian, M. (1972). Corti-coadrenal overactivity and hyperlipidemia in prolonged emotional stress. *Hormones, 3*, 167–174.

Assmann, G., & Schulte, H. (1987). The prospective cardiovascular Munster Study: Prevalence and prognostic significance of hyperlipidemia in men with systemic hypertension. *American Journal of Cardiology, 59*, 9G–17G.

Beaglehole, R., Foulkes, M. A., Prior, I. A. M., & Eyles, E. (1980). Cholesterol and mortality in New Zealand Maoris. *British Medical Journal, 280*, 285–287.

Beischer, D. (1956). Effect of simulated flight stress on concentration of serum cholesterol and lipoproteins. *Journal of Aviation Medicine, 27*, 260–266.

Benton, D. (1995). Do low cholesterol levels slow mental processing? *Psychosomatic Medicine, 57*, 50–53.

Bjorntorp, P. (1995). Neuroendocrine abnormalities in human obesity. *Metabolism, 44*(Suppl. 2), 38–41.

Bloch, S., & Brackenridge, C. (1972). Psychological performance and biochemical factors in medical students under examination stress. *Journal of Psychosomatic Research, 16*, 25–33.

Bonaa, K. H., & Thelle, D. S. (1991). Association between blood pressure and serum lipids in a population: The Tromso Study. *Circulation, 83*, 1305–1314.

Bookstein, L., Gidding, S. S., Donovan, M., & Smith, F. A. (1990). Day-to-day variability of serum cholesterol, triglyceride, and high-density-lipoprotein cholesterol levels. *Archives of Internal Medicine, 150*, 1653–1657.

Brindley, D. N., McCann, B. S., Niaura, R., Stoney, C. M., & Suarez, E. C. (1993). Stress and lipoprotein metabolism: Modulators and mechanisms. *Metabolism, 42*(Suppl. 1), 3–15.

Brown, S. L., Botsis, A., & van Praag, H. M. (1994). Serotonin and aggression. In M. Hillbrand (Ed.), *Psychobiology of aggression*. Binghamton, NY: Haworth Press.

Cade, J. E., Barker, D. J. P., Margetts, B. M., & Morris, J. A. (1988). Diet and inequalities in health in three English towns. *British Medical Journal, 296*, 359–1362.

Campbell, D., & Rahe, R. (1974). Serum uric acid and cholesterol variability for men aboard a Polaris submarine. *Military Medicine, 129*, 462–465.

Canner, P. L., Berge, K. G., Wenger, N. K., Stamler, J., Friedman, L., Prineas, R. J., & Friedewald, W. (1986). Fifteen year mortality in the Coronary Drug Project patients: Long-term benefits with niacin. *Journal of the American College of Cardiology, 8*, 245–255.

Carlson, L. A., Levi, L., & Oro, L. (1972). Stressor-induced changes in plasma lipids and urinary excretion of catecholamines, and their modification by nicotinic acid. *Acta Medica Scandinavica*, Suppl. 528, 91–105.

Carlson, L. A., & Rosenhamer, G. (1988). Reduction of mortality in Stockholm Ischaemic Heart Disease Secondary Prevention Study by combined treatment with clofibrate and nicotinic acid. *Acta Medica Scandinavica, 223*, 405–418.

Carruthers, M., & Taggart, P. (1973). Vagotonicity of violence: Biochemical and cardiac responses to violent films. *British Medical Journal, 3*, 384–389.

Cathey, C., Jones, H., Naughton, J., Hammarsten, J., & Wolf, S. (1962). The relation of life stress to serum lipids in patients with coronary artery disease. *American Journal of Medicine, 244,* 421–425.

Chapman, J. M., Reeder, L. G., Massey, F. J., Borune, E. R., Picken, B., Browning, G. C., Coulsen, A. H., & Zimmerman, J. H. (1966). Relationships of stress, tranquilizers and serum cholesterol levels in a sample population under study for coronary heart disease. *American Journal of Epidemiology, 83,* 537–546.

Christian, J. C., Borhani, N. O., Castelli, W. P., Fabsitz, R., Norton, J. A., Reed, T., Rosenman, R. H., Wood, P. D., & Yu, P. L. (1987). Plasma cholesterol variation in the National Heart, Lung and Blood Institute Twin Study. *Genetic Epidemiology, 4,* 433–446.

Cigolini, M., Seidell, J. C., Targher, G., Deslypere, J. P., Ellsinger, B. M., Charzewska, J., Crux, A., & Bjorntorp, P. (1995). Fasting serum insulin in relation to components of the metabolic syndrome in European healthy men: The European Fat Distribution Study. *Metabolism, 44,* 35–40.

Clarke, N. P., Arnold, E. L., Foulds, E. L., Brown, D. M., Eastmed, D. R., & Parry, E. M. (1975). Serum urate and cholesterol levels in Air Force Academy cadets. *Aviation Space & Environmental Medicine, 46,* 1044–1048.

Committee of Principal Investigators. (1980). Report of a WHO co-operative trial on primary prevention of ischemic heart disease using clofibrate to lower serum cholesterol mortality follow-up. *The Lancet, 2,* 379–384.

Coccaro, E. F., & Astill, J. L. (1990). Central serotonergic function in parasuicide. *Progress in Neuro-Psychopharmacology and Biological Psychiatry, 14,* 663–674.

Cowan, L. D., O'Connell, D., Criqui, M. H., Barrett-Connor, E., Bush, T., & Wallace, R. B. (1990). Cancer mortality and lipid levels: The LRC Program Mortality Follow-up Study. *American Journal of Epidemiology, 131,* 468–482.

Cummings, P., & Psaty, B. M. (1994a). The association between cholesterol and death from injury. *Annals of Internal Medicine, 120,* 848–855.

Cummings, P., & Psaty, B. (1994b). Injury, death, and cholesterol: [Letter to the editor]. *Archives of Internal Medicine, 121,* 719–720.

Davey Smith, G., & Pekkanen, J. (1992). Should there be a moratorium on the use of cholesterol lowering drugs? *British Medical Journal, 304,* 431–434.

Davis, C. E., & Havlik, R. J. (1977). Clinical trials of lipid lowering and coronary artery disease prevention. In B. M. Rifkind & R. I. Levy (Eds.), *Hyperlipidemia: Diagnosis and therapy* (pp. 79–92). New York: Grune & Stratton.

Dayton, S., Pearce, M. L., Hashimoto, S., Dixon, W. J., & Tomiyasu, U. (1969). A controlled clinical trial of a diet high in unsaturated fat in preventing complications of atherosclerosis. *Circulation, 39*(Suppl. 2), 1–63.

Dean, J. D., Jones, C. J. H., Hutchinson, S. J., Peters, J. R., & Henderson, A. H. (1991). Hyperinsulinemia and microvascular angina ("syndrome X"). *The Lancet, 337,* 456–457.

De Backer, G., Kornitzer, M., Dromaix, M., Peeters, H., & Kittel, F. (1987). Irregular working hours and lipid levels in men. In G. Schlist, & H. Norl (Eds.), *Expanding horizons in atherosclerosis research* (pp. 217–224). Berlin, Germany: Springer-Verlag.

Deger, G. (1986). Effect of terazosin on serum lipids. *American Journal of Medicine, 80,* 82–85.

Dimsdale, J. E., & Herd, A. (1982). Variability of plasma lipids in response to emotional arousal. *Psychosomatic Medicine, 44,* 413–430.

Dimsdale, J. E., Herd, J. A., & Hartley, J. H. (1978). Epinephrine mediated increases in plasma cholesterol. *Psychosomatic Medicine, 45,* 227–232.

Dimsdale, J. E., & Moss. J. (1980). Plasma catecholamines in stress and exercise. *Journal of the American Medical Association, 243,* 340–342.

Dimsdale, J. E., & Ziegler, M. G. (1991). What do plasma and urinary measures of catecholamines tell us about response to stressors? *Circulation, 83*(Suppl. II), II36–II42.

Dreyfuss, F., & Czaczkes, J. W. (1959). Blood cholesterol and uric acid of healthy medical students under stress of an examination. *Archives of Internal Medicine, 103,* 708–711.

Dujovne, V. F., & Houston, B. K. (1991). Hostility-related variables and plasma lipid levels. *Journal of Behavioral Medicine, 14,* 555–565.

Dzau, V. J., & Sacks, F. (1987). Regulation of lipoprotein metabolism by adrenergic mechanisms. *Journal of Cardiovascular Pharmacology, 10*(Suppl. 9), 52–56.

Egan, B. M., Weder, A. B., Petrin, J., & Hofman, R. G. (1991). Neurohumoral and metabolic effects of short-term dietary NaCl restriction in man. *American Journal of Hypertension, 4,* 416–421.

Esler, M. (1990). Neural regulation of the cardiovascular system. In D. G. Byrne & R. H. Rosenman (Eds.), *Anxiety and the heart* (pp. 159–185). Washington, DC: Hemisphere.

Feinleib, M. (1981). On a possible inverse relationship between serum cholesterol and cancer mortality. *American Journal of Epidemiology, 114,* 5–10.

Feinleib, M. (1982). Summary of a workshop on cholesterol and noncardiovascular disease mortality. *Preventive Medicine, 11,* 360–367.

Fliser, D., Nowak, R., Allendorf-Ostwald, N., Kohl, B., Hubinger, A., & Ritz, E. (1993). Serum lipid changes on low salt diet: Effects of alpha-1-adrenergic blockade. *American Journal of Hypertension, 6,* 320–324.

Fliser, D., Nowak, R., & Ritz, E. (1991). Serum lipid changes with low salt diet and influence of ACE-inhibition. *American Journal of Hypertension, 4,* 20A.

Floras, J. S., & Hara, K. (1993). Sympathoneural and hemodynamic characteristics of young subjects with mild hypertension. *Journal of Hypertension, 11,* 647–655.

Fowkes, F. G. R., Leng, G. C., Donnan, P. T., Deary, I. J., Riemersma, R. A., & Housley, E. (1992). Serum cholesterol, triglycerides, and aggression in the general population. *The Lancet, 340,* 995–998.

Francis, K. (1979). Psychologic correlates of serum indicators of stress in man: A longitudinal study. *Psychosomatic Medicine, 41,* 617–629.

Freedman, D. S., Byers, T., Barrett, D. H., Stroup, N. E., Eaker, E., & Monroe-Blum, H. (1995). Plasma lipid levels and psychologic characteristics in men. *American Journal of Cardiology, 141,* 507–517.

Frick, M. H., Elo, O., Haapa, K., Heinonen, O. O., Heisalmi, P., Helo, P., Huttinen, J. K., Kaitaniemi, P., Koskinen, P., Manninen, V., Maenpaa, H., Malkonen, M., Manttari, M., Norola, S., Paternack, A., Pikkarainen, J., Romo., M., Sjoblom, T., & Nikkila, E. A. (1987). Helsinki Heart Study: Primary prevention trial with gemfibrozil in middle-aged with dyslipidemia. *New England Journal of Medicine, 317,* 1237–1245.

Friedman, M., & Rosenman, R. H. (1959). Association of a specific overt behavior pattern with increases in blood cholesterol, blood clotting time, incidence of arcus senilis and clinical coronary artery disease. *Journal of the American Medical Association, 169,* 1286–1296.

Friedman, M., Rosenman, R. H., & Byers, S. O. (1964). Serum lipids and conjunctival circulation after fat ingestion in men exhibiting Type A behavior pattern. *Circulation, 29,* 874–886.

Friedman, M., Rosenman, R. H., & Carroll, V. (1958). Changes in the serum cholesterol and blood-clotting time in men subjected to cyclic variation of occupational stress. *Circulation, 17,* 852–861.

Gallerini, M., Manfredini, R., Caracciolo, S., Scapoli, C., Molinari, S., & Fersini, C. (1988). Serum cholesterol concentrations in parasuicide. *British Medical Journal, 310,* 1532–1536.

Garcia-Palmieri, M. R., Costas, R., Cruz-Vidal, M., Cortes-Alicea, M., Patterne, D., Rojas-Franco, L., Sorlie, P. D., & Kannel, W. B. (1978). Urban–rural differences in coronary heart disease in a low incidence area: The Puerto Rico Heart Study. *American Journal of Epidemiology, 107,* 206–215.

Glueck, C. J., Tieger, M., Kunkel, R., Hamer, T., Tracy, T., & Speirs, J. (1994). Hypocholesteremia and affective disorders. *American Journal of Medicine, 308,* 218–225.

Gottschalk, L., Stone, W., Glaser, G., & Iacono, J. (1969). Anxiety and plasma free fatty acids. *Life Sciences, 8*(Part II), 61–68.

Gray, R. F., Corrigan, F. M., Strathdee, A., Skinner, E. R., van Rhijn, A. G., & Horrobin, D. F. (1993). Cholesterol metabolism and violence: A study of individuals convicted of violent crimes. *NeuroReport, 4,* 754–756.

Groen, J. J., Tijong, B., Kamminger, C. E., & Willebrands, A. F. (1962). The influence of nutrition, individuality and some other factors, including various forms of stress on the serum cholesterol; an experiment of nine months duration. *Voeding, 13,* 556–573.

Groover, M., Jernigan, J., & Martin, C. (1962). Variations in serum lipid concentration and coronary artery disease. *American Journal of Medicine, 239,* 133–139.

Grundy, S. M., & Griffin, A. C. (1959a). Effects of periodic mental stress on serum cholesterol levels. *Circulation, 19*, 496–498.

Grundy, S. M., & Griffin, A. C. (1959b). Relationship of periodic mental stress to serum lipoprotein and cholesterol levels. *Journal of the American Medical Association, 171*, 1794–1796.

Hagan, R. D., Upton, S. J., Avakian, E. V., & Grundy, S. (1986). Increases in serum lipid and lipoprotein levels with movement from the supine to standing position in adult men and women. *Preventive Medicine, 15*, 18–27.

Hammarsten, J., Cathey, C., Redmond, R., & Wolf, S. (1957). Serum cholesterol, diet and coronary artery disease [Abstract]. *Journal of Clinical Investigation, 36*, 897.

Harlan, W. R., Oberman, A., Mitchell, R. E., & Graybiel, A. (1967). Constitutional and environmental factors related to serum lipid and lipoprotein levels. *Annals of Internal Medicine, 66*, 540–572.

Hatch, F. T., Reisell, P. K., Poon-King, T. M. W., Canellas, G. P., & Lees, R. S. (1966). A study of coronary heart disease in young men: Characteristics and metabolic studies of patients and comparison with age-matched healthy men. *Circulation, 33*, 679–703.

Heller, D. A., de Faire, U., Pedersen, N. L., Dahlen, G., & McClearn, G. E. (1993). Genetic and environmental influences on serum lipid levels in twins. *New England Journal of Medicine, 328*, 1150–1156.

Hillbrand, M., & Foster, H. G. (1993). Serum cholesterol and severity of aggression. *Psychological Reports, 72*, 270.

Hillbrand, M., Spitz, R. T., & Foster, H. G. (1995). Serum cholesterol and aggression in hospitalized male forensic patients. *Journal of Behavioral Medicine, 18*, 33–43.

Hjemdahl, P. (1990). Physiology of the autonomic nervous system as related to cardiovascular function. In D. G. Byrne & R. H. Rosenman (Eds.), *Anxiety and the heart* (pp. 95–158). Washington, DC: Hemisphere.

Hjermann, I., Holme, I., & Leren, P. (1986). Oslo Study Diet and Antismoking Trial: Results after 102 months. *American Journal of Medicine, 80*, 7–11.

Holme, I. (1990). An analysis of randomized trials evaluating the effects of cholesterol reduction on total mortality and CHD incidence. *Circulation, 82*, 1916–1924.

Hopkins, P. N. (1992). Effects of dietary cholesterol on serum cholesterol: A meta-analysis and review. *American Journal of Clinical Nutrition, 55*, 1060–1070.

Horowitz, C., & Bronte-Stewart, B. (1962). Mental stress and serum lipid variation in ischemic heart disease. *American Journal of Medical Sciences, 244*, 272–281.

Howard, B. V., Schneiderman, N., Falkner, B., Haffner, S. M., & Laws, A. (1993). Insulin, health behaviors, and lipid metabolism. *Metabolism, 42*(Suppl. 1), 25–35.

Howes, L. G., Krum, H., & Louis, W. J. (1987). Plasma cholesterol levels are dependent on sympathetic activity. *Journal of Hypertension, 5*(Suppl. 5), S361–S363.

Howes, L. G., Krum, H., & Louis, W. J. (1988). Increase in plasma cholesterol on subject's standing correlates with increase in plasma norepinephrine. *Clinical Chemistry, 34*, 988.

International Collaborative Group. (1992). Circulating cholesterol level and risk of death from cancer in men aged 40 to 69 years: Experience of an international collaborative group. *Journal of the American Medical Association, 248*, 2853–2859.

Iribarren, C., Reed, D. M., Burchfiel, C. M., & Dwyer, J. H. (1995). Serum total cholesterol and mortality: Confounding factors and risk modification in Japanese-American men. *Journal of the American Medical Association, 273*, 1926–1932.

Isles, C. G., Hole, D. J., Gillis, C. R., Hawthorne, V. M., & Lever, A. F. (1989). Plasma cholesterol, coronary heart disease, and cancer in the Renfrew and Paisley survey. *British Medical Journal, 198*, 920–924.

Ismail, A. H., & Young, R. J. (1977). Effect of chronic exercise on the multivariate relationship between selected biochemical and personality variables. *Multivariate Behavior Research, 12*, 49–67.

Iso, H., Jacobs, A. R., Wentworth, A., Neaton, J. D., & Cohen, J. D. (1989). Serum cholesterol levels and six-year mortality from stroke in 350,977 men screened for the MRFIT. *New England Journal of Medicine, 320*, 904–910.

Jacobs, D., Blackburn, H., Higgins, M., Reed, D., Iso, H., McMillan, G., Neaton, J., Nelson, J., Potter, J., Rifkind, B., Rossouw, J., Shekelle, R., & Yusuf, S. (1992). Report of the Conference on Low Blood Cholesterol: Mortality associations. *Circulation, 86,* 1046–1060.

Jacobs, D. R., Muldoon, M. F., & Rastam, L. (1995). Invited Commentary: Low blood cholesterol, nonillness mortality, and other nonatherosclerotic disease mortality: A search for causes and confounders. *American Journal of Cardiology, 141,* 518–522.

Jenkins, C. D., Hames, C. G., Zyzanski, S. J., Rosenman, R. H., & Friedman, M. (1969). Psychological traits and serum lipids: Part I. Findings from the California Psychological Inventory. *Psychosomatic Medicine, 31,* 115–128.

Jenkins, C. D., Rosenman, R. H., & Friedman, M. (1966). Components of the coronary-prone behavior pattern: Their relation to silent myocardial infarction and blood lipids. *Journal of Chronic Diseases, 19,* 599–609.

Jorgensen, R. S., Nash, J. K., Lasser, N. J., Hymovitz, N., & Langer, A. W. (1988). Heart rate acceleration and its relationship to total serum cholesterol, triglycerides, and blood pressure reactivity in men with mild hypertension. *Psychophysiology, 25,* 39–44.

Julius, S., & Jamerson, K. (1994). Sympathetics, insulin resistance and coronary risk in hypertension: The "chicken and egg" question. *Journal of Hypertension, 12,* 495–502.

Kagan, A., McGee, D. L., Yano, K., Rhoads, G. G., & Nomura, A. (1981). Serum cholesterol and mortality in a Japanese-American population: The Honolulu Heart Program. *American Journal of Epidemiology, 114,* 11–20.

Kahn, J. P., Gully, R. J., Cooper, T. B., Perumal, A. S., Thomas, T. M., & Klein, D. F. (1987). Correlation of Type A behavior with adrenergic density: Implications for coronary artery disease pathogenesis. *Lancet, 2,* 937–939.

Kaplan, J. R., Manuck, S. B., Clarkson, T. B., Lussso, F. M., Taub, D. M., & Miller, E. W. (1993). Social stress and atherosclerosis in normocholesteremic monkeys. *Science, 220,* 733–735.

Kaplan, J. R., Manuck, S. B., & Schively, C. (1991). The effects of fat and cholesterol on social behavior in monkeys. *Psychosomatic Medicine, 53,* 634–642.

Kaplan, R. M., Manuck, S. B., & Shumaker, S. (1992). Does cholesterol lowering cause increases in depression, suicide and accidents? In H. S. Friedman (Ed.), *Hostility, coping & health,* (pp. 117–123). Washington, DC: American Psychological Association.

Kaplan, J. R., Shively, C. A., Fontenot, B., Morgan, T. T., Howell, S. M., Manuck, S. M., Muldoon, M. F., & Mann, J. J. (1994). Demonstration of an association among dietary cholesterol, central serotonergic activity and social behavior in monkeys. *Psychosomatic Medicine, 56,* 479–484.

Kasl, S. V., Cobb, S., & Brooks, G. W. (1968). Changes in serum uric acid and cholesterol levels in men undergoing job loss. *Journal of the American Medical Association, 206,* 1500–1507.

Katan, M. B., Beynen, A. C., De Vries, J. H. M., & Nobels, A. (1986). Existence of consistent hypo- and hyperresponders to dietary cholesterol in man. *American Journal of Epidemiology, 123,* 221–234.

Kellaway, G. S. M., & Lubbe, W. F. (1986). Transdermal antihypertensive therapy with clonidine (catapres-TTS). *Hypertension, 4,* 125–127.

Ketterer, M. W., Brymer, J., Rhoads, K., Kraft, P., & Goldberg, D. (1994). Lipid-lowering therapy and violent death: Is depression a culprit? *Stress Medicine, 10,* 233–237.

Keys, A., Mickelsen, O., Miller, E. V. O., Hayes, E. R., & Todd, R. L. (1951). Concentration of serum cholesterol in the blood serum of normal man and its relation to age. *Journal of Clinical Investigation, 29,* 1347–1353.

Kjeldsen, W. E., Westheim, A., Lande, K., Gjesdal, K., Leren, P., Enger, E., & Eide, I. K. (1988). Sodium depletion increases platelet and plasma catecholamines in hypertensive men. *Hypertension, 11,* 477–482.

Knutsson, A. (1989). Relationships between serum triglycerides and gamma glutamyl transferase among shift and day workers. *Journal of Internal Medicine, 226,* 337–339.

Kornitzer, M., Dramaix, M., de Backer, G., & Thilly, C. (1977). Cholesterolemia and psychosociobiological variables: The Belgian Multifactor Preventive Trial in CVD. *Heart Bulletin, 8,* 147–154.

Kozarevic, Dj., McGee, D., Vojvodic, N., Gordon, T., Racic, Z., Zukel, W., & Dawber, T. (1981). Serum cholesterol and mortality: The Yugoslavia Cardiovascular Disease Study. *American Journal of Epidemiology, 114*, 21–28.

Kristiansson, K., Sigfusson, N., Sigvaldason, H., & Thorgeirsson, G. (1995). Glucose tolerance and blood pressure in a population-based cohort study of males and females: The Reykjavik Study. *Journal of Hypertension, 13*, 581–586.

Kritchevsky, S. B. (1992). Dietary lipids and the low blood cholesterol–cancer association. *American Journal of Epidemiology, 135*, 509–520.

Kromhout, D., Bosschieter, E. B., Drijver, M., & Coulander, C., de L. (1988). Serum cholesterol and 25-year incidence of and mortality from myocardial infarction and cancer. *Archives of Internal Medicine, 148*, 1051–1055.

Krone, W., Muller-Wieland, D., Nagele, H., Behnke, B., & Greten, H. (1985). Effect of adrenergic antihypertensives and calcium antagonists on LDL receptor activity and cholesterol synthesis in human mononuclear leukocytes. *Arteriosclerosis, 5*, 543a.

Kuhl, J., Beck, E., Gershberg, H., Street, E., & Ralli, E. (1955). Effect of cold water stress on blood and urine constituents in 55 normal male subjects. *Metabolism, 4*, 143–152.

Kunihara, M., & Oshima, T. (1983). Effects of epinephrine on plasma cholesterol in rats. *Journal of Lipid Research, 24*, 639–644.

Kyes, R. C., Botchin, M. B., Kaplan, J. R., Manuck, S. B., & Mann, J. J. (1995). Aggression and brain serotonergic responsivity: Responses to slides in male macaques. *Physiology and Behavior, 57*, 205–208.

Lake, C. R.. Ziegler, M. G., Coleman, M. D., & Kopin, T. J. (1979). Hydrochlorothiazide-induced sympathetic hyperactivity in hypertensive patients. *Clinical Pharmacology Therapy, 26*, 428–477.

Lang, C. M. (1967). Effects of psychic stress on atherosclerosis in the squirrel monkey. *Proceedings of Society for Experimental Biology and Medicine, 126*, 30–34.

Lardinois, C. K., & Neuman, S. L. (1988). The effects of antihypertensive agents on serum lipids and lipoproteins. *Archives of Internal Medicine, 148*, 1280–1288.

LaRosa, J. C., Bush, D., Criqui, M. H., Getz, G. S., Goto, A. M., Grundy, S. M., Nakita, L., Robertson, R. M., Weisfeldt, M. L., & Cleeman, J. I. (1990). The cholesterol facts: A summary of the evidence relating dietary fats, serum cholesterol and coronary heart disease. A joint statement by the American Heart Association and the National Heart, Lung, and Blood Institute. *Circulation, 81*, 1721–1733.

Law, M. R., Thompson, S. G., & Wald, N. J. (1994). Assessing possible hazards of reducing serum cholesterol. *British Medical Journal, 308*, 373–379.

Lewis, B., & Tikkanen, M. J. (1984). Low blood cholesterol and mortality: Causality, consequence and confounders. *American Journal of Cardiology, 73*, 80–85.

Lind, L., Lithell, H., Gustafsson, I. B., Pollare, T., & Ljunghall, S. (1992). Metabolic cardiovascular risk factors and sodium sensitivity in hypertensive subjects. *American Journal of Hypertension, 5*, 502–505.

Lindberg, G., Larsson, G., & Setterlind, D. (1994). Serum lipids and mood in working men and women. *Journal of Epidemiology Community Health, 48*, 364–368.

Lindberg, G., Rastam, L., Gullberg, B., & Eklund, G. A. (1992). Low serum cholesterol concentration and short term mortality from injuries in men and women. *British Medical Journal, 305*, 277–279.

Lipid Research Clinics Investigators. (1992). The Lipid Research Clinics Coronary Primary Prevention Trial: Results of 6 years of post-trial follow-up. *Archives of Internal Medicine, 152*, 1399–1410.

Lipid Research Clinics Program. (1984). The Lipid Research Clinics Coronary Primary Prevention Trial Results: I. Reduction in incidence of coronary heart disease. *Journal of the American Medical Association, 251*, 351–364.

Luft, F. C., Rankin, L. I., Henry, D. P., Bloch, R., Grim, C. E., Weyman, A. E., Murray, R. H., & Weinberger, M. H. (1979). Plasma and urinary norepinephrine values at extremes of sodium intake in normal man. *Hypertension, 1*, 261–266.

Lundberg, U., Hedman, M., Melin, B., & Frankenhaeuser, M. (1989). Type A behavior in healthy males and females as related to physiological reactivity and blood lipids. *Psychosomatic Medicine, 51*, 113–122.

Markel, A., & Brook, G. J. (1994). Cancer and hypocholesteremia. *Israel Journal of Medical Sciences, 30*, 787–793.

Martin, M. J., Hulley, S. B., Browner, W. S., Kuller, L. H., & Wentworth, D. (1986). Serum cholesterol, blood pressure, and mortality: Implications from a cohort of 361,662 men. *The Lancet, 2*, 933–936.

Mattiasson, I., Lindgarde, F., Nilsson, J. A., & Theorell, T. (1990). Threat of unemployment and cardiovascular risk factors: Longitudinal study of quality of sleep and serum cholesterol concentration in men threatened with redundancy. *British Medical Journal, 301*, 461–466.

McCormick, J., & Skrabanek, P. (1988). Coronary heart disease is not preventable by population interventions. *The Lancet, 2*, 839–841.

Megargee, E. I. (1985). The dynamics of aggression and their application to cardiovascular disorders. In M. A. Chesney & R. H. Rosenman (Eds.), *Anger and hostility in cardiovascular and behavioral disorders* (pp. 31–38). Washington, DC: Hemisphere.

Melamed, S. (1994). Life stress, emotional reactivity and their relation to plasma lipids in employed women. *Stress Medicine, 10*, 167–175.

Miettinen, M., Turpeinen, O., Karvonen, M. J., Elosuo, & Paavilainen, E. (1972). Effect of cholesterol-lowering diet on mortality from coronary heart disease and other causes— A 12-year clinical trial in men and women. *The Lancet, 2*, 835–838.

Modest, G. (1992). Long-term mortality after primary prevention for cardiovascular disease [Letter to the editor]. *Journal of the American Medical Association, 267*, 2184.

Mogadam, M., Ahmed, S. W., Mensh, A. H., & Godwin, I. D. (1991). Within-person fluctuations of serum cholesterol and lipoproteins. *Archives of Internal Medicine, 150*, 1645–1648.

Morgan, R. E., Palinkas, L. A., Barrett-Connor, E. L., & Wingard, D. L. (1993). Plasma cholesterol and depressive symptoms in older men. *The Lancet, 341*, 75–79.

Morris, D. L., Borhani, N. O., Fitzsimmons, E., Hardy, R. J., Hawkins, C. M., Kraus, J. F., Labarthe, D. R., Mastbaum, L., & Payne, G. H. (1983). Serum cholesterol and cancer in the Hypertension Detection and Follow-up Program. *Cancer, 52*, 1754–1759.

Muldoon, M. F. (1994). Injury, death, and cholesterol [Letter to the editor]. *Archives of Internal Medicine, 121*, 719–720.

Muldoon, M. F., Bachen, E. A., Manuck, S. B., Waldstein, S. R., Bricker, P. L., & Bennett, J. A. (1991). Acute cholesterol responses to mental stress and change in posture. *Archives of Internal Medicine, 152*, 775–780.

Muldoon, M. F., Herbert, T. B., Patterson, S. M., Kameneva, M., Raible, R., & Manuck, S. B. (1995). Effects of acute psychological stress on serum lipid levels, hemoconcentration, and blood viscosity. *Archives of Internal Medicine, 155*, 615–620.

Muldoon, M. F., Kaplan, J. R., Manuck, S. B., & Mann, J. J. (1992). Effects of a low-fat diet on brain serotonergic responsivity in cynomolgus monkeys. *Biological Psychiatry, 31*, 739–742.

Muldoon, M. F., & Manuck, S. B. (1992). Health care through cholesterol reduction: Are there unforeseen risks? *Annals of Behavioral Medicine, 14*, 101–108.

Muldoon, M. F., Manuck, S. B., & Matthews, K. A. (1990). Lowering cholesterol concentrations and mortality: A quantitative review of primary prevention trials. *British Medical Journal, 301*, 309–314.

Muldoon, M. F., Rossouw, J. E., Manuck, S. B., Glueck, C. J., Kaplan, J. R., & Kaufmann, P. G. (1993). Low or lowered serum cholesterol and risk of death from suicide or trauma. *Metabolism, 42*(Suppl. 1), 45–56.

Neaton, J. D., Blackburn, H., Jacobs, D., Kuller, L., Lee, D.-J., Sherwin, R., Shih, J., Stamler, J., Wentworth, D., & the MRFIT Group. (1992). Serum cholesterol level and mortality findings for men screened in the Multiple Risk Factor Intervention Trial. *Archives of Internal Medicine, 152*, 1490–1500.

Neil, H. A. W., Roe, I., Godlee, R. J. P., Moore, J. W., Clark, G. M. G., Brown, J., Thorogood, M., Stratton, I. M., Lancaster, T., Mant, D., & Fowler, G. H. (1995). Randomised trial of lipid lowering dietary advice in general practice: The effects of serum lipids, lipoproteins, and antioxidants. *British Medical Journal, 310*, 569–573.

Newman, T. B., Browner, W. S., & Hulley, S. B. (1992). Long-term mortality after primary prevention for cardiovascular disease [Letter to the editor]. *Journal of the American Medical Association, 267*, 2183–2184.

Niaura, R., Herbert, P. N., McMahon, N., & Sommerville, L. (1992). Regressive coping and blood lipids in men and women. *Psychosomatic Medicine, 54*, 698–706.

Niaura, R., Herbert, P. N., Saritelli, A. L., Goldstein, M. G., Flynn, M. M., Follick, M. J., Gorkin, L., & Ahern, D. K. (1991). Lipid and lipoprotein responses to episodic occupational and academic stress. *Archives of Internal Medicine, 151*, 2172–2179.

Niaura, R., Stoney, C. M., & Herbert, P. N. (1992). Lipids in psychological research: The last decade. *Biological Psychology, 34*, 1–43.

O'Donnell, L., O'Mear, N., Owens, D., Johnson, A., Collins, P., & Tomkin, G. (1987). Plasma catecholamines and lipoproteins in chronic psychological stress. *Journal of the Royal Society of Medicine, 80*, 339–344.

O'Donnell, L., Owens, D., McGee, C., Devery, R., Hession, P., Collins, P., Johnson, A., & Tomkin, G. (1988). Effects of catecholamines on serum lipoproteins of normally fed and cholesterol-fed rabbits. *Metabolism, 37*, 910–915.

Oliver, M. F. (1990). Might treatment of hypercholesterolaemia increase non-cardiac mortality? *The Lancet, 337*, 1530–1531.

Orth-Gomer, K. (1994). Lipid lowering through work stress reduction. *International Journal of Behavioral Medicine, 1*, 204–214.

Palmblad, J., Karlsson, C., Levi, L., & Lindberg, L. (1979). The erythrocyte sedimentation rate and stress. *Acta Medica Scandinavica, 205*, 517–520.

Patterson, S. M., Gottdiener, J. S., Hecht, G., Vargot, S., & Krantz, D. (1993). Effects of acute mental stress on serum lipids: Mediating effects of plasma volume. *Psychosomatic Medicine, 55*, 525–532.

Paul, O., & Hennekens, C. H. (1991). The latest report from Finland: A lesson in expectations. *Journal of the American Medical Association, 266*, 1267–1268.

Paul, O., & Hennekens, C. H. (1992). Long-term mortality after primary prevention for cardiovascular disease [Letter to the editor]. *Journal of the American Medical Association, 267*, 2185–2186.

Pekkanen, J. (1993). Lowering cholesterol concentrations and mortality [Letter to the editor]. *British Medical Journal, 2*, 835–838.

Peterson, J., Keith, R., & Wilcox, A. (1962). Hourly changes in serum cholesterol concentration. *Circulation, 25*, 798–803.

Peterson, J., Wilcox, A., Haley, M., & Keith, R. (1960). Hourly variation in total serum cholesterol. *Circulation, 22*, 247–253.

Petersson, B., Trell, E., & Hood, B. (1984). Premature death and associated risk factors in urban middle-aged men. *American Journal of Medicine, 77*, 418–426.

Peto, R., Yusuf, S., & Collins, R. (1991). Cholesterol-lowering trial results in their epidemiologic context. *Journal of the American College of Cardiology, 17*, III–451.

Pinter, E., Tolir, G., Guyda, H., & Katsarkas, A. (1979). Hormonal and free fatty acid changes during strenuous flight in novice and trained personnel. *Psychoneuroendocrinology, 4*, 79–82.

Puska, P., Tuomilehto, J., Nissanen, A., Salonen, J. T., Vartiainen, E., Pietinen, P., Koskela, K., & Korhonen, H. J. (1989). The North Karelia Project: 15 years of community-based prevention of coronary heart disease. *Annals of Medicine, 21*, 169–173.

Rahe, R., Rubin, R., & Arthur, R. (1974). The three investigator's study: Serum uric acid, cholesterol variability during stresses of everyday life. *Psychosomatic Medicine, 36*, 258–268.

Rahe, R. H., Rubin, R. T., Arthur, R. J., & Clark, R. B. (1968). Serum uric acid and cholesterol variability: A comprehensive view of underwater demolition team training. *Journal of the American Medical Association, 206*, 2875–2880.

Rahe, R. H., Rubin, R. T., Gunderson, E. K., & Arthur, R. J. (1971). Psychological correlates of serum cholesterol in men. *Psychosomatic Medicine, 33*, 399–410.

Rahe, R., Ryman, D., & Biersner, R. (1976). Serum uric acid, cholesterol, and psychological moods throughout stressful naval training. *Aviation Space & Environmental Medicine, 47*, 883–888.

Ramsay, L. E., Yeo, W. W., & Jackson, P. R. (1991). Dietary reduction of serum cholesterol concentration: Time to think again. *British Medical Journal, 303*, 953–957.

Ravnskov, U., (1992). Cholesterol lowering trials in coronary heart disease: Frequency of and outcome. *British Medical Journal, 305*, 15–19.

Reynolds, R. C. (1974). Community and occupational influences in stress at Cape Kennedy: Relationships to heart disease. In R. S. Eliot (Ed.), *Stress and the Heart* (pp. 33–50). New York: Futura.

Robinson, D., Ferns, G. A., Bevan, E. A., Stocks, J., Williams, P. T., & Galton, D. J. (1987). High density lipoprotein subfractions and coronary risk factors in normal men. *Arteriosclerosis, 7*, 341–346.

Romon, M., Nuttens, M.-C., Fievet, C., Pot, P., Bard, J. M., Furon, D., & Fruchart, J. C. (1992). Increased triglyceride levels in shift workers. *American Journal of Medicine, 93*, 259–262.

Rose G., & Shipley, M. J. (1980). Plasma lipids and mortality: A source of error. *The Lancet, 1*, 523–526.

Rosenman, R. H. (1989). Results of the Multicenter Antihypertensive Treatment Trials: Therapeutic implications and the role of the sympathetic nervous system. *American Journal of Hypertension, 2*(Suppl. 2, Part 2), 313S–338S.

Rosenman, R. H. (1990). Type A behavior pattern: A personal overview. *Journal of Social Behavior and Personality, 5*, 1–24.

Rosenman, R. H. (1991). Type A behavior pattern and coronary heart disease: The hostility factor. *Stress Medicine, 7*, 245–254.

Rosenman, R. H. (1993a). The questionable roles of the diet and serum cholesterol in the incidence of ischemic heart disease and its 20th century changes. *Homeostasis in Health and Disease (Prague), 34*, 1–44.

Rosenman, R. H. (1993b). Relationships of neurogenic and psychological factors to regulation and variability of serum lipids. *Stress Medicine, 9*, 133–140.

Rosenman, R. H., Brand, F. J., Jenkins, C. D., Friedman, M., Straus, R., & Wurm, M. (1975). Coronary heart disease in the Western Collaborative Group Study: Final follow-up experience of 8 years. *Journal of the American Medical Association, 233*, 872–877.

Rosenman, R. H., & Friedman, M. (1957). Changes in the serum cholesterol and blood clotting time in men subjected to cyclic variation of emotional stress [Abstract]. *Circulation, 16*, 391.

Rosenman, R. H., & Friedman, M. (1974). Neurogenic factors in pathogenesis of coronary heart disease. *Medical Clinics of North America, 58*, 269–279.

Rosenman, R. H., & Friedman, M. (1961). Association of a specific overt behavior pattern in females with blood and cardiovascular findings. *Circulation, 24*, 1173–1184.

Rossouw, J. E., Canner, P. O., Hulley, S. B. (1991). Deaths from injury, violence, and suicide in secondary prevention trials of cholesterol-lowering. *New England Journal of Medicine, 325*, 1813.

Rossouw, J. E., Lewis, B., & Rifkind, B. M. (1990). The value of lowering cholesterol after myocardial infarction. *New England Journal of Medicine, 323*, 1112–1120.

Ruppert, M., Diehl, J., Kolloch, R., Overlack, A., Kraft, K., Gobel, B., Hittel, N., & Stumpe, L. (1991). Short-term dietary sodium restriction increases serum lipids and insulin in salt-sensitive and salt-resistant normotensive adults. *Klinische Wochenschrift, 69*(Suppl. 25), 51–57.

Ryman, A. (1994). Cholesterol, violent death, and mental disorder. *British Medical Journal, 309*, 421–422.

Salmond, C. E., Beaglehole, R., & Prior, I. A. M. (1985). Are low cholesterol values associated with excess mortality? *British Medical Journal, 290*, 422–424.

Sane, A., & Kukreti, S. (1978). Effect of preoperative stress on serum cholesterol levels in humans. *Experentia, 34*, 213–214.

Santiago, J. M., & Dalen, J. E. (1994). Cholesterol and violent behavior. *Archives of Internal Medicine, 154*, 1317–1321.

Schuitt, A. J., Dekker, J. M., Schouten, E. G., & Kok, F. J. (1993). Low serum cholesterol and death due to accidents, violence, or suicide [Letter to the editor]. *The Lancet, 341*, 827.

Schuit, A. J., Van Dijk, L. C. M. J., Dekker, J. M., Schouten, E. G., & Kok, F. J. (1993). Inverse association between serum total cholesterol and cancer mortality in Dutch civil servants. *American Journal of Epidemiology, 137,* 966–976.

Segers, M., & Mertens, C. (1976). Relationships between anxiety, depression, self-ratings and CHD risk factors among obese, normal and lean individuals. *Journal of Psychosomatic Research, 20,* 25–35.

Seltzer, C. C. (1990). Changes in risk factors and the decline in mortality from cardiovascular disease [Letter to the editor]. *New England Journal of Medicine, 323,* 1705.

Shekelle, R. B., Gale, M., Ostfeld, A. M., & Paul, O. (1983). Hostility, risk of coronary heart disease, and mortality. *Psychosomatic Medicine, 45,* 109–114.

Sherwin, R. W., Wentworth, D. N., Cutler, J. A., Hulley, S. B., Kuller, L. H., & Stamler, J. (1987). Serum cholesterol levels and cancer mortality in 361,662 men screened for the Multiple Risk Factor Intervention Trial. *Journal of the American Medical Association, 257,* 943–948.

Shively, C. A., Knox, S. S., Sherwin, B. B., Walsh, B. W., & Wilson, P. W. F. (1993). Sex steroids, psychological factors, and lipid metabolism. *Metabolism, 42*(Suppl. 1), 16–24.

Siegel, J. M. (1984). Anger and cardiovascular risk in adolescents. *Journal of Health Psychology, 3,* 293–313.

Siegrist, J., Matchinger, H., Cremer, P., & Seidel, D. (1988). Atherogenic risk in men suffering from occupational stress. *Atherosclerosis, 69,* 211–218.

Sletten, I. W., Nilsen, J. A., Young, R. C., & Anderson, J. T. (1964). Blood lipids and behavior in mental-hospital patients. *Psychosomatic Medicine, 26,* 261–266.

Sloane, R. B., Davidson, P., Holland, L., & Payne, R. W. (1962). Aggression and effects of upbringing in normal students. *Archives of General Psychiatry, 7,* 374–384.

Sloane, R. B., Habib, A., Eveson, M. B., & Payne, R. W. (1961). Some behavioral and other correlates of cholesterol metabolism. *Journal of Psychosomatic Research, 5,* 183–186.

Spence, D., Manuck, S. B., Munoz, C., Cheung, H., Huff, M., Dennis, B., & Borkowski, K. (1990). Hemodynamic and endocrine effects of mental stress in untreated borderline hypertension. *American Journal of Hypertension, 3,* 859–862.

Sprague, H. B. (1966). The search for the "coronary" archetype and the Damocles test [Editorial]. *Circulation, 33,* 676–678.

Staessen, J., Amery, A., Birkenhager, W., Bulpitt, C., Clement, D., de Leeuw, P., Deruyttere, M., De Schaepdryver, A., Dollery, C., & Fagard, R. (1990). Is a high serum cholesterol level associated with longer survival in elderly hypertensives? *Journal of Hypertension, 8,* 755–761.

Stalder, M., Pometta, D., & Suenram, A. (1982). Relationship between plasma insulin levels and high density lipoprotein cholesterol levels in healthy men. *Diabetologia, 21,* 544–548.

Stamler, J. (1987). Serum cholesterol levels and cancer mortality in 361,662 men screened for the Multiple Risk Factor Intervention Trial. *Journal of the American Medical Association, 257,* 943–948.

Stemmerman, G. N., Chyou, P.-H., Kagan, A., Nomura, A. M. Y., & Yano, K. (1991). Serum cholesterol and mortality among Japanese-American men: The Honolulu (Hawaii) Heart Program. *Archives of Internal Medicine, 151,* 969–972.

Stewart, M. A, & Stewart, S. G. (1981). Serum cholesterol in antisocial personality: A failure to replicate earlier findings. *Neuropsychobiology, 7,* 9–11.

Stoker, D. J., & Wynn, V. (1966). Effect of posture on the plasma cholesterol level. *British Medical Journal, 1,* 336–338.

Stoney, C. M., Matthews, K. A., McDonald, R. H., & Johnson, C. A. (1988). Sex differences in lipid, lipoprotein, cardiovascular, and neuroendocrine responses to acute stress. *Psychophysiology, 25,* 645–656.

Strandberg, T. E., for the Helsinki Businessmen Study Group. (1992). Long-term mortality after primary prevention for cardiovascular disease [Letter to the editor]. *Journal of the American Medical Association, 267,* 2185.

Strandberg, T. E., Salomaa, V. V., Naukkarinen, V. A., Vanhanen, H. T., Sarna, S. J., & Miettinen, T. A. (1991). Long-term mortality after 5-year multifactorial primary prevention of cardiovascular diseases in middle-aged men. *Journal of the American Medical Association, 266,* 1225–1229.

Suarez, E. C., Williams, R. B., Jr., Kuhn, C. M., Zimmerman, E. H., & Schanberg, S. M. (1991). Biobehavioral basis of coronary-prone behavior in middle-aged men: Part II. Serum cholesterol, the Type A behavior pattern, and hostility as interactive modulators of physiological reactivity. *Psychosomatic Medicine, 53*, 528–537.

Sugden, P. H. (1992). Serum cholesterol, triglycerides, and aggression. *The Lancet, 340*, 1350.

Sytkowski, P. A., Kannel, W. B., & D'Agostino, R. B. (1990). Changes in risk factors and the decline in mortality from cardiovascular disease: The Framington Heart Study. *New England Journal of Medicine, 322*, 1635–1641.

Sytkowski, P. A., Kannel, W. B., & D'Agostino, R. B. (1991). Changes in risk factors and the decline in mortality from cardiovascular disease [Letter to the editor]. *New England Journal of Medicine, 323*, 1706.

Taggart, P., & Carruthers, M. (1971). Endogenous hyperlipemia induced by emotional stress of racing driving. *The Lancet, 1*, 363–366.

Taggart, P., Carruthers, M., & Somerville, W. (1973). Electrocardiogram, plasma catecholamines and lipids and their modification by oxprenolol during public speaking,. *The Lancet, 2*, 341–346.

Tan, M. H., Wilmhurst, E. G., Gleason, R. E., & Soeldner, J. S. (1973). Effect of posture on serum lipids. *New England Journal of Medicine, 289*, 416–419.

Thelle, D., Forde, O. H., Try, K., & Lehman, E. H. (1976). The Tromso Study. *Acta Medica Scandinavica, 200*, 107–118.

Theorell, T. (1975). Selected illnesses and somatic factors in relation to two psychosocial stress indices—A prospective study of middle-aged construction building workers. *Journal of Psychosomatic Research, 20*, 7–20.

Theorell, T., & Akerstedt, T. (1976). Day and night work: Changes in cholesterol, uric acid, glucose and potassium in serum and circadian patterns of urinary catecholamine excretion. *Acta Medica Scandinavica, 200*, 47–53.

Theorell, T., & Emlund, N. (1993). On physiologic effects of positive and negative life changes—A longitudinal study. *Journal of Psychosomatic Research, 37*, 653–659.

Theorell, T., Lind, E., Froberg, J., Karlsson, C., & Levi, L. (1972). A longitudinal study of 21 patients with coronary heart disease: Life changes, catecholamine excretion and related biochemical reactions. *Psychosomatic Medicine, 34*, 505–516.

Thomas, C. B., & Murphy, E. A. (1958). Further studies on cholesterol levels in Johns Hopkins medical students: The effects of stress at examination. *Journal of Chronic Diseases, 81*, 661–670.

Troisi, R. J., Weiss, S. T., Parker, D. R., Sparrow, D., Young, J. B., & Landsberg, L. (1991). Relation of obesity and diet to sympathetic nervous system activity. *Hypertension, 17*, 699–677.

van Doornen, L. J. P. (1980). The coronary risk personality: Psychological and psychophysiological aspects. *Psychotherapy Psychosomatics, 34*, 204–215.

van Doornen, J. P., & Orlebeke, J. F. (1982). Stress, personality and serum cholesterol level. *Journal of Human Stress, 8*, 24–29.

Virkkunen, M. (1979). Serum cholesterol in anti-social personality. *Neuropsychobiology, 5*, 27–30.

Virkkunen, M. (1983). Serum cholesterol levels in homicidal offenders: A low cholesterol level is connected with a habitually violent tendency under the influence of alcohol. *Neuropsychobiology, 10*, 65–69.

Virkkunen, M., Horrobin, D. F., Jenkins, D. K., & Manku, M. S. (1987). Plasma phospholipid essential fatty acids and prostaglandins in alcoholic, habitually violent, and impulsive offenders. *Biological Psychiatry, 22*, 1087–1096.

Virkkunen, M., & Penttinen, H. (1984). Serum cholesterol in aggressive conduct disorder: A preliminary study. *Biological Psychiatry, 19*, 435–439.

Voldet, G., Scheidegger, P., & Garbone, G. (1959). Modifications of serum proteins and lipids in melancholic syndromes. *Encephale, 48*, 510–516.

Weidmann, P., Beretta-Piccoli, C., Meier, A., Keusch, G., Gluck, Z., & Ziegler, W. H. (1983). Antihypertensive mechanism of diuretic treatment with chlorthalidone: Complementary roles of sympathetic axis and sodium. *Kidney International, 23*, 320–326.

Weidner, G., Connor, S. L., Hollis, J. F., & Connor, W. E. (1992). Improvements in hostility and depression in relation to dietary change and cholesterol lowering. *Annals of Internal Medicine, 117*, 820–823.

Weidner, G., Sexton, G., McClelland, R., Connor, S. L., & Matarazzo, J. D. (1987). The role of Type A behavior and hostility in an elevation of plasma lipids in adult women and men. *Psychosomatic Medicine, 49*, 136–145.

Wertlake, P. T., Wilcox, A. A., Haley, M. I., & Peterson, J. E. (1958). Relationship of mental and emotional stress to serum cholesterol levels. *Proceedings of the Society for Experimental Biology and Medicine, 97*, 163–165.

Williams, R. B., Jr., Suarez, E. C., Kuhn, C. M., Zimmerman, E. H., & Schanberg, S. M. (1990). Biobehavioral basis of coronary-prone behavior in middle-aged men: Part I: Evidence for chronic SNS activation in Type As. *Psychosomatic Medicine, 57*, 517–527.

Wolf, S., McCabe, W. R., Yamamoto, J., Adsett, C., & Schottstaedt, W. (1962). Changes in serum lipids in relation to emotional stress during rigid control of diet and exercise. *Circulation, 26*, 379–384.

Wright, R. (1995, March 22). The biology of violence. *The New Yorker*, pp. 768–777.

Young, J. B, Troisi, R. J., Weiss, S. T., Parker, D. R., Sparrow, D., & Landsberg, L. (1992). Relationship of catecholamine excretion to body size, obesity, and nutrient intake in middle-aged and elderly men. *American Journal of Clinical Nutrition, 56*, 827–834.

Yusuf, S., Wittles, J., & Friedman, L. (1988a). Overview of results of randomized clinical trials in heart disease: I. Treatments following myocardial infarction. *Journal of the American Medical Association, 260*, 2088–2093.

Yusuf, S., Wittles, J., & Friedman, L. (1988b). Overview of results of randomized clinical trials in heart disease: II. Unstable angina, heart failure, primary prevention with aspirin, and risk factor modification. *Journal of the American Medical Association, 260*, 2259–2263.

3

Lipids, Personality, and Stress: Mechanisms and Modulators

Catherine M. Stoney and Sheila West

In 1982, Dimsdale and Herd wrote a review article of published studies investigating the relationship between psychological stress and lipid concentrations. A majority of those studies had been performed 2 or more decades previously, and their review demonstrated widespread (although not universal) support for the notion that psychological stress has the ability to alter lipid levels. Limitations in both the accuracy of the methods for measuring lipid concentrations, as well as the specific lipid particles that could be identified, restricted these early studies, but the overwhelming support for the notion that stress can impact lipid concentrations provided the impetus for researchers in the 1980s and 1990s to continue this line of investigation. Ten years after the publication of the Dimsdale and Herd review, we (Niaura, Stoney, & Herbert, 1992) undertook a more recent review of these later studies. Like the earlier analysis, our review also found support for the notion that stress and lipids are related, but the more recent studies allowed a more fine grained analysis of the conditions under which stress is associated with changes in lipid concentrations. In our descriptive review, we concluded that *acute* stress (i.e., laboratory-based, achievement-focused stressors that last on the order of minutes to a few hours) and *episodic* stress (i.e., naturalistic acute stressors that occur with some degree of periodicity, such as exam stress) frequently are associated with increases in total cholesterol, low density lipoprotein-cholesterol (LDL-c), and (less consistently) triglyceride concentrations. Little support for the notion that free fatty acids change in response to acute stress could be found in the later investigations.

In contrast to the very consistent findings among investigations of acute and episodic stress, our review found more restricted evidence for the notion that chronic (i.e., persistent and pervasive) stressors are associated with significant elevations in the atherogenic lipids. However, these overall conclusions obscured interesting variability among studies. Specifically, we noted that when the nature of the chronic stress is severe and threatening (but not when it is mild), increases in the atherogenic lipids are typically apparent. Consequently, for chronic stress at least, the severity of the stressor appears to play a role in the magnitude of association with lipid concentrations.

We recently followed up this descriptive review by performing a meta-analysis on these same data (unpublished analyses). The meta-analysis provided analytic support for the findings of our descriptive review and specifically shows overall significant elevations in cholesterol, LDL-c, and triglycerides during stress, with stronger support for these associations during acute stress relative to chronic stress. These analyses reinforce the notion that stress can significantly impact the atherogenic lipids.

Thus, there is compelling evidence that psychological factors such as stress do show consistent and reliable associations with the atherogenic lipids. Individual differences in both the subject characteristics and the stressors themselves dictate the magnitude of the association with lipid concentrations. What has not been adequately addressed in the literature to date, however, is elucidation of the potential mechanisms by which lipids and lipoproteins come to be altered during stress. This has been a major thrust of the work from our laboratory; accordingly, the purpose of this chapter is to provide an overview of these potential mechanisms.

The model guiding our own work investigating the mechanisms responsible for the stress–lipid relationship is presented in Figure 1. Briefly, psychological factors are presumed to exert influence on lipid concentrations through several nonexclusionary pathways. The major pathways— behavioral and environmental influences, hemoconcentration, hormonal influences, and metabolic influences—are each discussed in turn. Note that as work in this area becomes more biologically sophisticated, modifications to these and other potential pathways are not only possible but also likely and desirable.

Behavioral and Environmental Influences

The effects of stress on lipid profiles may be mediated in part by behavioral and environmental factors such as diet, coffee and alcohol intake, exercise, smoking, and seasonal changes in lipid concentrations. Because of their direct and interactive effects on the lipid profile (see Figure 1), behavioral and seasonal changes are particularly important to assess in chronic and episodic stress situations in which individuals are being evaluated over an extended period of time. The effects of these variables in influencing the acute-stress lipid response are less clear but worthy of further investigation. For example, athletes have a higher metabolic rate, so they may show faster rate or smaller magnitude patterns of lipid response to acute stress.

Diet

Dietary factors can have profound effects on lipid concentrations, and to the extent that stress influences eating behaviors (Robbins, Everitt, & Sahakian, 1981; Robbins & Fray, 1980), this is one mechanism through which stress may indirectly alter lipoprotein concentrations. Stress-induced eat-

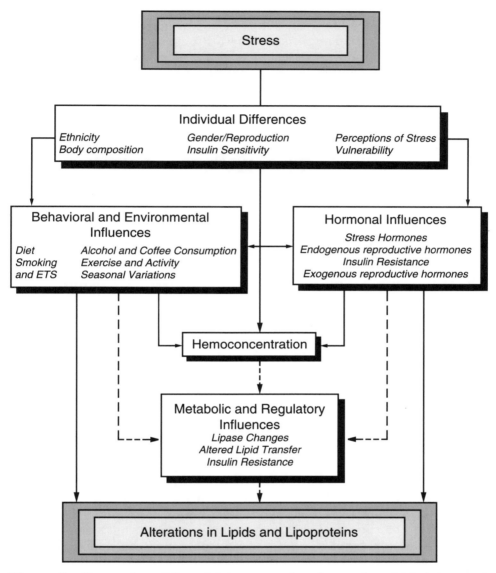

Figure 1. Proposed model explaining several pathways by which behavioral stress (acute, chronic, and episodic) might impact on lipid and lipoprotein concentrations. ETS = environmental tobacco smoke.

ing has been observed in both human and animal studies, although consistent effects are not reported in all paradigms (for review, see Greeno & Wing, 1994). In studies of acute laboratory stress, the most consistent finding to date is that women who normally exert considerable effort to restrain their eating (i.e., through chronic dieting) are most vulnerable to stress-induced eating (Baucom & Aiken, 1981; Greeno & Wing, 1994). There is also evidence that gender may mediate the effects of acute stress on eating behavior. Grunberg and Straub (1992) offered male and female participants a choice of sweet, salty, and bland foods while participants viewed stressful and nonstressful videos. Compared with their gender-matched control groups, stressed women ate more sweet foods and consumed more total calories, whereas stressed men ate less than their unstressed counterparts. Thus, in studies of acute stress, significant changes in the amount and type of food consumed were observed, and the direction of such changes differed among men and women.

The impact of stress-induced changes in food choice can be more readily observed in studies of episodic or chronic stress. In one such study (McCann, Warnick, & Knopp, 1990), increases in perceived stress resulting from an increased workload were correlated with increased total cholesterol concentrations in office workers. However, the large increase in workload was also associated with increased consumption of total calories, fats, and percentage of calories from fat, thereby obscuring changes due to psychological stress alone. The stress-related changes in diet may have clinical significance because of their profound effects on lipoprotein metabolism and on body composition. In support of this argument, body mass index is greater in individuals who are experiencing stressful life events and negative emotions (Bradley, 1985; Rookus, Burema, & Frijters, 1988; Trevisan et al., 1986), and increased dietary intake of cholesterol and saturated fats increase plasma concentrations of total cholesterol and triglycerides (Kris-Etherton et al., 1988).

Alcohol and Coffee Consumption

Alcohol and coffee consumption are also particularly relevant to the discussion of dietary influences on lipid concentrations. Increased consumption of both alcohol (Conway, Vickers, Ward, & Rahe, 1981) and coffee (Shapiro, Lane, & Henry, 1986) have been observed in response to occupational stress, negative life events, and acute stress. Because both dietary factors have also been shown to influence lipid concentrations, they may partly explain the stress–lipid relationship.

Alcohol has complicated effects on lipid metabolism, because it can increase concentrations of high density lipoprotein-cholesterol (HDL-c), very low density lipoprotein (VLDL) cholesterol, and triglycerides (Hulley & Gordon, 1981). The increase in HDL-c has been thought to be responsible, at least in part, for the cardioprotective effects of moderate alcohol ingestion (Hulley & Gordon, 1981; Yano, Rhoads, & Kagan, 1977). Metabolically, acute alcohol ingestion inhibits hepatic triglyceride lipase activity (HTGLA). This enzyme is most likely responsible for catabolizing VLDL and degrading HDL, particularly the phospholipid components of these lipoproteins. Thus, the alcohol-induced inhibition of HTGLA leads to a transient elevation in HDL and VLDL concentrations (Goldberg, Tall, & Krumholz, 1984). Because these effects are apparent even after acute alcohol intake, researchers would be well advised to consider these transient effects when investigating lipid responsivity to both chronic and acute stressors.

Regarding coffee consumption, both the type of coffee (caffeinated vs. decaffeinated) and its method of preparation determine its effect on lipoprotein metabolism (Battig, 1991; Kokjohn, Graham, & McGregor, 1993; Superko, Brotz, Williams, Albers, & Wood, 1991). For example, prospective studies have shown that caffeinated coffee has no effect on total cholesterol, LDL-c, apolipoprotein B, and triglyceride levels, but individuals who switch to decaffeinated coffee show elevated levels of LDL and apolipoprotein B. The increase in LDL may be due to the observed changes in HTGLA and lipoprotein lipase activity (LPLA), two of the lipid-metabolizing enzymes (Superko et al., 1991). Finally, several prospective investigations have shown that drinkers of boiled coffee have higher levels of total cholesterol than those drinking filtered coffee (Battig, 1991; Kokjohn et al., 1993). It is therefore important to assess consumption of all foods and drinks, even those that do not contain fats, in studies of the effects of stress on lipid concentrations.

Exercise and Activity

In concert with changes in diet, changes in exercise and physical activity may accompany periods of high stress and thus contribute to changes in both body mass index and lipid concentrations. Although relatively few investigations have examined the effect of life stress on adherence to exercise regimens, some data suggest that stress modulates the degree of exercise adherence. For example, Klonoff, Annechild, and Landrine (1994) reported that among sedentary women who were invited to attend free and convenient aerobics classes, 73% of the variance in attendance rate could be explained by a model that included height, weight, trait anxiety level, physical symptoms, and intensity of daily hassles. Perceived severity of daily stress alone accounted for 17% of the variance in attendance. These data demonstrated that women who experienced a greater intensity of daily stressors, but not necessarily a greater number of stressful events, were less likely to adhere to a fitness program. To the extent that these findings generalize to other populations, alterations in physical activity level represent an important pathway through which stress may influence lipid levels.

Because of the robust relationship between regular physical exercise and low levels of atherosclerotic disease (Kannel, Wilson, & Blair, 1985; Paffenbarger, Hyde, Wing, & Steinmetz, 1984), extensive studies of the effects of exercise training on lipid and lipoprotein metabolism have been conducted (for review see Durstine & Haskell, 1994; Pronk, 1993; Schieken, 1991). Multiple investigations have reported that trained athletes, compared with sedentary controls, have a less atherogenic lipid profile, including lower levels of triglycerides and VLDL and higher levels of HDL (Durstine & Haskell, 1994; Schieken, 1991). However, there are some exceptions to the notion that endurance exercise results in a more favorable lipid profile (Allison, Iammarino, Metz, Skrinar, Kuller, & Robertson, 1981), and most studies report no effect of exercise on concentrations of total cholesterol or LDL, perhaps because increased HDL is balanced by decreases in the cholesterol content of other lipoproteins (Schieken, 1991).

More recently, it has become clear that regular exercise may impact atherogenesis by altering subclass distribution of the major lipoproteins. For example, runners have been shown to have lower levels of small, dense LDL, the more atherogenic form of LDL, as well as higher levels of HDL_2, the metabolically active form of HDL, which participates in cholesteryl ester−triglyceride exchange (Williams, Krauss, Vranizan, & Wood, 1990; Williams et al., 1986). Furthermore, improvements in the lipid profile may be dose dependent, because time spent running each week (Durstine et al., 1987) and number of miles run per week (Williams et al., 1990) are positively correlated with HDL levels in runners. In general, prospective investigations of exercise training or prolonged bouts of acute exercise are associated with decreases in triglycerides and triglyceride-rich VLDL, with increases in HDL levels (Durstine & Haskell, 1994; Pronk, 1993; Sady et al., 1986). Decreased body weight and body fat alone may be responsible for a portion of the lipid-lowering effect, particularly with regard to the chronic-exercise-training studies (Williams et al., 1986; Wood et al., 1988).

Several investigators have suggested that the effects of exercise on lipid concentrations can be explained by alterations in HTGLA and LPLA during exercise training (Seip et al., 1993; Thompson et al., 1991). Although changes in the atherogenic lipids resulting from exercise training may be explained by the observed changes in lipase activity, the metabolic changes are not sufficient to explain the magnitude of exercise-induced increase in HDL concentrations. For example, changes in LPLA are not correlated either with the size of the change observed in HDL concentrations (Seip et al., 1993), or with alterations in triglyceride clearance following prolonged exercise (Sady et al., 1986). A possible explanation was recently offered (Seip et al., 1993) by investigators who found that prolonged exercise training (9−12 months) significantly decreased cholesteryl ester transfer protein levels. Cholesteryl ester transfer protein may have prevented the degradation of HDL (Lagrost, 1994; Tall, 1992, 1993). Parenthetically, the pattern of lipid responses to a single, acute bout of exercise contrasts with that of prolonged exercise training but is less relevant to studies of behavioral stress and so is not detailed here.

In conclusion, exercise training results in increases in HDL and decreases in triglycerides and VLDL. These moderate changes can be partially explained by changes in body mass and plasma volume, but metabolic factors may also play a role. Lipoprotein levels are strongly influenced by the synergistic actions of endothelial enzymes responsible for lipoprotein metabolism (HTGLA and LPLA) and the proteins involved in cholesterol transport (lecithin:cholesterol acyltransferase and cholesteryl ester transfer protein [CETP]), which are themselves altered by exercise.

Smoking

Periods of high stress are also associated with increases in smoking and a greater incidence of relapse in smoking cessation programs (Cohen & Lichtenstein, 1990). This maladaptive coping response has a dose-dependent (Muscat, Harris, Haley, & Wynder, 1991), deleterious effect on virtually all lipoproteins (Craig, Palomaki, & Haddow, 1989). A meta-analysis of 54 published studies demonstrated that in relation to nonsmokers, smokers have 3%–10% higher serum concentrations of total cholesterol, VLDL, triglycerides, and apolipoprotein B and concomitant 4%–6% lower concentrations of HDL and apolipoprotein A-I (Craig et al., 1989). To further investigate this relationship, Craig et al. (1989) were also able to statistically demonstrate significant dose–response relationships for smoking and lipid levels. Other investigations have found even more striking differences in HDL in smokers. For example, Moffatt (1988) found that smokers have HDL levels that are 15%–20% lower than nonsmokers; importantly, smoking cessation is associated with reversal of this effect (Moffatt, 1988). Even nonsmokers exposed to environmental tobacco smoke are susceptible to these effects (see Figure 1). For example, adolescents exposed to environmental tobacco smoke have significantly higher total cholesterol:HDL ratios and lower HDL compared with controls matched for age, gender, and body mass index (Feldman et al., 1991). Environmental tobacco smoke also has been shown to increase atherosclerotic plaque development in lipid-fed rabbits (Sun, Zhu, Sievers, Glantz, & Parmley, 1994), an animal model that has much in common with human lipid metabolism.

Atherogenic lipid changes associated with smoking may be due to higher rates of CETP-mediated lipid-transfer activity in smokers (Dullaart, Hoogenberg, Dikkeschei, & van Tol, 1994); acute elevations in catecholamines and cortisol as each cigarette is smoked (Pomerleau, 1992); and a diet higher in saturated fats (Fisher & Gordon, 1985; Herbert & Kabat, 1990). In women, cigarette smoking appears to have antiestrogenic effects and thus may reduce the beneficial lipid effects of both exogenous (Jensen & Christiansen, 1988) and endogenous (Michnovicz, Herschkopf, Naganuma, Bradlow, & Fishman, 1986) estrogens. In a study of postmenopausal women, both smokers and nonsmokers exhibited decreases in LDL and total cholesterol in response to hormone replacement therapy. However, these changes were twice as large in nonsmokers (Jensen & Christiansen, 1988). In the group receiving oral administration of hormones, lower serum levels of estradiol were achieved in the smokers, suggesting that the deleterious effects of smoking on hormone-induced lipid changes were due to changes in hepatic metabolism of estradiol. In support of this conclusion, smoking has been shown to dramatically reduce the bioavailability of estradiol in premenopausal women by altering its hepatic metabolism (Michnovicz et al., 1986). Thus, the deleterious effects of smoking on the lipid profile are multifaceted, dose dependent, and reversible. Consequently, stress-related changes in smoking behaviors should be carefully monitored in studies of episodic or chronic stress, and smoking behaviors in general should be noted in acute-stress studies.

Seasonal Variations

Studies of chronic and episodic stress are particularly sensitive to seasonal variations in lipoprotein levels. Gordon et al. (1988) followed 1,446 men in a nationwide program to reduce dietary fat and cholesterol. They reported that HDL, LDL, and total cholesterol increased significantly in midwinter, whereas triglycerides reached their peak in mid-October during each year of the 7-year study. These seasonal changes could not be explained by climatic differences in ambient temperature, number of daylight hours, or seasonal changes in body mass index but might be attributable to changes in health behaviors and seasonal alterations in plasma volume (Gordon et al., 1988).

In conclusion, adjustments in behavioral and environmental factors are plausible mechanisms through which chronic stress may impact lipid levels. In addition, they also represent critical individual differences, which must be taken into account in cross-sectional studies of high- and low-stressed participants. Indeed, these behavioral factors may interact with race, gender, and other individual differences to determine the impact that stress has on lipid levels. Stress-induced changes in lipids may also be masked or confounded by seasonal variations in lipid profile or by the use of female sex hormones in oral contraceptives or hormone replacement therapy. Furthermore, individual differences such as race and gender may determine who is vulnerable to stress-related changes in health behaviors. When stress-induced alterations in health behaviors are observed, these individual differences may also interact to determine the magnitude of the changes in lipid levels.

Hemoconcentration

Since the beginning of the century, physiological and psychological stress has been known to induce *polycythemia*, which is a relative hemoconcentration of the blood usually due to contracted plasma volume. Such plasma-volume shifts have been noted in response to acute behavioral stress, chronic psychological stress, and physical and postural stress (Jern, Jern, & Wadenvik, 1991; Mattiasson, Lindgarde, Nilsson, & Theorell, 1990; Muldoon et al., 1992, 1995; van Beaumont, Young, & Greenleaf, 1974; see Figure 1). Mild-to-moderate polycythemia is also apparent in a subset of individuals who are hypertensive or Type A or who smoke, drink alcohol excessively, or use diuretics (Emery, Whitcomb, & Frohlich, 1974; Jern et al., 1991; Smith & Landaw, 1978). Polycythemia is particularly interesting because individuals with polycythemia secondary to hypertension (termed *relative polycythemia*) are at markedly greater risk for mortality and morbidity associated with thromboembolic complications

(Burge, Johnson, & Prankerd, 1975). The importance of mild polycythemia, such as occurs during stress, is unknown.

The mechanisms for stress-associated plasma-volume shifts are poorly understood. Some candidate mechanisms include hemodynamic-induced fluid shifts; changes in red cell mass and size (i.e., changes in mean corpuscular volume); and stress-induced changes in kidney function, resulting in changes in clearance of fluid by the kidneys. However it occurs, the ultimate result of the hemoconcentration leads to an indirect increase in the concentration of all nondiffusible constituents of blood (i.e., large proteins and large particles), including cholesterol and the lipoproteins.

Some investigators believe that this mild polycythemia is the sole mechanism by which stress impacts lipid concentrations (Muldoon et al., 1992; Patterson, Gottdiener, Hecht, Vargot, & Krantz, 1993), because changes that occur in the lipoproteins during acute stress occur too rapidly to be explained by alterations in lipoprotein synthesis. Several pieces of data support this contention, including the disappearance of elevated atherogenic lipoproteins and triglycerides during some stressors (i.e., mathematical) after plasma-volume-shift correction (Muldoon et al., 1992; Patterson et al., 1993). The hemoconcentration hypothesis (Muldoon et al., 1992) does not diminish the possible importance of stress-induced lipid elevations, because an elevation in the atherogenic lipids during a time when endothelial cell damage might be expected (i.e., as might occur with catecholamines released during psychological stress) suggests a viably important etiologic role for such lipid elevations in the progression of atherogenesis.

Perhaps more important, there are several pieces of evidence from our laboratory and others that do not support the hemoconcentration hypothesis as the sole mechanism to explain acute-stress-induced lipid elevations. These data suggest that other mechanisms are operating (alone or in combination with plasma-volume changes) to explain acute-stress-induced lipid elevations. At least three pieces of data suggest that changes in plasma volume do not entirely explain the stress-associated elevations in cholesterol and the lipoproteins. First, a number of published studies show that after appropriate correction for changes in plasma volume (Dill & Costill, 1974; van Beaumont, 1972), the stress effects for total cholesterol, LDL, and triglycerides remain statistically significant in both young and middle-aged men and women (Stoney, Matthews, McDonald, & Johnson, 1988). Second, the nature of the psychological stressor appears to determine the extent to which plasma-volume changes occur during acute stress. This quite likely plays a role in reconciling our consistent findings with those of Muldoon et al. (1992) and Patterson et al. (1993). In this latter study, the math stressor produced small changes in lipoproteins before adjustment for plasma volume, and in both studies, the relatively larger changes in plasma volume that occurred accounted for most of the lipoprotein changes. In our studies, however, the use of several stressors has demonstrated that the potency of the stressor plays a role in determining whether lipid changes are substantial and maintained after correction for plasma volume. In our studies, for example, the math stressor used typically produces half the magnitude increase in LDL and total cholesterol than does a more potent speech stressor. The correction for changes in plasma volume diminishes lipid responses to both stressors, but changes that occur during speech remain significant, whereas the changes during math stress are sometimes not. Relatedly, the extent to which the stressors induce a pressor response may also dictate the extent to which plasma-volume changes occur, because hemodynamic forces can push fluid across the vascular bed and into the interstitial space, effectively causing a change in plasma volume. Third, the magnitude change from baseline in plasma volume is typically about 1%–3% during acute stress. The concomitant fluctuations in plasma concentrations of LDL and total cholesterol range between a 4% and a 10% change from baseline. This is further evidence that hemoconcentration alone cannot explain LDL and total cholesterol fluctuations during acute stress.

There are at least two implications of the foregoing. First, researchers in this area must be cognizant of the role of plasma-volume shifts in potentially modifying the concentrations of all blood constituents with a high molecular weight and of the well-documented relative hemoconcentration that occurs during stress. Toward this end, the use of the equation offered by Dill and Costill (1974) is most useful in providing a means of identifying and mathematically correcting changes in plasma volume (see Appendix). These authors recommend using both hematocrit and hemoglobin in the calculation of plasma volume, as the use of hematocrit alone can lead to an inaccurate estimate of plasma-volume changes because mean corpuscular volume (red blood cell size) can change without alterations in plasma volume occurring (van Beaumont, 1972). Second, it is clear that at least during some types of psychological experiences, other mechanisms are operating to explain the elevations in the atherogenic lipids and lipoproteins during stress. The identification of these additional mechanisms is essential in attempting to understand both the characteristics of the lipid stress response, as well as the clinical implications of these responses.

Hormonal Influences

Although it is clear that a large number of individual differences that are associated with lipid concentrations have been identified (e.g., age or body fat), our purpose here is to describe some of the parameters that are more directly relevant to behavioral and psychological factors. To this end, we discuss the role of reproductive hormones, because these hormones have been postulated to mediate the stress response (Matthews, 1989; Stoney, Davis, & Matthews, 1987). In addition, we describe some of the effects of several hormones that are involved in the stress response.

Gender and Endogenous Reproductive Hormones

Gonadal steroids are potent regulators of hepatic cholesterol metabolism (Sacks & Walsh, 1994; Shively, Knox, Sherwin, Walsh, & Wilson, 1993;

Walsh et al., 1991), and they may alter lipid metabolism indirectly by changing the distribution of adipose tissue (Rebuffe-Scrive, 1988; Wakatsuki & Sagara, 1995). Relative to men (Lipid Research Clinics, 1980) and postmenopausal women of the same age (Bush et al., 1987; Lobo, 1991; Matthews et al., 1989), premenopausal women have lower levels of LDL and total cholesterol and higher levels of HDL. In fact, prior to menopause, average HDL levels are 10 mg/dl higher in women than in men and are primarily in the form of the metabolically active particle HDL_2 (Lipid Research Clinics, 1980).

The interaction of endogenous reproductive hormones, lipids, and stress was directly investigated in a few studies. Long-term psychological stress and its behavioral effects produce changes in endogenous levels of gonadal steroids, which in turn can alter lipid profiles. In females, change in weight (Harlow & Matanoski, 1991), psychological stress (Chatterton, 1990; Shively et al., 1993), and exercise training (Gindoff, 1989) impair ovarian function, thus altering the patterns of the menstrual cycle and, subsequently, circulating levels of the estrogens and progesterone. In nonhuman primates, social stress induces ovarian dysfunction in subordinate females (Adams, Kaplan, Clarkson, & Koritnik, 1984). This stress-induced decrease in estradiol increases concentrations of serum cholesterol, decreases levels of HDL, and accelerates the development of atherosclerotic plaques (for review, see Clarkson, 1994, and Shively et al., 1993). In at least one study, the severity of atherosclerotic disease in subordinate females was equivalent to that observed in ovariectomized animals. This provides additional evidence that the estrogens mediate this effect (Shively et al., 1993).

Chronic and episodic stress may alter lipid profiles in susceptible individuals indirectly through changes in gonadal steroid concentrations. An additional study provides indirect evidence that premenopausal women have lower lipid levels than do postmenopausal women, even when both groups are undergoing the chronic stress of divorce (Kushnir & Kristal-Boneh, 1995). However, the authors do not directly test this hypothesis, and part of their findings may reflect the lipid increases that are normally apparent during aging as a function of changes in lipase activity (Brodows & Campbell, 1972). Finally, we have preliminary data to show that chronic occupational stress in airline pilots is associated with smaller magnitude lipid levels in premenopausal women, relative to men. These latter two studies do not directly test whether the chronic nature of the stressors alters ovarian hormone functioning in women. Future investigations should include these hormonal assessments.

Lipid reactivity may also be moderated by hormonal status in acute-stress studies (Brindley, McCann, Niaura, Stoney, & Suarez, 1993). For example, men (Stoney et al., 1988) and postmenopausal women (Owens, Stoney, & Matthews, 1993) exhibit significantly greater lipid responses to acute stress compared with premenopausal women, again suggesting that the estrogens that normally circulate may play an important role in determining lipid responsivity to stress. It is currently not known whether hormone replacement therapy alters this response in women. In conclusion, stress may impact lipoprotein levels by decreasing gonadal steroid concentrations, and individuals who differ in reproductive hormonal status may also differ in their stress responses.

Exogenous Reproductive Hormones

Recent meta-analyses suggest that use of estrogen replacement therapy among women reduces the risk of cardiovascular disease by 50%, in part by preventing atherogenic changes in the lipid profile (Grady et al., 1992; Stampfer & Colditz, 1991). For example, one study demonstrated that HDL levels were 16% higher and LDL levels were 15% lower in women given 3 months of oral estrogen replacement therapy, compared with levels in women who received placebo (Nabulsi et al., 1993; Walsh et al., 1991). Although elevations in VLDL triglycerides are commonly observed with estrogen replacement therapy, most of the additional VLDL is directly cleared from the circulation. This may explain reduced levels of LDL (Walsh et al., 1991).

The beneficial metabolic effects of oral estrogen replacement therapy may result from decreased activity of HTGLA (Applebaum-Bowden et al., 1989; Colvin, Auerbach, Case, Hazzard, & Applebaum-Bowden, 1991) and LPLA (Wakatsuki & Sagara, 1995), together with increased production of hepatic LDL receptors (Ma, Yamamoto, Goldstein, & Brown, 1986). Oral androgens, in contrast, increased postheparin HTGLA activity in male weight lifters, resulting in a 71% decrease in HDL_2 (Thompson et al., 1989). Thus, orally administered androgens and, potentially, the androgenic progestins may reduce HDL levels and attenuate the lipid improvements observed with unopposed estrogen (for review, see Derman, 1995; Haffner & Valdez, 1995; LaRosa, 1995). The extent to which these effects differ among men and women is not known.

Several investigators have reported that among some women, combined estrogen–progestin treatment results in beneficial changes in the lipoproteins, although these changes are smaller than those observed with unopposed estrogen (V. T. Miller et al., 1991; Sherwin & Gelfand, 1989; The Writing Group for the PEPI Trial, 1995). Synthetic progestins, which are used also in oral contraceptives, vary widely in their androgenic activity, and newer progestins with low androgenic activity (e.g., desogestrel and norgestrel) may have minimal effects on lipid metabolism (Godsland et al., 1994; for review, see Darney, 1995). Although the use of highly androgenic progestins has been shown to attenuate the estrogen-induced lipid benefits, studies in nonhuman primates indicate that this does not result in greater severity of atherosclerosis (Adams, Clarkson, Koritnik, & Nash, 1987).

Unfortunately, no published studies have explored the impact of exogenous reproductive hormones on lipid reactivity. These studies might suggest, however, a mechanism for the role of stress in altering lipid concentrations in women. Given the role of exogenous hormones in altering lipid concentrations, one might expect an alteration to stress-induced lipid concentrations among those given exogenous hormones.

Influence of the Stress Hormones

Increased sympathetic nervous system activity during stress typically results in rapid and profound increases in the catecholamines (norepinephrine and epinephrine), glucocorticoids (cortisol in humans), and glucagon. The increase in catecholamines, cortisol, and glucagon, in turn, causes lipolysis and subsequent release of fatty acids into the circulation. These direct effects of stress have several metabolic consequences on lipids and lipoproteins.

Increased circulation of fatty acids may occur from lipolysis, as described above, or may occur either indirectly from stress-associated changes in diet or directly as a result of increased synthesis by cortisol and insulin. These increased fatty acids, however they occur, stimulate hepatic glucose production and thereby increase sources of available energy. Cortisol and fatty acids increase both insulin resistance and the synthesis of hepatic triglycerides. Very low density lipoprotein secretion is stimulated also by increased circulating cortisol and fatty acids. Because insulin regulates triglyceride synthesis and the hepatic production of VLDL, the decreased activity of insulin during stress inhibits regulation of triglyceride and VLDL production. The finding that insulin increases hepatic LDL receptors, which clear circulating LDL, further supports insulin's role in regulating lipid metabolism. Both insulin resistance and increased cortisol suppress the hepatic LDL receptors and catabolism, thereby resulting in delayed LDL clearance.

Increased neuroendocrine activity can stimulate adipose beta receptors, which may result in decreases in lipoprotein lipase and hepatic triglyceride lipase activity. Specifically, lipoprotein lipase originates from extrahepatic tissues and plays an important role in the removal of triglycerides from chylomicrons and the large VLDL particles (Robinson, 1970) at the vascular endothelium (Blanchette-Mackie & Scow, 1971). Hepatic triglyceride lipase originates from the liver and serves primarily to remove triglycerides from intermediate-density lipoproteins and HDL_2 (Patsch, Prasad, Gotto, Bengtsson-Olivecrona, 1984; Tikkanen, Nikkila, Kuusi, & Sipinen, 1982). Animal and human data show that LPLA is inhibited by norepinephrine and cortisol (Jansen & Hulsmann, 1985; W. C. Miller, Gorski, Oscai, & Palmer, 1989), in turn decreasing clearance of triglycerides, decreasing HDL concentrations, and increasing VLDL, IDL, and LDL levels (Huttunen, Ehnolm, Kekki, & Nikkila, 1976). Our work in this area has preliminarily shown that individuals with higher LPLA during rest show smaller elevations in triglyceride responses to stress. Those individuals with higher HTGLA during rest have greater elevations in the atherogenic lipids and norepinephrine during acute stress. In contrast to the effects of cortisol and norepinephrine, epinephrine decreases VLDL secretion and increases LDL uptake by stimulating $alpha_1$ receptors. These actions appear to be similar to the effects of insulin, in that glucose uptake and glycolysis are increased (Brindley et al., 1993; Standaert, Farese, Cooper, & Pollet, 1988).

Both acute and chronic behavioral stress typically induce rapid elevations in the catecholamines and cortisol. Changes in insulin resistance, adipose beta receptors, and lipase activity during stress are not typically examined, however, and the effects of these stress hormones on the cascade of metabolic events are simply not known. Although no studies have directly tested the ability of psychological stress to mediate lipid concentrations through the hormonal pathways described above, researchers in this area would be well advised to consider these variables when trying to understand the mechanisms of stress-induced lipid elevations.

Metabolic Influences

There are no published studies available that have directly tested the hypothesis that lipid metabolism is altered during psychological stress, but several pieces of intriguing evidence suggest such a mechanism for stress-induced lipid elevations. First, it is clear from the previous section that the well-documented stimulation of the sympathetic nervous system that occurs during stress has the ability to alter lipoprotein lipase and hepatic triglyceride lipase activity. Alterations in lipase activity would presumably result in subsequent changes in levels of circulating lipids and lipoproteins (see Figure 1). Second, data from the exercise literature suggest that exercise training may alter the fractional catabolic rate of endogenous triglyceride, which results in an improved lipid profile. For example, it has been shown that athletes have 25% faster triglyceride clearance rates and 33% higher LPLA, relative to healthy, sedentary controls (Sady, Cullinane, Saritelli, Bernier, & Thompson, 1988). Behavioral stress might be considered to represent a dynamic state in which increased energy mobilization in excess of metabolic demand occurs. Consequently, physiological effects due to stress might be expected to be in direct contrast to those in response to physical exercise.

The final piece of evidence suggesting that psychological factors may impact on lipid metabolism comes from preliminary evidence from our laboratory showing that individuals with certain psychological characteristics have slower triglyceride metabolism to an intravenous fat load (Stoney, 1994). Specifically, those scoring high on measures of hostility and perceived stress had slower triglyceride metabolic responses relative to individuals scoring low on these parameters. Interestingly, the higher risk individuals also had significantly higher levels of total and LDL cholesterol, suggesting that the metabolic differences resulted in the expected different lipid profiles. Work in our laboratory is currently extending these findings to examine these metabolic parameters more dynamically.

Conclusion

The purpose of this chapter was to outline several potential pathways by which psychological stress might directly and indirectly alter lipid and lipoprotein concentrations. Specifically, our intention was to encourage active participation in this area of research and to promote keen awareness of the biological underpinnings of stress-induced alterations in lipid and lipoprotein concentrations. It is our belief that only through such a physiologically based perspective will the importance of psychological stress on long-term health consequences become apparent.

References

Adams, M. R., Clarkson, T. B., Koritnik, D. R., & Nash, H. A. (1987). Contraceptive steroids and coronary artery atherosclerosis in cynomolgus macaques. *Fertility and Sterility, 47,* 1010–1018.

Adams, M. R., Kaplan, J. R., Clarkson, T. B., & Koritnik, D. R. (1984). Ovariectomy, social status, and atherosclerosis in cynomolgus monkeys. *Arteriosclerosis, 5,* 192–200.

Allison, T. G., Iammarino, R. M., Metz, K. F., Skrinar, G. S., Kuller, L. H., & Robertson, R. J. (1981). Failure of exercise to increase high density lipoprotein cholesterol. *Journal of Clinical Research, 1,* 257–265.

Applebaum-Bowden, D., McLean, P., Steinmetz, A., Fontana, D., Matthys, C., Warnick, G. R., Cheung, M., Albers, J. J., & Hazzard, W. R. (1989). Lipoprotein, apolipoprotein, and lipolytic enzyme changes following estrogen administration in postmenopausal women. *Journal of Lipid Research, 30,* 1895–1906.

Battig, K. (1991). Coffee, cardiovascular, and behavioral effects: Current research trends. *Reviews on Environmental Health, 9,* 53–84.

Baucom, D. H., & Aiken, P. A. (1981). Effect of depressed mood in eating among obese and nonobese dieting and nondieting persons. *Journal of Personality and Social Psychology, 41,* 577–585.

Blanchette-Mackie, E. J., & Scow, R. O. (1971). Sites of lipoprotein lipase activity in adipose tissue perfused with chylomicrons: Electron microscope cytochemical study. *Journal of Cell Biology, 51,* 1–25.

Bradley, P. J. (1985). Conditions recalled to have been associated with weight gain in adulthood. *Appetite, 6,* 235–241.

Brindley, D. N., McCann, B. S., Niaura, R., Stoney, C. M., & Suarez, E. C. (1993). Stress and lipoprotein metabolism: Modulators and mechanisms. *Metabolism, 42*(Suppl. 1), 3–15.

Brodows, R. G., & Campbell, R. G. (1972). Effect of age on post-heparin lipase. *New England Journal of Medicine, 287,* 969–970.

Burge, P. S., Johnson, W. S., & Prankerd, T. A. J. (1975). Morbidity and mortality in pseudopolycythemia. *Lancet, I,* 1266–1269.

Bush, T. L., Barrett-Connor, E., Cowan, D., Criqui, M. H., Wallace, R. B., Suchindran, C. M., Tyroler, H. A., & Rifkind, B. M. (1987). Cardiovascular mortality and noncontraceptive use of estrogen in women: Results from the Lipid Research Clinics follow up study. *Circulation, 75,* 1102–1109.

Chatterton, R. T. (1990). The role of stress in female reproduction: Animal and human considerations. *International Journal of Fertility, 35,* 8–13.

Clarkson, T. B. (1994). Estrogens, progestins, and coronary heart disease in cynomolgus monkeys. *Fertility and Sterility, 62*(Suppl. 2), 147S–151S.

Cohen, S., & Lichtenstein, E. (1990). Perceived stress, quitting smoking, and smoking relapse. *Health Psychology, 9,* 466–478.

Colvin, P. L., Auerbach, B. J., Case, L. D., Hazzard, W. R., & Applebaum-Bowden, D. (1991). A dose–response relationship between sex hormone induced change in hepatic triglyceride lipase and high-density lipoprotein cholesterol in postmenopausal women. *Metabolism, 40,* 1052–1056.

Conway, T. L., Vickers, R. R., Ward, H. W., & Rahe, R. H. (1981). Occupational stress and variation in cigarette, coffee, and alcohol consumption. *Journal of Health and Social Behavior, 22,* 155–165.

Craig, W. Y., Palomaki, G. E., & Haddow, J. E. (1989). Cigarette smoking and serum lipid and lipoprotein concentrations: An analysis of published data. *British Medical Journal, 298*, 784–788.

Darney, P. D. (1995). The androgenicity of progestins. *The American Journal of Medicine, 98*(Suppl. 1A), 104S–110S.

Derman, R. J. (1995). Effects of sex steroids on women's health: Implications for practitioners. *The American Journal of Medicine, 98*(Suppl. 1A), 137S–143S.

Dill, D. B., & Costill, D. L. (1974). Calculation of percentage changes in volumes of blood, plasma, and red cells in dehydration. *Journal of Applied Physiology, 37*, 247–248.

Dimsdale, J. E., & Herd, J. A. (1982). Variability of plasma lipids in response to emotional arousal. *Psychosomatic Medicine, 44*, 413–430.

Dullaart, R. P. F., Hoogenberg, K., Dikkeschei, B. D., & van Tol, A. (1994). Higher plasma lipid transfer protein activities and unfavorable lipoprotein changes in cigarette-smoking men. *Arteriosclerosis and Thrombosis, 14*, 1581–1585.

Durstine, J. L., & Haskell, W. L. (1994). The effects of exercise training on plasma lipids and lipoproteins. *Exercise and Sports Science Reviews, 22*, 477–521.

Durstine, J. L., Pate, R. R., Sparling, P. B., Wilson, G. E., Senn, M. D., & Bartoli, W. P. (1987). Lipid, lipoprotein, and iron status of elite women distance runners. *International Journal of Sports Medicine, 8*, 119–123.

Emery, A. C., Whitcomb, W. H., & Frohlich, E. D. (1974). "Stress" polycythemia and hypertension. *Journal of the American Medical Association, 229*, 159–162.

Feldman, J., Shenker, R., Etzel, R. A., Spierto, F. W., Lilienfield, D. E., Nussbaum, M., & Jacobson, M. S. (1991). Passive smoking alters lipid profiles in adolescents. *Pediatrics, 88*, 259–264.

Fisher, M., & Gordon, T. (1985). The relation of drinking and smoking habits to diet: The Lipid Clinics Prevalence Study. *The American Journal of Clinical Nutrition, 41*, 623–630.

Gindoff, P. R. (1989). Menstrual function and its relationship to stress, exercise and bodyweight. *Bulletin of the New York Academy of Medicine, 65*, 774–786.

Godsland, I. F., Crook, D., Simpson, R., Proudler, T., Felton, C., Lees, B., Anyaoku, V., Devenport, M., & Wynn, V. (1994). The effects of different formulations of oral contraceptive agents on lipid and carbohydrate metabolism. *New England Journal of Medicine, 323*, 1375–1381.

Goldberg, C. S., Tall, A. R., & Krumholz, S. (1984). Acute inhibition of hepatic lipase and increase in plasma lipoproteins after alcohol intake. *Journal of Lipid Research, 25*, 714–720.

Gordon, D. J., Hyde, J., Trost, D. C., Whaley, F. S., Hannan, P. J., Jacobs, D. R., & Ekelund, L.-G. (1988). Cyclic seasonal variation in plasma lipid and lipoprotein levels: The Lipid Research Clinics Coronary Primary Prevention Trial placebo group. *Journal of Clinical Epidemiology, 41*, 679–689.

Grady, D., Rubin, S. M., Petitti, D. B., Fox, C. S., Black, D., Ettinger, B., Ernster, V. L., & Cummings, S. R. (1992). Hormone replacement therapy to prevent disease and prolong life in postmenopausal women. *Annals of Internal Medicine, 117*, 1016–1037.

Greeno, C. G., & Wing, R. R. (1994). Stress-induced eating. *Psychological Bulletin, 115*, 444–464.

Grunberg, N. E., & Straub, R. O. (1992). The role of gender and taste class in the effects of stress on eating. *Health Psychology, 11*, 97–100.

Haffner, S. M., & Valdez, R. A. (1995). Endogenous sex hormones: Impact on lipids, lipoproteins, & insulin. *The American Journal of Medicine, 98*(Suppl. 1A), 40S–47S.

Harlow, S. D., & Matanoski, G. M. (1991). The association between weight, physical activity, and stress and variation in the length of the menstrual cycle. *American Journal of Epidemiology, 133*, 38–49.

Herbert, J. R., & Kabat, G. C. (1990). Differences in dietary intake with smoking status. *European Journal of Clinical Nutrition, 44*, 185–193.

Hulley, S. B., & Gordon, S. A. (1981). Alcohol and high density lipoprotein cholesterol: Causal inference from diverse study designs. *Circulation, 64*, 57–63.

Huttunen, J. K., Ehnolm, C., Kekki, M., & Nikkila, E. A. (1976). Post-heparin plasma lipoprotein lipase and hepatic lipase in normal subjects and in patients with hypertriglyceridaemia: Correlations to sex, age, & various parameters of triglyceride metabolism. *Clinical Science and Molecular Medicine, 50,* 249–260.

Jansen, H., & Hulsmann, W. C. (1985). Enzymology and physiological role of hepatic lipase. *Biochemical Society Transactions, 3,* 24–26.

Jern, S., Jern, C., & Wadenvik, H. (1991). "Polycythaema of stress" in subjects with Type A and Type B behaviour patterns. *Journal of Psychosomatic Research, 35,* 91–98.

Kannel, W. B., Wilson, P., & Blair, S. N. (1985). Epidemiological assessment of the role of physical activity and fitness in development of cardiovascular disease. *American Heart Journal, 109,* 876–885.

Klonoff, E. A., Annechild, A., & Landrine, H. (1994). Predicting exercise adherence in women: The role of psychological and physiological factors. *Preventive Medicine, 23,* 257–262.

Kokjohn, K., Graham, M., & McGregor, M. (1993). The effect of coffee consumption on serum cholesterol levels. *Journal of Manipulative and Physiological Therapeutics, 16,* 1255–1274.

Kris-Etherton, P. M., Krummel, D., Russell, M. E., Dreon, E., Mackey, S., Borchers, J., & Wood, P. D. (1988). The effect of diet on plasma lipids, lipoproteins, and coronary heart disease. *Journal of the American Dietetic Association, 88,* 1373–1400.

Kushnir, T., & Kristal-Boneh, E. (1995). Blood lipids and lipoproteins in married and formerly married women. *Psychosomatic Medicine, 57,* 116–120.

Lagrost, L. (1994). Regulation of cholesteryl ester transfer protein (CETP) activity: Review of in vitro and in vivo studies. *Biochimica et Biophysica Acta, 1215,* 209–236.

LaRosa, J. C. (1995). Androgens and women's health: Genetic and epidemiologic aspects of lipid metabolism. *The American Journal of Medicine, 98*(Suppl. 1A), 22S–26S.

Lipid Research Clinics. (1980). *Populations studies: Data book. Volume 1: The prevalence study.* (NIH Publication No. 80-1527, pp. 1–134). Bethesda, MD: National Institutes of Health.

Lobo, R. A. (1991). Effects of hormonal replacement on lipids and lipoproteins in postmenopausal women. *Journal of Clinical Endocrinology and Metabolism, 73,* 925–930.

Ma, P. T., Yamamoto, T., Goldstein, J. L., & Brown, M. S. (1986). Increased mRNA for low density lipoprotein receptors in the livers of rabbits treated with 17 alpha-ethinyl estradiol. *Proceedings of the National Academy of Sciences, USA, 83,* 792–796.

Matthews, K. A. (1989). Interactive effects of behavior and reproductive hormones on sex differences in risk for coronary heart disease. *Health Psychology, 8,* 373–387.

Matthews, K. A., Meilahn, E., Kuller, L. H., Kelsey, S. F., Caggiula, A. W., & Wing, R. R. (1989). Menopause and risk factors for coronary heart disease. *New England Journal of Medicine, 321,* 641–646.

Mattiasson, I., Lindgarde, F., Nilsson, J. A., & Theorell, T. (1990). Threat of unemployment and cardiovascular risk factors: Longitudinal study of quality of sleep and serum cholesterol concentrations in men threatened with redundancy. *British Medical Journal, 301,* 461–466.

McCann, B. S., Warnick, G. R., & Knopp, R. H. (1990). Changes in plasma lipids and dietary intake accompanying shifts in perceived work-load and stress. *Psychosomatic Medicine, 52,* 97–107.

Michnovicz, J. J., Herschkopf, R. J., Naganuma, H., Bradlow, H. L., & Fishman, J. (1986). Increased 2-hydroxylation of estradiol as a possible mechanism for the anti-estrogenic effect of cigarette smoking. *New England Journal of Medicine, 315,* 1305–1309.

Miller, V. T., Muesing, R. A., La Rosa, J. C., Stoy, D. B., Phillips, E. A., & Stillman, R. J. (1991). Effects of conjugated equine estrogen with and without three different progestogens on lipoproteins, high density lipoprotein subfractions, and apolipoprotein A-I. *Obstetrics and Gynecology, 77,* 235–240.

Miller, W. C., Gorski, J., Oscai, L. B., & Palmer, W. K. (1989). Epinephrine activation of heparin-nonreleasable lipoprotein lipase in 3 skeletal muscle fiber types of the rat. *Biochemical and Biophysical Research Communications, 164,* 615–619.

Moffatt, R. J. (1988). Effects of cessation of smoking on serum lipids and high density lipoprotein-cholesterol. *Atherosclerosis, 74,* 85–89.

Muldoon, M. F., Bachen, E. A., Manuck, S. B., Waldstein, S. R., Bricker, P. L., & Bennett, J. A. (1992). Acute cholesterol responses to mental stress and change in posture. *Archives of Internal Medicine, 152*, 775–780.

Muldoon, M. F., Herbert, T. B., Patterson, S. M., Kameneva, M., Raible, R., & Manuck, S. B. (1995). Effects of acute psychological stress on serum lipid levels, hemoconcentration, and blood viscosity. *Archives of Internal Medicine, 155*, 615–620.

Muscat, J. E., Harris, T. E., Haley, N. J., & Wynder, E. L. (1991). Cigarette smoking and plasma cholesterol. *American Heart Journal, 121*, 141–147.

Nabulsi, A. A., Folsom, A. R., White, A., Patsch, W., Heiss, G., Wu, K. K., & Skzlo, M. (1993). Association of hormone-replacement therapy with various cardiovascular risk factors in postmenopausal women. *New England Journal of Medicine, 328*, 1069–1075.

Niaura R., Stoney, C. M., & Herbert, P. N. (1992). Lipids in psychological research: The last decade. *Biological Psychology, 34*, 1–43.

Owens, J. F., Stoney, C. M., & Matthews, K. A. (1993). Menopausal status influences ambulatory blood pressure levels and blood pressure changes during mental stress. *Circulation, 88*, 2794–2802.

Paffenbarger, R. S., Hyde, R. T., Wing, A. L., & Steinmetz, C. H. (1984). A natural history of athleticism and cardiovascular health. *Journal of the American Medical Association, 252*, 491–495.

Patsch, J. R., Prasad, S., Gotto, A. M., Jr., & Bengtsson-Olivecrona, G. (1984). Postprandial lipemia: A key for the conversion of high density lipoprotein 2 into high density lipoprotein 3 by hepatic lipase. *Journal of Clinical Investigation, 74*, 2017.

Patterson, S. M., Gottdiener, J. S., Hecht, G., Vargot, S., & Krantz, D. S. (1993). Effects of acute mental stress on serum lipids: Mediating effects of plasma volume. *Psychosomatic Medicine, 55*, 525–532.

Pomerleau, O. F. (1992). Nicotine and the central nervous system: Biobehavioral effects of cigarette smoking. *The American Journal of Medicine, 93*(Suppl. 1A), 1A2S–1A7S.

Pronk, N. P. (1993). Short term effects of exercise on plasma lipids and lipoproteins in humans. *Sports Medicine, 16*, 431–448.

Rebuffe-Scrive, M. (1988). Steroid hormones and distribution of adipose tissue. *Acta Medica Scandinavica, 723*, 143–146.

Robbins, T. W., Everitt, B. J., & Sahakian, B. J. (1981). Stress-induced eating in animals. In L. A. Cioffi, W. P. T. James, & T. B. Van Etallie (Eds.), *The body weight regulatory system: Normal and disturbed mechanisms* (pp. 289–297). New York: Raven Press.

Robbins, T. W., & Fray, P. J. (1980). Stress-induced eating: Fact, fiction or misunderstanding? *Appetite, 1*, 103–133.

Robinson, D. S. (1970). The function of the plasma triglycerides in fatty acid transport. In M. Florkin & E. M. Stotz (Eds.), *Comprehensive biochemistry: Vol. 18: Lipid biochemistry* (pp. 51–116). Amsterdam: Elsevier.

Rookus, M. A., Burema, J., & Frijters, J. E. R. (1988). Changes in body mass index in young adults in relation to number of life events experienced. *International Journal of Obesity, 12*, 29–39.

Sacks, F. M., & Walsh, B. W. (1994). Sex hormones and lipoprotein metabolism. *Current Opinion in Lipidology, 5*, 236–240.

Sady, S. P., Cullinane, E. M., Saritelli, A., Bernier, D., & Thompson, P. D. (1988). Elevated high-density lipoprotein cholesterol in endurance athletes is related to enhanced plasma triglyceride clearance. *Metabolism, 37*, 568–572.

Sady, S. P., Thompson, P. D., Cullinane, E. M., Kantor, M. A., Domagala, E., & Herbert, P. N. (1986). Prolonged exercise augments plasma triglyceride clearance. *Journal of the American Medical Association, 256*, 2552–2555.

Schieken, R. M. (1991). Effects of exercise on lipids. *Annals of the New York Academy of Sciences, 623*, 269–274.

Seip, R. L., Moulin, P., Cocke, T., Tall, A., Kohrt, W. M., Mankowitz, K., Semenkovich, C. F., Ostlund, R., & Schonfeld, G. (1993). Exercise training decreases plasma cholesteryl ester transfer protein. *Arteriosclerosis and Thrombosis, 13*, 1359–1367.

Shapiro, D., Lane, J. D., & Henry, J. P. (1986). Caffeine, cardiovascular reactivity, and cardiovascular disease. In K. A. Matthews, S. M. Weiss, T. Detre, T. M. Dembroski, B. Falkner, S. B. Manuck, & R. B. Williams, Jr. (Eds.), *Handbook of stress, reactivity, and cardiovascular disease* (pp. 311–327). New York: Wiley.

Sherwin, B. B., & Gelfand, M. M. (1989). A prospective one year study of estrogen and progestin in postmenopausal women: Effects on clinical symptoms and lipoprotein lipids. *Obstetrics and Gynecology, 73*(5, Pt. 1), 759–766.

Shively, C. A., Knox, S. S., Sherwin, B. B., Walsh, B. W., & Wilson, P. W. F. (1993). Sex steroids, psychosocial factors, and lipid metabolism. *Metabolism, 42*(9, Suppl. 1), 16–24.

Smith, J. R., & Landaw, S. A. (1978). Smokers' polycythemia. *New England Journal of Medicine, 298*, 6–10.

Stampfer, M. J., & Colditz, G. A. (1991). Estrogen replacement and coronary heart disease: A quantitative assessment of the epidemiological evidence. *Preventative Medicine, 20*, 47–63.

Standaert, M. L., Farese, R. B., Cooper, D. R., & Pollet, R. J. (1988). Insulin-induced glycerolipid mediators and the stimulation of glucose transport in BC3H-1 myocytes. *Journal of Biological Chemistry, 263*, 8696–8705.

Stoney, C. M. (1994). Lipid metabolism is related to psychological characteristics [Abstract]. *Psychosomatic Medicine, 56*, 176.

Stoney, C. M., Davis, M. C., & Matthews, K. A. (1987). Sex differences in physiological responses to stress and coronary heart disease: A causal link? *Psychophysiology, 24*, 127–131.

Stoney, C. M., Matthews, K. A., McDonald, R. H., & Johnson, C. A. (1988). Sex differences in lipid, lipoprotein, cardiovascular, and neuroendocrine responses to stress. *Psychophysiology, 25*, 645–656.

Sun, Y., Zhu, B., Sievers, R. E., Glantz, S. A., & Parmley, W. W. (1994). Metoprolol does not attenuate atherosclerosis in lipid-fed rabbits exposed to environmental tobacco smoke. *Circulation, 89*, 2260–2265.

Superko, H. R., Bortz, W., Jr., Williams, P. T., Albers, J. J., & Wood, P. D. (1991). Caffeinated and decaffeinated coffee effects on plasma lipoprotein cholesterol, apolipoproteins, and lipase activity in a controlled, randomized trial. *American Journal of Clinical Nutrition, 54*, 599–605.

Tall, A. R. (1992). Metabolic and genetic control of HDL cholesterol levels. *Journal of Internal Medicine, 231*, 661–668.

Tall, A. R. (1993). Plasma cholesteryl ester transfer protein. *Journal of Lipid Research, 34*, 1255–1274.

Thompson, P. D., Cullinane, E. M., Sady, S. P., Chenevert, C., Saritelli, A. L., Sady, M. A., & Herbert, P. N. (1989). Contrasting effects of testosterone and stanozolol on serum lipoprotein levels. *Journal of the American Medical Association, 261*, 1165–1168.

Thompson, P. D., Cullinane, E. M., Sady, S. P., Flynn, M. M., Chenevert, C. N., & Herbert, P. N. (1991). High density lipoprotein metabolism in endurance athletes and sedentary men. *Circulation, 84*, 140–152.

Tikkanen, M. J., Nikkila, E. A., Kuusi, T., & Sipinen, S. (1982). High density lipoprotein-2 and hepatic lipase: Reciprocal changes produced by estrogen and norgestrel. *Journal of Clinical Endocrinology and Metabolism, 54*, 1113.

Trevisan, M., Celentano, E., Meucci, C., Farinaro, E., Jossa, F., Krogh, V., Giumetti, D., Panico, S., Scottoni, A., & Mancini, M. (1986). Short-term effect of a natural disaster on coronary heart disease risk factors. *Arteriosclerosis, 6*, 491–494.

van Beaumont, W. (1972). Evaluation of hemoconcentration from hematocrit measurements. *Journal of Applied Physiology, 32*, 712–713.

van Beaumont, W., Young, H. L., & Greenleaf, J. E. (1974). Plasma fluid and blood constituent shifts during heat exposure in resting man. *Aerospace Medicine, 45*, 176–181.

Wakatsuki, A., & Sagara, Y. (1995). Lipoprotein metabolism in postmenopausal and oophorectomized women. *Obstetrics and Gynecology, 85*, 523–528.

Walsh, B. W., Schiff, I., Rosner, B., Greenberg, L., Ravnikar, V., & Sacks, F. M. (1991). Effects of postmenopausal estrogen replacement on the concentrations and metabolism of plasma lipoproteins. *New England Journal of Medicine, 325*, 1196–1204.

Williams, P. T., Krauss, R. M., Vranizan, K. M., & Wood, P. D. S. (1990). Changes in lipo-protein subfractions during diet-induced and exercise-induced weight loss in moderately overweight men. *Circulation, 81,* 1293–1304.

Williams, P. T., Krauss, R. M., Wood, P. D., Lindgren, F. T., Giotas, C., & Vranizan, K. M. (1986). Lipoprotein subfractions of runners and sedentary men. *Metabolism, 35,* 45–52.

Wood, P. D., Stefanick, M. L., Dreon, D. M., Frey-Hewitt, B., Garay, S. C., Williams, P. T., Superko, H. R., Fortmann, S. P., Albers, J. J., Vranizan, K. M., Ellsworth, N. M., Terry, R. B., & Haskell, W. L. (1988). Changes in plasma lipids and lipoproteins in overweight men during weight loss through dieting as compared with exercise. *New England Journal of Medicine, 319,* 1173–1179.

The Writing Group for the PEPI Trial. (1995). Effects of estrogen or estrogen/progestin regimens on heart disease risk factors in postmenopausal women. *Journal of the American Medical Association, 273,* 199–208.

Yano, K., Rhoads, F. F., & Kagan, A. (1977). Coffee, alcohol and risk of coronary heart disease among Japanese men living in Hawaii. *New England Journal of Medicine, 297,* 405–409.

Appendix
Calculation of Plasma Volume Changes

The equation offered by Dill and Costill (1974) uses both hematocrit and hemoglobin to calculate change in plasma volume. The first step of the equation is to calculate plasma volume at baseline, as follows:

$$PV_{base} = 100 - hematocrit_{base},$$

where $hematocrit_{base}$ is the hematocrit assessed at the baseline period.

The second step is to calculate plasma volume during stress. This is accomplished in the following calculation:

$$PV_{stress} = [100 \times (hemoglobin_{base}/hemoglobin_{stress})] \times hematocrit_{stress},$$

where $hemoglobin_{base}$ is the baseline value of hemoglobin, $hemoglobin_{stress}$ is the stress value of hemoglobin, and $hematocrit_{stress}$ is the value of the hematocrit during stress. This calculation would be repeated for as many different stressors as are included in the protocol, with each of these periods represented by different values of hemoglobin and hematocrit.

The changes in plasma volume that are calculated are applied as a correction to lipid concentration during stress, as follows:

$$Lipid_{corrected} = Lipid_{stress} \times PV_{stress}/PV_{base}$$

or

$$Lipid_{corrected} = Lipid_{stress} \times [1 - (\%PV/100)],$$

where $Lipid_{corrected}$ = corrected lipid value, $Lipid_{stress}$ = lipid concentration during stress, and $\%PV$ = percentage change in plasma volume. These equations are essentially identical and either can be used. However, we prefer the former, because it has less rounding error.

Part II

Lipids and Psychological Distress

4

Anxiety Disorders and Serum Lipids

Chris Hayward

This chapter, unlike most chapters in this book, is concerned with the possible link between anxiety disorders and hyperlipidemia rather than with low serum lipids. Questions regarding serum lipid levels in anxiety patients were stimulated by reports of increased cardiovascular mortality in those with anxiety disorders (Coryell, Noyes, & Clancy, 1982; Coryell, Noyes, & House, 1986). A possible explanation for the higher than expected mortality of these patients is that those with anxiety disorders have higher levels of known cardiovascular disease (CVD) risk factors. This chapter provides an overview of studies regarding anxiety and cardiovascular disease risk and examines in detail the handful of studies measuring serum lipid levels in patients with anxiety disorders.

Anxiety and Cardiovascular Disease Risk

Six studies have examined CVD outcomes in patients with anxiety disorders. In two studies, there was a higher than expected death rate from diseases of the circulatory system in patients with panic disorder (Coryell et al., 1982, 1986). In a third study, anxiety neurosis was associated with higher rates of death from arteriosclerotic disease (Sims & Prior, 1982). A fourth study, which used the Epidemiologic Catchment Area database (Weissman, Livingston-Bruce, Leaf, Florio, & Holzer, 1991), found an association between panic disorder and CVD, although medical diagnoses in this study were determined by self-report (Weissman, Markowitz, Ouellette, Greenwald, & Kahn, 1990). Two studies failed to observe a relationship between anxiety disorders and CVD (Allgulander & Lavori, 1991; Martin, Cloninger, Guze, & Clayton, 1985). All of these six studies were retrospective, did not control for known CVD risk factors, and, with the exception of one study (Weissman et al., 1990), used registries for the purpose of case identification.

The studies reporting a relationship between self-reported anxiety and the risk of subsequent CVD in nonclinical populations are more compelling. Five of seven studies reported significant findings (Haines, Imeson, & Meade, 1987; Kawachi et al., 1994; Medalie et al., 1973; Paffenbarger, Wolf, Notkin, & Thorne, 1966; Thiel, Parker, & Bruce, 1973). With one exception (Thiel et al., 1973), these studies had large samples, were prospective, and reported increased risks of CVD among the anxious ranging from one and one half to six times greater than expected. In the two most recent studies (Haines et al., 1987; Kawachi et al., 1994), in which the reported effects were largest, results were adjusted for the effect of known CVD risk factors. In both of these studies, the risk of CVD was specifically related to the Phobic Anxiety subscale of the Crown–Crisp Experiential Index (Crown & Crisp, 1966). In the study by Kawachi et al., the risk of sudden coronary death was greater than the risk of nonsudden coronary death. The most extreme risk of sudden coronary death (relative risk = 10.8, confidence interval = 2.2–52.5) was associated with an *always* response to the query, "Do you feel panicky in crowds?" Unfortunately, four of the prospective studies involved only men. Anxiety is more common in women. Thus, it is important to replicate these findings in women.

Anxiety and Serum Lipid Levels

If anxiety does influence cardiovascular risk, it may do so indirectly by affecting known CVD risk factors. The effect of anxiety on cardiovascular risk factors and the possibility that anxious patients engage in risk-associated behavior to relieve anxiety have been neglected in behavioral cardiovascular research. Studies that explore the specific relationship between serum lipids and anxiety are discussed below.

Four studies reported cholesterol levels in participants with panic disorder (these are summarized in Table 1). An additional study correlated a scaled measure of anxiety with cholesterol levels in a sample of depressed persons (Fava, Abraham, Pava, Shuster, & Rosenbaum, 1996). Another study assessed the frequency of hypercholesterolemia in a large nonclinical sample who were given a measure of phobic anxiety (Kawachi et al., 1994). All of these studies are reviewed in detail below.

In the first study of plasma lipid levels in patients with panic disorder (Hayward, Taylor, Roth, King, & Agras, 1989), 74 women and 28 men with panic disorder or agoraphobia had fasting lipid levels measured before they participated in a pharmacological-treatment trial. Eighty-four participants met the *Diagnostic and Statistical Manual of Mental Disorders* (American Psychiatric Association, 1980) criteria for panic disorder, and 18 participants had agoraphobia with panic attacks. The triglycerides, total cholesterol, and low density lipoprotein (LDL) and high density lipoprotein (HDL) cholesterol levels in the patients were compared with expected values from the Lipid Research Clinic's program reference ranges by age and sex (National Institutes of Health, 1980). Women, but not men, had mean cholesterol and LDL cholesterol values that exceeded predicted levels. For the women, 46% of the patient group had total cholesterol values that exceeded the 75th percentile, and 43% had LDL cholesterol levels that exceeded the 75th percentile.

Hayward et al. (1989) offered a possible mechanism for the findings in this study involving the sympathetic nervous system. Sympathetic activation increases the activity of lipoprotein lipase, which results in an

Table 1.   Studies of Serum Lipids and Panic Disorder

Study	Sample		Results				
	Type	Size and gender	Total cholesterol		Pooled total cholesterol		Effect size
			M	SD	M	SD	
Hayward, Taylor, Roth, King, and Agras (1989)	Panic disorder	74 F	208	37	—	37 F	0.54 F
	Control	28 M	202	38	—	—	
		National average (F)	188	—	—	—	
Tancer, Stein, Moul, and Uhde (1990)	Panic disorder	56 F	194.4	36.9	194.4	36.9	0.15 pooled M–F
		24 M	195.4	33.4			
	Control	56 F	187.7	36.5	187.7	36.5	0.13 F
		24 M	190.6	36.4			0.18 M
Bajwa, Asnis, Sanderson, Irfan, and van Praag (1992)	Panic disorder	13 F	—	—	224.7	43.5	1.01 pooled M–F
		17 M	—	—			
	Control	13 F	—	—	183.6	37.7	
		17 M	—	—			
Freedman et al. (1995)	Panic disorder	85 M	211	41	211	41	0.02 M
	Control	1,237 M	212	41	212	41	

Note: F = female, M = male. Cholesterol was measured in milligrams per deciliter.

increase of free fatty acid in the serum. Theoretically, the hypothesized alteration in adrenergic function observed in patients with panic disorder (Charney & Redmond, 1983; Neese, Cameron, Curtis, McCann, & Huber-Smith, 1984; Villacres, Hollifield, & Katon, 1987) could alter lipid metabolism by affecting sympathetic regulation of lipoprotein lipase activity. If this were true, total cholesterol and LDL might also correlate with pertinent clinical variables related to panic, such as avoidance and panic attack frequency. This hypothesis was tested by correlating the total cholesterol and LDL in female participants with the frequency of panic attacks and a measure of phobic avoidance. The frequency of panic attacks was significantly correlated with total cholesterol level ($r_s = .25$, $N = 66$, $p < .05$), which suggests a relationship between frequency of panic attacks and total cholesterol. However, the correlation coefficient was not large, and it represented the only significant correlation of eight analyses performed. The limitations of this study include the facts that no control group was used and that the sample size for men was relatively small.

A second study (Bajwa, Asnis, Sanderson, Irfan, & van Praag, 1992) confirmed previous findings that patients with panic disorder have higher total serum cholesterol levels than normal persons (Hayward et al., 1989). In addition, this study found that elevated cholesterol levels were particularly associated with panic disorder, in comparison with major depression, and that patients with histories of anxiety disorders among those with major depression had elevated cholesterol levels also.

The serum cholesterol levels of patients with panic disorder were compared with those of age- and sex-matched patients with major depression and with those of normal control participants ($n = 30$ for each study group, with 17 male and 13 female participants in each group). The two groups of patients met *Diagnostic and Statistical Manual of Mental Disorders* (American Psychiatric Association, 1987) criteria (Spitzer & Williams, 1987) and had been drug free for a period of 3 weeks. The control participants were screened for psychiatric disorders. Potential participants who reported alcohol or drug abuse or dependence during the past 6 months; had abnormal electrocardiograms; or had unstable medical conditions such as hypertension, diabetes mellitus, or asthma were excluded from the study.

Total serum cholesterol levels in the groups studied were significantly different. Patients with panic disorder had a mean cholesterol level of 224.7 mg/dl, which was significantly different from that of patients with major depression ($M = 189.8$ mg/dl) and normal control participants ($M = 183.6$ mg/dl; $p < .002$). In addition, patients with major depression who also had histories of anxiety disorders ($n = 9$) had higher cholesterol levels than did patients with major depression who did not have histories of anxiety disorders ($n = 21$).

To ensure that a concurrent medical condition was not responsible for the elevated cholesterol levels of the patients with panic disorder, Bajwa et al. (1992) conducted analyses that included only patients without medical diagnoses and their age- and sex-matched normal control participants. The cholesterol levels of the healthy patients with panic disorder ($n = 17$)

were significantly higher than those of the control participants. The cholesterol levels of healthy depressed patients who had no history of anxiety disorder (n = 16) were not significantly different from those of their age- and sex-matched controls. However, healthy depressed patients with histories of anxiety disorders (n = 4) had significantly higher cholesterol levels than depressed patients.

Bajwa et al. (1992) suggested two possible explanations for their findings. First, anticipatory anxiety may be responsible for the elevations in cholesterol levels of patients with panic disorder, who experience substantial anticipatory anxiety related to the stressful onset of panic attacks. Second, higher cholesterol levels in patients with panic disorder may be a result of induction of lipoprotein lipase, as suggested by Hayward et al. (1989).

Note that cholesterol levels of all participants in the study were not markedly elevated but were within normal range (150–250 mg/dl). The study was limited in that HDL or LDL cholesterol levels (which are considered to be more specifically correlated with risk or coronary heart disease) were not measured. In addition, when the findings were analyzed excluding participants with concurrent medical conditions, the sample sizes became very small (n = 4 in one case).

Another study reported that patients with panic disorder do not have elevated serum cholesterol values compared with controls (Tancer, Stein, Moul, & Uhde, 1990). Total serum cholesterol levels were assessed in 80 patients who met *DSM–III–R* criteria for panic disorder and 80 normal controls, who were matched for age and gender (there were 24 men and 56 women in each group). All participants in the study (N = 160) were determined as healthy by their history and by physical and laboratory examinations. A subset of the panic disorder patients (n = 68) completed the Spielberger State Anxiety Inventory within 3 days of phlebotomy.

Mean serum cholesterol levels did not significantly differ among diagnostic groups: Panic disorder patients had a mean serum cholesterol level of 194.4 mg/dl (SD = 36.9), compared with the control group's mean cholesterol level of 187.7 mg/dl (SD = 36.5, t (158) = 1.14, p = .26). Male panic disorder patients had mean levels of 195 mg/dl (SD = 33.4), compared with 190.6 mg/dl (SD = 36.4) for the controls (t (46) = 0.47, p = .64). Taking 200 mg/dl as the cutoff for elevated serum cholesterol (Grundy, 1986), 37.5% of the male panic disordered patients and 28.8% of the male normal controls had elevated cholesterol levels (N = 24, p = .24). There was no significant correlation between State Anxiety ratings and serum cholesterol levels in the subset of 68 patients (Tancer et al., 1990).

This study concluded that if cardiac mortality was, in fact, increased in patients with panic disorder, hypercholesterolemia alone would appear to be an insufficient cause. In this study, comparisons for serum cholesterol levels for men, but not for women, were analyzed separately. Because Hayward et al.'s (1989) study observed differences in serum cholesterol levels for women, but not for men, analyzing the women separately would have been useful.

In a fourth study (Freedman et al., 1995) 3,490 male veterans were evaluated as part of a study comparing the health of Vietnam veterans to veterans who served in other areas during the same time period. The Diagnostic Interview Schedule was administered in a cross-sectional design when the participants were between the ages of 31 and 45 years. The Diagnostic Interview Schedule is a structured psychiatric interview that can be administered by trained laypeople (Robins et al., 1985). It provides diagnoses for a number of psychiatric disorders. Total cholesterol, HDL, and triglyceride values were obtained after an overnight fast.

The results indicated that the 85 participants with panic disorder had a total cholesterol level ($M = 211$, $SD = 41$) that did not significantly differ from those without a psychiatric diagnosis ($n = 1,237$, $M = 212$, $SD = 41$). Other anxiety disorders assessed included generalized anxiety disorder (GAD), obsessive–compulsive disorder, and post-traumatic stress disorder. Only the participants with GAD had total cholesterol levels that were significantly higher than those without this diagnosis (M for GAD ever = 216, $SD = 41$; M for GAD within the last month = 222, $SD = 41$). Those with GAD demonstrated significantly higher triglyceride levels also; compared with those without GAD.

The association between GAD and higher cholesterol and triglyceride levels could not be attributed to differences in alcohol consumption, cigarette smoking, body weight, or educational status. Freedman et al. (1995) speculated that the higher cholesterol and triglyceride levels in those with GAD might be mediated by catecholamines or elevated cortisol, although this study did not assess catecholamine or cortisol levels.

The limitations of this study were the absence of women and the participation of veterans only; however, its methodologic strengths included a large sample size, a nonclinical population, and adjustment for confounding variables such as body weight and cigarette smoking.

Fava et al. (1996) conducted a study that explored the possible relationship between coronary artery disease risk factors and anger and anxiety, in a sample of 127 depressed outpatients. Fava et al. (1996) observed that increased anxiety scores were associated with higher cholesterol levels and with prolonged QTc intervals on the echocardiogram. In addition, patients who had experienced anger attacks showed a trend toward higher cholesterol levels as compared with patients without those attacks.

This study defined *anger attacks* as sudden outbursts of anger inappropriate to the situation, accompanied by autonomic arousal symptoms such as tachycardia, sweating, and flushing. Participants were classified as having anger attacks when they reported having experienced the following four conditions over the previous 6 months: irritability; overreaction to minor annoyances; occurrence of anger attacks, with at least one occurring within the past month; and experience during at least one of the attacks of four or more extreme reactions (tachycardia, hot flashes, chest tightness, paresthesia, dizziness, shortness of breath, sweating, trembling, panic, feeling out of control, feeling like attacking others, attacking physically or verbally, or throwing or destroying objects).

Participants in this study ($N = 178$) were participating in the open phase of a double-blind study on the long-term efficacy of fluoxetine, had been diagnosed with major depressive disorder, as determined by *DSM–III–R* criteria, and had a Hamilton Rating Scale for Depression (HAM–D–17) score greater than or equal to 16 both at screening and baseline (Hamilton, 1960). Patients with serious suicidal risk, serious or unstable mental illness, pregnancy, substance abuse disorders, or current use of psychotropic drugs other than fluoxetine were excluded. The study included a 12-week open phase of fluoxetine treatment of 20 mg/day.

Of all the participants in the study, 138 patients (42 male and 96 female) volunteered to participate in the add-on study on anger in depression. They had been free of antidepressants for at least 2 weeks before entering the 12-week fluoxetine-treatment trial. Each participant was administered the Anger Attacks Questionnaire (Fava et al., 1991), a self-rating instrument that assesses the presence or absence of anger attacks during the previous month, at baseline and 8 weeks later. Of the 127 depressed patients evaluated, 56 (44%) reported the presence of anger attacks. There was no difference in age between depressed patients with and without anger attacks or in the severity of their depression at baseline, as assessed by the HAM–D–17 score.

In addition to the Anger Attacks Questionnaire, 133 patients in the overall study were administered the Symptom Questionnaire (Kellner, 1987), a 92-item self-rating questionnaire with four scales: Anxiety, Depression, Somatization, and Anger/Hostility. The Anger/Hostility scale consists of items such as "feeling angry" or "not feeling kind to people," whereas the Anxiety scale consists of items such as "feeling restless" or "feeling jumpy."

Several CVD risk factors were evaluated in all participants at baseline visit, including serum cholesterol levels. A significant positive relationship was found between anxiety and cholesterol, even after adjusting for age, body mass index (BMI), and gender. No statistically significant associations were observed for the relationship between anger and irritability and CVD risk factors.

This study found that cholesterol levels were associated with increased anxiety scores among depressed patients. The depressed-patient group as a whole, however, had cholesterol levels within the normal range. This was in keeping with findings of a previous study, which showed that depressed patients had cholesterol levels no different from those of control participants (Oxenkrug et al., 1983). Higher cholesterol levels have been reported in depressed patients with histories of anxiety disorders as compared with patients with depression alone (Bajwa et al., 1992). In addition, patients with anger attacks had a trend toward higher cholesterol levels than did patients without those attacks, in keeping with a prior report of high hostility scores associated with elevated levels of plasma cholesterol (Weidner, Sexton, McLellarn, Connor, & Matarazzo, 1987).

Finally, in the study referred to earlier, by Kawachi et al. (1994), 33,999 U.S. male health professionals were prospectively evaluated, to determine the relation between phobic anxiety and the subsequent incidence of CVD. A strong association between phobic anxiety and sudden death was found, but in addition, participants with phobic symptoms more frequently reported a history of hypertension, elevated cholesterol, and diabetes.

This study began in 1986, when male health professionals age 40 to 76 years completed a mailed questionnaire on CVD risk factors, medical history, and diet. Follow-up questionnaires were sent every 2 years after the beginning of the study. All participants were asked to complete the Phobic Anxiety scale of the Crown–Crisp Experiential Index, as part of the 1988 questionnaire. The final questionnaire was mailed in 1990. In addition to the self-assessment of phobic anxiety, information was obtained on the participants' medical history, smoking habit, weight, height, level of physical activity, alcohol intake, and family history of myocardial infarction. Self-assessments of hypertension, hypercholesterolemia, and diabetes mellitus also were elicited.

Hypercholesterolemia was more frequently reported by participants with symptoms of phobic anxiety. Approximately 15% of those with low levels of phobic anxiety reported hypercholesterolemia, versus 19.2% of those who scored greater than or equal to 4 on the Crown–Crisp Phobic Anxiety scale. This study was limited in that its sample consisted of male health care professionals. Therefore, results may not be generalizable to the general population, because most of those affected with phobic anxiety are women. In addition, all data were self-reported.

Discussion

Although there is compelling evidence that anxiety, particularly phobic anxiety, is associated with increased CVD mortality, the evidence that this is due to elevated serum lipids in the anxious is variable. Two of four studies measuring lipids in anxiety disordered persons found differences compared with controls. The effect sizes (as shown in Table 1) ranged from 0.02 to 1.01. There are no data yet with regard to phobic disorders and serum lipids. This would be a useful contribution, because phobic anxiety appears to be most related to CVD risk. The following three factors may influence the observed association between anxiety and elevated levels of cholesterol, if in fact there is one: diet, exercise, and bias of sample.

Those with anxiety disorders may consume a diet that is higher in fat than people who do not suffer from these disorders. Anxiety is often associated with overeating or binge eating. If anxious participants did eat a higher fat diet than nonanxious participants, one might expect them to have higher BMIs than others. The one study reviewed that reported BMI did not find a difference between panic disordered participants and controls (Hayward et al., 1989).

Patients with anxiety disorders may be less physically fit than the general population. Two studies demonstrated that patients with panic disorder were less fit than controls (Gaffney, Fenton, Lane, & Lake, 1988; Taylor et al., 1987). Physical fitness may indirectly lower cholesterol by reducing BMI; however, it does increase HDL ("good" cholesterol), which contributes to total serum cholesterol levels.

Studies of clinical samples with anxiety disorders may be biased in that they include only those participants who suffer from disorders who either are seeking treatment or responding to advertisements. However, we know from the Epidemiologic Catchment Area study that nearly half of those with anxiety disorders never seek treatment. Those who do seek treatment for these conditions may be more likely to have one or more other health conditions, because those with two disorders are more likely to seek treatment in general (Berkson's bias; Berkson, 1946). For example, those with concerns about hypercholesterolemia may be more likely to seek treatment than those who have panic disorder and have normal lipid levels. The study by Freedman et al. (1995) is important in this regard in that it represents the only study of a nonclinical sample.

Finally, the possible relationship among serum lipids, anxiety, and serotonin is worthy of mention. Apter et al. (1990) argued that serotonin hypofunction underlies affective disorders, anxiety disorders, and disorders of impulse. Also, the low cholesterol levels found among those with impulse disorders have been hypothesized to be mediated by serotonin hypofunction (Engelberg, 1992). The findings from this review, however, suggest that the anxious do not have low levels of serum lipids and, in fact, may have increased serum lipids. This would not be in keeping with a hypothesis that links anxiety disorders, affective disorders, and impulse disorders with serotonin hypofunction and hypocholesterolemia. On the other hand, if anxiety disorders are conceptualized as disorders of over-control in contrast to impulse control disorders, then the higher lipid levels in the anxious are complementary to lower lipid levels observed in the impulsive.

Conclusion and Recommendations for Future Research

In conclusion, there is some evidence that subjects with anxiety symptoms and disorders may have slightly higher cholesterol levels. The differences observed however are not large enough to represent clinical significant effects. Therefore the observed increase in CVD mortality among the anxious may not be mediated by difference in lipids.

More research on self-reported anxiety and relative risk of subsequent CVD in women is needed. Four of the seven prospective studies overviewed in this chapter involved only men, and anxiety disorders are 2–3 times more common in women. The study of plasma lipid levels in patients with panic disorder should be analyzed separately by gender. More detailed studies of patients with panic disorder and serum cholesterol values, controlling for BMI and diet, are needed. Finally, the studies that indicate a relation between phobic anxiety and subsequent CVD are important to replicate.

References

Allgulander, C., & Lavori, P. W. (1991). Excess mortality among 3,302 patients with "pure" anxiety neurosis. *Archives of General Psychiatry, 48*, 599–602.

American Psychiatric Association. (1980). *Diagnostic and statistical manual of mental disorders* (3rd ed.). Washington, DC: Author.

American Psychiatric Association. (1987). *Diagnostic and statistical manual of mental disorders* (3rd ed., rev.). Washington, DC: Author.

Apter, A., van Praag, H. M., Plutchik, R., Sevy, S., Korn, M., & Brown, S. L. (1990). Interrelationships among anxiety, aggression, impulsivity, and mood: A serotonergically linked cluster? *Psychiatry Research, 32*, 191–199.

Bajwa, W. K., Asnis, G. M., Sanderson, W. C., Irfan, A., & van Praag, H. M. (1992). High cholesterol levels in patients with panic disorder. *American Journal of Psychiatry, 149*, 376–378.

Berkson, J. (1946). Limitations of the application of fourfold table analysis to hospital data. *Biometrics, 2*, 47–53.

Charney, D. S., & Redmond, D. E. (1983). Neurobiologic mechanisms in human anxiety: Evidence supporting central noradrenergic hyperactivity. *Neuropharmacology, 22*, 1531–1536.

Coryell, W., Noyes, R., & Clancy, J. (1982). Excess mortality in panic disorder: A comparison with primary unipolar depression. *Archives of General Psychiatry, 39*, 701–703.

Coryell, W., Noyes, R., Jr., & House, J. D. (1986). Mortality among outpatients with anxiety disorders. *American Journal of Psychiatry, 143*, 508–510.

Crown, S., & Crisp, A. H. (1966). A short clinical diagnostic self-rating scale for psychoneurotic patients: The Middlesex Hospital questionnaire. *British Journal of Psychiatry, 112*, 917–923.

Dimsdale, J. E., & Herd, J. A. (1982). Variability of plasma lipids in response to emotional arousal. *Psychosomatic Medicine, 44*, 413–429.

Engelberg, H. (1992). Low serum cholesterol and suicide. *The Lancet, 399*, 727–728.

Fava, M., Abraham, M., Pava, J., Shuster, J., & Rosenbaum, J. (1996). Cardiovascular risk factors in depression: The role of anxiety and anger. *Psychosomatics, 37*, 31–37.

Freedman, D. S., Byers, T., Barrett, D. H., Stroup, N. E., Eaker, E., & Monroe-Blum, H. (1995). Plasma lipid levels and psychologic characteristics of men. *American Journal of Epidemiology, 141*, 507–517.

Gaffney, F. A., Fenton, B. J., Lane, L. D., & Lake, C. R. (1988). Hemodynamic, ventilatory, and biochemical responses of panic patients and normal controls with sodium lactate infusion and spontaneous panic attacks. *Archives of General Psychiatry, 45*, 53–60.

Grundy, S. M. (1986). Cholesterol and coronary heart disease: A new era. *Journal of the American Medical Association, 256*, 2849–2858.

Haines, A. P., Imeson, J. D., & Meade, T. W. (1987). Phobic anxiety and ischaemic heart disease. *British Medical Journal* [Clinical Research], *295*, 297–299.

Hamilton, M. (1960). A rating scale for depression. *Journal of Neurology and Neurosurgical Psychiatry, 23*, 56–62.

Hayward, C., Taylor, C. B., Roth, W. T., King, R., & Agras, W. S. (1989). Plasma lipid levels in patients with panic disorder or agoraphobia. *American Journal of Psychiatry, 146*, 917–919.

Kawachi, I., Colitz, G. A., Ascherio, A., Rimm, E. B., Giovannucci, E., Stamfer, M. J., & Willett, W. C. (1994). Prospective study of phobic anxiety and risk of coronary heart disease in men. *Circulation, 89*, 1992–1997.

Kellner, R. A. (1987). Symptom questionnaire. *Journal of Clinical Psychiatry, 48*, 268–274.

Martin, R. L., Cloninger, R., Guze, S. B., & Clayton, P. J. (1985). Mortality in a follow-up of 500 psychiatric outpatients: II. Cause-specific mortality. *Archives of General Psychiatry, 42*, 58–66.

Medalie, J. H., Snyder, M., Groen, J. J., Neufeld, H. N., Goldbourt, U., & Riss, E. (1973). Angina pectoris among 10,000 men: 5-year incidence and univariate analysis. *American Journal of Medicine, 55*, 583–594.

National Institutes of Health. (1980). *The Lipids Research Clinics Population Studies Data Book* (Vol. 1, pp. 22–81, NIH Publication No. 80-1527). Washington, DC, National Heart, Lung and Blood Institute, Division of Heart and Vascular Diseases, Lipid Metabolism Branch.

Neese, R. M., Cameron, O. G., Curtis, C. G., McCann, D. S., & Huber-Smith, M. J. (1984). Adrenergic function in patients with panic anxiety. *Archives of General Psychiatry, 41*, 771–776.

Oxenkrug, G. F., Branconnier, R. J., Harto-Truax, N., & Cole, J. O. (1983). Is serum cholesterol a biological marker for major depressive factor? *American Journal of Psychiatry, 140*, 920–921.

Paffenbarger, R. S., Wolf, P. A., Notkin, J., & Thorne, M. C. (1966). Chronic disease in former college students: I. Early precursors of fatal coronary heart disease. *American Journal of Epidemiology, 83*, 314–328.

Robins, L. N., Helzer, J. E., Orvaschel, H., Anthony, J. C., Blazer, D. G., Burnam, A., & Burke, J. D. (1985). The Diagnostic Interview Schedule. In W W. Easton and L. G. Kessler (Eds.), *Epidemiologic field methods in psychiatry: The NIMH epidemiologic catchment area program* (pp. 143–170). Orlando: Academic Press, Inc.

Sims, A., & Prior, P. (1982). Arteriosclerosis related deaths in severe neurosis. *Comprehensive Psychiatry, 23*(2), 181–185.

Spitzer, R. L., & Williams, J. B. W. (1987). Structured clinical interview for *DSM–III–R*— Patient edition (SCID–P, Version 1.0). Washington, DC: American Psychiatric Press.

Tancer, M. E., Stein, M. B., Moul, D. E., & Uhde, T. W. (1990). Normal serum cholesterol in panic disorder. *Biological Psychiatry, 27*, 99–101.

Taylor, C. B., King, R., Ehlers, A., Margraf, J., Clark, D., Hayward, C., Roth, W. T., & Agras, W. S. (1987). Treadmill exercise test and ambulatory measures in panic attacks. *American Journal of Cardiology, 60*, 48j–52j.

Thiel, H. G., Parker, D., & Bruce, T. A. (1973). Stress factors and the risk of myocardial infarction. *Journal of Psychosomatic Research, 17*, 43–57.

Villacres, E. C., Hollifield, M., & Katon, W. J. (1987). Sympathetic nervous system activity in panic disorder. *Journal of Psychiatric Research, 21*, 313–321.

Weidner, G., Sexton, G., McLellarn, R., Connor, S. L., & Matarazzo, J. D. (1987). The role of type A behavior and hostility in an elevation of plasma lipids in adult women and men. *Psychosomatic Medicine, 49*, 136–145.

Weissman, M. M., Livingstone-Bruce, M., Leaf, P. J., Florio, L. P., & Holzer III, C. (1991). Affective Disorders. In L. N. Robins and D. A. Regier (Eds.), *Psychiatric disorders in America* (pp. 53–80). New York: The Free Press.

Weissman, M. M., Markowitz, J. S., Ouellette, R., Greenwald, S., & Kahn, J. P. (1990). Panic disorder and cardiovascular/cerebrovascular problems: Results from a community survey. *American Journal of Psychiatry, 147*, 1504–1508.

5

Lipids and the Coronary-Prone Personality

Lorenz J. P. van Doornen

The evidence for an association between psychological factors and risk of cardiovascular disease (CVD) has evoked the question of to what extent this association could be ascribed to the relationship of psychological factors to serum lipid levels. The best known description of the coronary-prone personality is the Type A behavior pattern. In the 1960s, Type A behavior was implicated as a predictor of CVD among achievement-oriented individuals. Researchers tried to demonstrate that Type A individuals had elevated cholesterol levels, to explain part of the Type A behavior pattern–CVD link. Later on, when the focus changed to hostility as the crucial toxic element of the Type A behavior pattern, the connection between hostility and lipid levels became a topic of interest. Depression and anxiety also have been suggested to be components of the coronary-prone personality. Consequently, the association among depression, anxiety, and lipid levels became the subject of several studies.

All of these studies had a common perspective: A personality factor, or a mood state was supposed to be causally related to an elevation of lipid levels. The studies were purely empirical in the sense that they simply looked for an association. In case an association was observed, this was often hypothesized to be attributable to the lipid-mobilizing effect of stress hormones, which, however, were in fact not measured.

Recently, there has been a revival of interest in the association between lipids and psychological variables. The impetus for this regained interest originates in reports from intervention trials that show that lowering cholesterol level might lead to an increase of non-illness-related mortality (mortality due to suicide or a violent crime or accident, see chapter 15 in this volume). The starting point of this more recent line of research differs in two respects from the former one. First, lowered, rather than elevated, cholesterol levels are supposed to be associated with psychological characteristics. Second, the supposed causality is reversed: Lipid levels are the origin instead of the consequence of a psychological state. For example, the studies in this area hypothesize that low cholesterol, or a rapid lowering of cholesterol by intervention, is associated with an increase of depressive and hostile feelings. This in turn might explain the association of low cholesterol with the incidence of non-illness-related mortality. Surprisingly, the opposite predictions had been made in the research field of the coronary-prone personality I first described. This potentially leads to contrasting findings that the same psychological variables (e.g., depression and hostility) are associated with both higher and lower lipid levels.

The purpose of the present chapter is to evaluate critically the evidence for an association between lipids and personality factors that are (or are supposed to be) components of the coronary-prone personality. These studies are a nearly complete coverage of lipids–personality studies, because practically only those personality factors have been studied that were deemed to be relevant with respect to CVD risk. The term *personality* in the title implies that my focus will be on relatively stable psychological characteristics, thereby excluding those studies looking at the association between acute or chronic stress or mood changes and lipids. A clear separation, however, between stable temperamental *traits* and more variable *states* is difficult to make. For example, Type A behavior has been characterized as a risk personality, a behavioral style, or a coping style. It certainly contains elements close to biologically rooted, temperament-like traits, but it is also a product of environmental factors. The same applies to the concepts of depression and hostility. There are certainly influences of stable characteristics, being inherited or originating in early life experiences, but at the same time, environmental factors such as life events do influence someone's depression or hostility.

In the sections that follow, I will evaluate the evidence for the association between lipids and lipoproteins, on one hand, and Type A behavior pattern, hostility, depression, and anxiety–neuroticism, on the other. I do not describe all studies in detail but, rather, focus on general methodological and theoretical problems in this field and try to come to global judgments on the solidity of findings in the different areas.

Type A Behavior Pattern and Lipid Levels

The characteristic elements of the Type A behavior pattern are achievement orientation, competitiveness, repressed hostile feelings, excessive impatience, overactivity, and a continuous sense of time urgency. The contrasting Type B behavior pattern is defined by the relative absence of these characteristics. Type A is traditionally measured by way of a Structured Interview, although a self-report measure of Type A behavior was developed (the Jenkins Activity Survey; JAS; Jenkins, Zyzanski, & Rosenman, 1971).

Some prospective studies have shown the predictive power of structured-interview-based Type A classification for the future development of CVD (see Matthews, 1988, for review). This association remained even after correction for traditional CVD risk factors and, thus, for cholesterol level. This does not exclude, however, that part of the association may be mediated by higher cholesterol levels in Type A persons.

The early studies by Friedman and Rosenman in the 1960s indeed suggested that Type A behavior was associated with elevated cholesterol and triglyceride levels (M. Friedman & Rosenman, 1959; Rosenman & Friedman, 1961) in both men and women. Correction for lifestyle variables such as smoking, physical activity, and diet did not eliminate the association. Also, Jenkins, Rosenman, and Friedman (1966) observed, by means of the California Personality Inventory, that overactivity (competition, aggression, and impatience—all central elements of Type A behavior) was associated with higher cholesterol levels. Several other small-scale studies from that period could not, however, confirm these findings (e.g., E. H. Friedman, Hellerstein, Eastwood, & Jones, 1968; Keith, Lown, & Stare, 1965). The same lability of findings characterizes our own studies in this field. I once observed that a test measuring impatience, overactivity, and goal-directed striving (all Type A characteristics) was significantly correlated (.32) with cholesterol level in 78 middle-aged men (van Doornen, 1980). Later, however, we found no correlation between Type A, as measured by the JAS questionnaire, and cholesterol in young adults (van Doornen & van Blokland, 1989). Data from Lundberg, Hedman, Melin, and Frankenhaeuser (1989) suggest that the association might be sex specific. In a group of 60 middle-aged men and women, an association between interview-based Type A score and cholesterol was observed in men (.37) but not in women. No associations were observed in either sex for high-density lipoproteins (HDLs) and triglycerides.

The alternation of positive and negative findings is characteristic for this research area. Niaura, Stoney, and Herbert (1992), as part of their general review on the relation between psychological variables and lipids, also summarized the results of the Type A–lipids studies. They cited 10 positive studies, but also 11 negative ones, which failed to find any association. Moreover, they concluded that in the positive studies, the results were inconsistent with respect to the influence of sex, age, race, and type of lipid measured. Perhaps this confusing picture is due to the lack of power or the influence of chance in these relatively small-scale studies.

Population-based, larger scale studies, however, do not offer a convincing picture either. In the Belgian Multifactor Prevention Trial, no association was found between cholesterol and Type A behavior pattern, as measured by questionnaire (Kornitzer, Kittel, Dramaix, & de Backer, 1983). In the Western Collaborative Group Study (WCGS) a weak association was found, but only in the younger age group (Rosenman et al., 1975). In the Multiple Risk Factor Intervention Trial (MRFIT), interview-based Type A score was unrelated to cholesterol level (Shekelle et al., 1985). In the 742 male and female young adults participating in the Family Heart Study, a significant but low correlation was found between JAS-derived Type A scores and cholesterol for men ($r = .18$), after controlling for age and body mass index (BMI). For women, a marginal correlation (.13) was observed. No relations occurred for HDL and triglycerides (Weidner, Sexton, McLellarn, Connor, & Matarazzo, 1987).

In conclusion, the smaller scale studies show inconsistent results, and the population-based studies show mainly negative results or very small effects. The results of studies are, however, difficult to compare. They differ widely in the extent to which correction for confounders such as age, body mass, and lifestyle variables is applied. Perhaps even more important is a conceptual problem. Though all studies attempted to measure Type A behavior pattern, it is clear that studies, in fact, differed with respect to what they actually measured. Even the most accepted operationalizations of Type A behavior pattern, the JAS and the structured interview, do not measure the same aspects of Type A and only share 20% to 25% variance. There is evidence that anxiety–neuroticism and depression are also elements of questionnaire-defined Type A. For example, the Type A questionnaire, as used in the Framingham Study, was even more strongly related to neuroticism (.41) and depression (.37) than to interview-defined Type A behavior pattern (Chesney, Black, Chadwick, & Rosenman, 1981). Because Type A behavior is an ill-defined and heterogenous concept and different instruments measure different aspects of this mosaic of characteristics, it is clear that already on a priori grounds, not much consistency can be expected with respect to a relation between Type A behavior pattern and lipid values. Even when assuming that structured interview is the most appropriate way of measuring Type A behavior pattern, there seems to be no evidence that studies relying on the structured interview were more successful in finding an association with lipids than studies using the JAS or other questionnaires.

Because the heterogeneity of the concept has been the main reason for the confusing set of results reported, focusing on the separate and crucial components may be a promising approach. The search for a "toxic" component of Type A behavior pattern, with respect to CVD risk, has pointed to hostility as a promising candidate. Similar to studies that tried to demonstrate the predictive value of hostility for CVD, several studies investigated the association between hostility and lipids and lipoproteins.

Hostility and Lipids

The terms *aggression*, *hostility*, and *anger* are often used interchangeably. The cluster of these concepts is often referred to as *AHA syndrome*. Nevertheless, they have a different meaning. *Anger* refers to an emotion but can also be considered a personality trait, referring to individual differences with respect to frequency or intensity of this emotional response. The term *aggression* refers to overt verbal or physical aggressive behavior toward others (Smith, 1992). Because *hostility* was considered to be specifically related to CVD risk, most of the studies looking for a relation with lipids and lipoproteins measured hostility rather than anger. The evidence for an association between aggression and (low) cholesterol is discussed in chapter 9 of this volume. In specifying hostility as the toxic component of global Type A, the hope was to have defined a more homogenous trait. Hostility, however, also appeared to be a multidimensional concept. It can be categorized into an attitudinal, an emotional, and a behavioral component. The *attitudinal* (or *cognitive*) component refers to negative attitudes and appraisals toward others, in other words, mistrust and cynicism. The *emotional* component includes emotions like anger, irritability, and annoyance. It has also been termed *neurotichostility*. The *behavioral* component, also described as *reactive* or *expressive hostility*, refers to aggressive antagonistic behavior (Dembroski & Costa, 1987). Concerning the measurement of these components, it is well accepted that the most often used scale, the Cook–Medley Hostility (Ho) Scale, mainly measures cynical hostility, although it also contains elements of expressive hostility (Smith, 1992). The Cook–Medley Ho Scale, moreover, contains a neurotic component. In the Western Electric Study, the Cook–Medley Ho score correlated .60 with neuroticism (Almada et al., 1991).

Another measure is the "potential for hostility," as derived from the Type A Structured Interview. It contains three subcomponents: hostile content, hostile intensity, and stylistic hostility (Dembroski & Costa, 1987). Less frequently, the Buss–Durkee Hostility Inventory has been used. The Assault, Verbal, and indirect Hostility subscales are supposed to measure expressive hostility. Neurotic hostility is measured by the Resentment and Suspicion subscales (Siegman, Dembroski, & Ringel, 1987). For a more detailed evaluation of the construct validity and psychometric properties of these instruments, see the concise review of the hostility concept by Smith (1992).

After the failure to replicate the predictive value of Type A behavior pattern for CVD in several studies (e.g., Appels et al., 1987; Ragland & Brand, 1988; Shekelle et al., 1985), the question rose of which components of the heterogenous Type A concept could be held responsible for the association with CVD risk. The attention focused on hostility as the possible toxic component. Indeed, in a study by Shekelle, Gale, Ostfeld, and Paul (1983), Ho scores predicted coronary events in a sample of 1,877 men after controlling for risk factors and confounders. Also, in the WCGS study, hostility, as measured with the Cook–Medley Ho scale, showed to be prospectively related to coronary death and total mortality (Almada et al., 1991). The MRFIT study showed that not global Type A behavior pattern, but total Potential for Hostility and the subcomponent Stylistic Hostility were significantly related to CVD incidence, at least in the age group under 47 years (Dembroski, MacDougall, Costa, & Grandits, 1989). Several other studies, however, failed to find an association (e.g., Hearn, Murray, & Luepker, 1989; McCranie, Watkins, & Brandsma, 1989), and also, recently, Maruta et al. (1993) reported negative findings. The issue of the relevance of hostility for CVD risk, or health in general, is still a matter of controversy, which is not discussed further here. See, for example, Barefoot (1993) for comments on this issue.

As during the time of "global Type A" studies, parallel to studies that tried to demonstrate the CVD predictive value of hostility, several studies investigated whether hostility was related to lipid values. Already in the 1960s, there were suggestions of an association between hostility and cholesterol levels. Sloane, Inglis, and Payne (1962) found substantial correlations (around .50), in a group of 33 students, between aggression and hostility, as assessed by psychiatric interview and cholesterol levels. Self-estimates of hostility, however, were unrelated to cholesterol. Harlan, Oberman, Mitchell, and Graybiel (1967) reported unrestrained, aggressive temperament and sociability (as measured with the Guilford–Zimmerman Temperament Survey) to be associated with higher cholesterol and triglyceride levels in a group of 441 former naval aviation cadets, after correction for confounders such as weight, diet, smoking, and physical activity. The 2 psychological characteristics were, however, the only scales out of 11 that showed some association, and they together explained only 1% of the variance in lipids. Siegel (1984) found no association in adolescents between anger measures and cholesterol. A later study that focused on anger observed trait anger to be significantly ($r = .41$) related to the low density lipoprotein (LDL) to HDL ratio among Black males (Johnson, Collier, Nazzaro, & Gilbert, 1992). Lundberg et al. (1989) found Type A interview–derived hostility and cholesterol to be correlated in women (.37) but not in men. Triglyceride level correlated .30 with hostility in men but not in women. Dujovne and Houston (1991) observed Cook–Medley Ho scores to be positively associated with cholesterol (.23) and LDL (.28) in 74 men, but not in women. In males and females together, expressive hostility, as measured with subscales of the Buss–Durkee Hostility Inventory, correlated .18 and .23 with cholesterol and LDL, respectively. These relations were obtained after correction for age, exercise, smoking, and body mass. *Neurotic hostility* (referring to hostility-related emotions such as anger and resentment) was unrelated to lipid values. No associations were observed for triglycerides and HDL.

The impression from these fairly small scale studies is that some association seems to exist, relatively independent of the instrument used. The sex specificity is unclear, and the results are inconsistent with respect to the type of lipid measured, triglycerides or cholesterol.

Hostility has been measured in population-based studies as well. Shekelle et al. (1983) observed no association between cholesterol and Cook–Medley Ho scores in a large population of males. In the Family Heart Study, hostility was measured by means of the Paranoid Ideation subscale of the Symptom Checklist (Derogatis, 1977), which measures mainly cynicism. No correlations between hostility and cholesterol were found, after controlling for age and BMI, not even when extreme groups were compared (Weidner, Sexton, McLellarn, Connor, & Matarazzo, 1987). In an analysis of a subsample of the MRFIT participants taking part in the Behavior Pattern Study, comprising 192 infarction patients and 384 controls, no association was observed between any of the interview-derived hostility subcomponents and cholesterol level (Dembroski et al., 1989). In the Whitehall study, Cook–Medley Ho scores were unrelated to cholesterol in 4,246 men and 1,742 women. The more recent hypothesis that hostility might be associated with very low cholesterol levels was not confirmed. Even in the lowest deciles of the cholesterol distribution, hostility scores were not higher (Davey-Smith, Shipley, Marmot, & Patel, 1990). In the Western Electric Study, Cook–Medley Ho scores were unrelated to cholesterol levels (Almada et al., 1991), though in this study these scores were prospectively related to coronary death. Also in the CARDIA study, comprising over 5,000 persons, no relation was observed between Cook–

Medley Ho scores and cholesterol or HDL levels (Scherwitz et al., 1992). In the North Carolina Alumni Heart Study, Ho scores were available from the initial screening, 21–23 years earlier, for 792 persons who had their lipids measured at follow-up. The highest quintile of the Ho distribution had a significantly higher total cholesterol:HDL ratio at follow-up. The partial correlation (controlling for age and sex) between lipid ratio and Ho score was only .09. Cross-sectionally (at follow-up), the correlation was .12 (Siegler, Peterson, Barefoot, & Williams, 1992). Siegler et al. referred to the CARDIA study to suggest a possible cause of this association. In that study, a high Ho score was associated with higher caloric intake. In the CARDIA study, however, as mentioned, Ho scores were not related to lipid values. One of the rare positive findings in a large group was obtained by Fowkes et al. (1992). In 1,592 men, they observed a correlation between scores on the subscale Hostile Acts of the Bedford-Foulds Personality Deviance Questionnaire and triglyceride levels, after correction for age, smoking, and alcohol consumption. The correlation was significant but low (.13). No associations were observed for cholesterol and HDL. *Extra punitiveness*, defined as hostile thoughts and denigratory attitudes, was inversely related to cholesterol in women, but only after adjustment for the just-mentioned possible confounders. Recently, in line with the series of negative results, in a group of 3,490 U.S. Army veterans, Freedman et al. (1995) observed no association between Minnesota Multiphasic Personality Inventory (MMPI) Manifest Hostility scores and cholesterol, HDL, or triglycerides.

Overall, the results of these large-scale studies do not support the impression one could have from the smaller studies that some relation might exist between hostility and lipids. In fact, the larger studies furnish hardly any evidence for such an association. One could argue that this is due to the often doubtful status of the most frequently used scale, that is, the Cook–Medley Hostility Scale, as a measure of hostility. Dembroski et al. (1989), however, using Type A interview–derived hostility did not find an association either.

The sparse and small positive correlations might well be due to incomplete correction for confounders. According to several studies, hostility is associated with adverse health behaviors, which in turn can influence lipid levels. Hostility seems to be associated with a higher prevalence of smoking and higher alcohol intake (Almada et al., 1991; Scherwitz et al., 1992; Shekelle et al., 1983). Some studies report on lower leisure activity and higher BMI (Houston & Vavak, 1991; Koskenvuo et al., 1988). In case a positive association is due to a factor not controlled for, this does not necessarily diminish its significance from a health perspective. The confounder, then, in fact, is an interesting mediator. Considering the absent or very small association between hostility and lipids, the effect of hostility on health-related behavior might even be more relevant with respect to health outcomes than the supposed effect of hostility on lipids. The tendency in studies is to be eager to control for the confounding effects of lifestyle variables, although several studies were far from successful in accomplishing this. The reason for this may be the silent assumption that a relation between hostility and lipids originates in the autonomic and neuroendocrine correlates of hostility and their effects on lipid metabolism. There is some evidence, indeed, that in response to interpersonal stressors, people with high hostility scores are sympathetically more reactive, as reflected in an exaggerated reactivity of their cardiovascular system. Smith (1992) reviewed the evidence for this "psychophysiological reactivity model" (p. 143) and concluded that the evidence was mixed when hostility was assessed by interview but rather consistent when the Cook–Medley Hostility Scale was used. Even then, this is only indirect evidence for the assumption that if people with high hostility scores have higher lipid levels, the levels are due to sympathoadrenal activity. It is a doubtful assumption that acute cardiovascular reactivity to stress is an indicator of generally elevated sympathetic tone. Even if this were the case, a further necessary assumption would be that basal lipid levels are related to sympathetic tone. Ward et al. (1994), however, found no association in 615 men between 24-hr urine adrenaline excretion and cholesterol levels, and even an inverse correlation (−.14) with triglycerides. Noradrenaline was not related to lipid levels. However attractive and plausible a stress–physiological mechanism for the hostility–lipids association may be, it needs empirical support.

Depression and Lipids

According to the meta-analysis of Booth–Kewley and Friedman (1987), depression is a relatively neglected psychological risk factor for CVD, which may be more powerful than Type A behavior. This conclusion, concerning the role of depression, however, was not drawn by Matthews (1988) in a later meta-analysis.

The same as has been the case for Type A behavior pattern and hostility, similar to the disputes about the status of depression as a risk factor, the association with lipids and lipoproteins has been investigated. With respect to depressive mood as a state variable, several earlier studies observed higher cholesterol levels at times when participants reported negative mood (van Doornen & Orlebeke, 1982). I focus further here on depression as a more stable personality characteristic. In our own research, we found some evidence for a relation between depression and lipids. In my earliest study, I observed a small but significant correlation of .27 between depression score and cholesterol in a group of 78 middle-aged men (van Doornen, 1980). In a later study of a group of 52 male and female college students, the Zung Depression score explained 24% of the variance in cholesterol level, but only for men (van Doornen & van Blokland, 1987). In a recently completed larger scale study on 360 middle-aged men and women, we compared the extreme quintiles of the distributions of lipids and lipoproteins with respect to a series of personality variables (van Doornen, Snieder, & Boomsma, 1996). In contrast to our earlier studies, depression–lipid associations were observed only for women. The women with high cholesterol levels (274 mg/dl) showed significantly ($p = .01$)

higher Zung Depression scores than the women with low cholesterol levels (156 mg/dl). The high- versus low-triglycerides groups also differed considerably ($p = .002$) with respect to Zung scores, in the same direction. No association occurred for HDL. These effects were obtained after exclusion of women using contraceptives or antihypertensive or lipid-lowering drugs and after correction for age, habitual level of physical activity, smoking, and alcohol consumption.

As mentioned, we observed no associations for men. This was in contrast to the results of the Lipid Research Clinic Study (Morgan, Palinkas, Barrett-Connor, & Wingard, 1993), in which an inverse relation between cholesterol and Beck Depression Inventory (Beck, Ward, Mendelson, Mock, & Erbaugh, 1961) scores was found. From 1,020 White men between 50 and 89 years, those with low cholesterol levels (<160 mg/dl) were compared with those in all higher categories. Only for men age 70 years and older was categorical depression (Beck Depression Inventory scores ≥13) significantly more manifest in the lowest cholesterol group as compared with the three higher cholesterol categories. After adjustment for possible confounders such as health status, weight, number of medications, and age, the difference remained significant. Across all participants, however, cholesterol only correlated −.10 with depression score. The same result was reported for an elderly French population. Elevated depression scores were evident for the lowest quintile of the cholesterol distribution as compared with all higher quintiles for both men and women, whereas the correlation between cholesterol and depression was close to zero in the total groups of men and women. No clear associations were found with HDL or triglycerides (DeAlberto, Ducimetiere, Mainard, & Alperovitch, 1993). In the Helsinki Aging Study (Strandberg, 1993), Zung Depression scores were also unrelated to cholesterol values in 621 elderly men and women. In contrast to the French study, in women, depression was associated with lower HDL and higher triglyceride levels. This finding, with respect to triglycerides, is in line with the just-mentioned results of our own study, in which middle-aged women with high triglyceride levels had higher Zung Depression scores. A clue for the origin of this association may be the well-known correlation between triglycerides and BMI. Indeed, in our study, the women in the highest quintile of the BMI distribution also had significantly higher Zung Depression scores, as compared with the women with the lowest BMI. This suggests that the stigmatization of being obese in women leads to higher depression scores in this group. Although some studies, indeed, found some evidence for this, a recent review on the psychological effects of obesity concluded that studies are inconsistent in this respect (M. A. Friedman & Brownell, 1995).

If depression were associated with elevated lipid levels, one should certainly be able to find this in groups with clinical depression. The influence, however, of other factors on lipids can be expected to be larger in these groups—factors such as extreme smoking, a low fitness level, and medication use. Lang and Haits (1968), indeed, observed higher cholesterol levels in patients with major depression, and even concluded that it might be a simple biological marker for major depression. Oxenkrug,

Branconnier, Harto-Truax, and Cole (1983), however, could not confirm this finding in a large group of depressed participants; neither could Yates and Wallace (1987), in a group of patients with bipolar affective disorder. Also Bajwa, Asnis, Sanderson, Irfan, and van Praag (1992) observed no difference between patients with major depression and sex- and age-matched controls. More recently, Freedman et al. (1995) in their study of 3,490 U.S. Army veterans, observed no association between either a diagnosis of major depression or two MMPI-derived depression scores and cholesterol level. So these studies on patient groups in general do not support the idea that depression and lipids are associated, neither in a negative nor in a positive way.

Some recent studies approached the relation between depression and lipids in an experimental way: manipulating lipids by diet or pharmacologically and measuring a possible change in depression. Glueck et al. (1993) showed a decrement in depressive symptoms of people with severe primary hypertriglyceridemia after a combined dietary and pharmacological intervention. Triglyceride decrement correlated .47 with improvement of depression. The effect was attributed to improved brain oxygenation, but the possibility of a nonspecific effect, increased self-efficacy, was also mentioned. Weidner, Connor, Hollis, and Connor (1992) studied the psychological effect of dietary intervention in a less extreme population. Change in diet was associated with a decrement in depression score (.19), as measured on the Hopkins Symptoms Checklist. But because 8 out of 9 subscores of the Hopkins Symptoms Checklist changed, nonspecific effects were also a plausible explanation here. Moreover, although dietary change was correlated with lowering cholesterol (.20), lowering cholesterol as such (which only amounted to 1% in the intervention group) was not related to the decrement in depression. These studies thus do not prove that lowering cholesterol is causally related to improvement in depression.

The attention in the field of the association between depression and CVD has switched to a related concept that seems to be promising with respect to CVD risk: vital exhaustion (VE). It has shown to be a short-term predictor of myocardial infarction risk (Appels & Mulder, 1988) and of new cardiac events after percutaneous transluminal coronary angioplasty (Kop et al., 1994). Although the concept of VE contains certain specific elements, there is considerable overlap with depression. Raikkonen, Keltikangas-Jarvinen, and Hautanen (1994) found the VE score to correlate .75 with a depression scale. In middle-aged men and women we observed substantial correlations (.70 and .63, respectively) between VE and Zung Depression scores (van Doornen et al., 1996).

In the two studies demonstrating the prospective value of VE for cardiac events, the prediction was independent of other risk factors, including cholesterol. Despite this, VE and cholesterol might have been correlated. Zero-order correlations were, however, not reported. In a study on the effect of stress on cholesterol (van Doornen & van Blokland, 1989), we measured cholesterol levels in a group of 33 academics on the day of their thesis defense and on a control day several weeks later. Vital exhaustion was significantly correlated with cholesterol level on the control day (.37).

The rise in cholesterol in anticipation of this stressful event correlated .41 with VE, which resulted in a high correlation (.60) between VE and cholesterol level on the day of thesis defense (van Doornen & van Blokland, 1989). Some evidence was found for a mediating role of noradrenaline in this association. Both VE and cholesterol level on the stressful day were significantly correlated with noradrenaline level on the stressful day (.32 and .34, respectively).

Another mechanism is suggested by the recent finding of an association between VE and deviations of insulin metabolism (Raikkonen et al., 1994), which is closely related to lipid metabolism. Because these studies suggest potential mechanisms underlying an association between VE and lipids, this association warrants further investigation.

Anxiety, Neuroticism, and Lipids

In a meta-analysis of studies on personality and coronary disease by Booth-Kewley and Friedman (1987), anxiety was significantly related to coronary risk, both in cross-sectional and prospective studies, although the effect size was moderate. To what extent can this be due to an association between anxiety–neuroticism and lipids?

In the Western Electric Study, Almada et al. (1991) found no association between neuroticism and cholesterol levels in 1,871 middle-aged men. Also, in this study, neuroticism showed no predictive value for coronary death. In data from our lab, we checked the association between State–Trait Personality Inventory (van der Plues, Spielberger, & Defares, 1980) Trait Anxiety scores and lipids and lipoproteins in 144 middle-aged men and 145 women (Boomsma et al., 1996). The extreme quintiles of cholesterol, LDL, HDL, and triglycerides were compared. The extreme cholesterol groups did not differ with respect to trait anxiety. For men only, the highest quintile of the LDL distribution showed significantly higher Trait Anxiety scores than the lowest quintile ($p < .007$), after correction for age, smoking, alcohol use, level of education, and habitual level of physical activity. No differences emerged for the other parameters, and no differences occurred for women.

The suggestion that repressed anxiety might be associated with cholesterol complicates the interpretation of a relationship between anxiety and lipids (Niaura, Herbert, McMahon, & Sommerville, 1992). In this study, repressed anxiety was attributed to those participants with low anxiety scores and high psychological defensiveness scores. Male repressors showed higher cholesterol levels than "true" participants scoring low for anxiety. Difficult to interpret, however, was the fact that in women, the opposite was found.

Effects of repressed anxiety on lipids may be observed only in extreme groups, such as phobics or panic patients. At least the repression factor will be of less influence in these groups. On the other hand, as was mentioned in the framework of depression, the influence of confounders will be larger in psychiatric patients groups. Hayward, Taylor, Roth, King, and

Agras (1989) observed that in a group of 102 patients with panic attacks, women had higher cholesterol values than population reference values. High density lipoproteins and triglycerides were normal. In contrast, Tancer, Stein, Moul, and Uhde (1990) found no difference in cholesterol level between 80 panic-disorder patients and 80 normal controls. Also, within the patient group, cholesterol and state anxiety were unrelated. In the earlier mentioned study by Bajwa et al. (1992), 30 panic-disorder patients had higher cholesterol levels than age- and sex-matched groups of depressive patients and controls. Moreover, within the group of depressive patients, those with a history of (current or past) anxiety disorders had higher cholesterol levels than the patients in which this was not the case. Recently Freedman et al. (1995) reported results from a study on a much larger population, with a high rate of psychiatric problems. It concerned 3,490 men who had served in the U.S. Army. As many as two thirds had psychiatric diagnoses, and more than half had alcohol-related problems. Those men with a diagnosis of generalized anxiety disorder had higher cholesterol levels than the rest of the study population. The association was independent from the diagnoses of depression, antisocial personality disorder, or hypochondriasis and remained after control for possible confounders such as age, smoking, and alcohol consumption. The diagnosis of panic disorder, however, was unrelated to lipid levels. Although significant, the effect of generalized anxiety disorder was quite small. The group had a 7-mg/dl higher cholesterol level than those without this diagnosis. Because as many as two thirds of this population had psychiatric diagnoses and more than half had alcohol-related problems, it is doubtful whether these findings are representative for the population of middle-aged men in general. These studies on anxiety and lipids indicate that some association may exist, although neither the data from normal groups nor from patient groups are very consistent.

Conclusion and Recommendations for Future Research

We must conclude that the efforts to associate psychological traits with lipid levels have not furnished a consistent picture. For Type A behavior pattern, a number of positive findings stand in contrast to a similar number of negative findings in the smaller scale studies. Moreover, within the category of positive studies, the results are inconsistent with respect to gender, age, race, and type of lipid or lipoprotein measured. The larger studies are mainly negative or show very small effects. This seems to be independent of the way Type A was measured. For hostility, the larger studies do not support the incidentally observed positive associations in the smaller studies. In some of our earlier studies, we found positive associations between depression and cholesterol both in young and middle-aged participants. In larger scale studies, the association was absent or very small. Moreover, depressive patients generally do not show deviations in lipid values. For anxiety–neuroticism, the evidence seems a bit stronger, but the results remain equivocal.

A major problem is that most studies that examine the personality–lipids relation do not (or do so incompletely) take into account that personality is only one of numerous factors that influence lipid levels. In the discussion of the relation between lipids and hostility, I have already mentioned that lifestyle factors are associated with both hostility and lipid levels. Apart from smoking, alcohol, and exercise, lipid levels also vary by age, social class, physical fitness, dietary habits, body mass, menopausal status, use of contraceptives, or use of antihypertensive medication. The difference among studies in controlling for these influences may enhance or reduce the chance of finding associations, which could be an explanation for the variety of results. Several of these factors are also (either positively or negatively) associated with personality variables. For example, lipid levels rise with age, whereas hostility scores decrease with age (Barefoot et al., 1991). Level of socioeconomic class is inversely related to both hostility (Barefoot et al., 1991; Carmelli, Rosenman, & Swan, 1988) and lipid levels. Heterogeneity with respect to social class, and not controlling for it, will enhance the chance of finding an association between hostility and lipids. The same argument applies to the other influencing factors just mentioned. In future studies, a careful control for the influence of these factors is needed. It is promising that one of the few studies that controlled for most of the confounders mentioned (Dujovne & Houston, 1991) observed a significant, but small, correlation between expressive hostility and LDL and cholesterol. The plea to control for confounders, however, also has its negative side. It is inspired by the ideal to find a pure, unconfounded association between a personality variable and a lipid level. This might be interesting from the psychophysiological view that the connection between personality variables and lipids is mediated by neuroendocrine processes. From the broader perspective, however, control for confounders may eliminate relevant information. Imagine a finding that depression in women was associated with elevated cholesterol levels, and that this association was mediated by the association of obesity with depression. From a health perspective, this is an interesting observation in itself, which will be eliminated if obesity is introduced as a covariate. For another example, if a relation between hostility and cholesterol disappeared after correction for social class, one would not conclude that there was in fact no association. It would suggest a larger variety of possible reasons for the association observed. Future studies certainly should include all factors that may influence or explain an association between personality traits and lipids, in case such an association is found. But the influence of these factors should be considered as potential mediators and not as noise or confounders.

Although the overall picture is confusing, I cannot deny that some studies, after proper control for mediating factors, indeed found an association between personality and lipids. Let us assume that some association exists between hostility, depression, or anxiety and lipid values but that the demonstration of it depends on (still unknown) methodological factors. Then the paradox has to be solved of why these traits would be associated with higher lipid values in the research area of cardiovascular risk, but with lower values in the research area focusing on the possible influence of low lipid levels on risk of suicide or violent acts. A first explanatory factor may be publication bias, which is the tendency to publish results that support the direction of the hypothesis. It is difficult to assess the impact of this factor for obvious reasons. Other explanatory options must also be considered. Probably, personality variables such as hostility or depression have little to do with committing violent crimes or suicide, respectively. The aspects of hostility as measured by questionnaire, and especially as measured with the Cook–Medley Hostility Scale, are different from the tendency to behave in a physically aggressive manner. For example, Megargee (1985) did not find any systematic or significant relationship between Ho score and criminal violence. Suicidal tendency is multifactorially determined and only to a limited extent a function of depression. In other words, because the normal variation of hostility and depression may have little to do with actual aggressive or suicidal behavior, their association with lipid values may have a different direction and are probably founded in different biological mechanisms. Another point that has to be considered is that the relation between lipids and psychological variables might show up only in the extremes of the distributions of lipids or psychological variables. For example, in the studies by De-Alberto et al. (1993) and Morgan et al. (1993), elevated depression scores were evident only in the lowest quintile of the cholesterol distribution, as compared with all higher quintiles, whereas the correlations between cholesterol and depression were close to zero in the whole group in both studies. With respect to hostility, however, this argument might not apply. Even the lowest decile of the cholesterol distribution in the Whitehall study showed normal hostility scores (Davey Smith et al., 1990).

A point that has been neglected so far is the interrelatedness of the psychological concepts measured. Most of the studies focus on one of them. The Cook–Medley Ho score is strongly related to neuroticism (Almada et al., 1991). Siegal (1986) observed high correlations between anger and trait anxiety. Overt hostility, as measured with the Buss–Durkee Hostility Inventory, correlates significantly with depression (Johnston, Rogers, & Russell Searight, 1991). It would be of interest to include all of them in one study and find out whether there was a common dimension that was related to lipid or lipoprotein levels. For the possible relationship of low lipid levels with aggressive or suicidal behavior, the suggestion made by Apter et al. (1990) that anxiety, aggression, depression, and impulsivity might be a serotonergically linked cluster is worth investigating.

A last point of concern is that within the category of positive studies, the studies do not correspond with respect to the type of lipid or lipoprotein with which an association is found and for which sex group the association holds. Cholesterol, triglycerides, and HDL have different roles in lipid metabolism and are connected in different ways to neuroendocrine processes. All studies are empirical in the sense that they simply look for associations without any preconceived idea of with which lipid or lipoprotein parameter an association is to be expected. In case a positive finding is obtained, no explanation is available for why this specifically occurred for this parameter and not for another. Future studies should go beyond the level of simply correlating psychological and lipid parameters and try to get insight into the origin of the associations. Future studies should, therefore, include neurohumoral parameters, to investigate their possible role as mediators. Estrogens, insulin, catecholamines, and cortisol are potential candidates.

References

Almada, S. J., Zonderman, A. B., Shekelle, R. B., Dyer, A. R., Daviglus, M. L., Costa, P. T., & Stamler, J. (1991). Neuroticism and cynicism and risk of death in middle-aged men: The Western Electric Study. *Psychosomatic Medicine, 53,* 165–175.

Appels, A., & Mulder, P. (1988). Excess fatigue as a precursor of myocardial infarction. *European Heart Journal, 9,* 758–764.

Appels, A., Mulder, P., van 't Hof, M., Jenkins, C. D., van Houtem, J., & Tan, F. (1987). A prospective study of the Jenkins Activity Survey as a risk indicator for coronary heart disease in the Netherlands. *Journal of Chronic Diseases, 40,* 959–965.

Apter, A., van Praag, H. M., Plutchik, R., Sevy, S., Korn, M., & Brown, S. L. (1990). Interrelationships among anxiety, aggression, impulsivity, and mood: A serotonergically linked cluster? *Psychiatry Research, 32,* 191–199.

Bajwa, W. K., Asnis, G. M., Sanderson, W. C., Irfan, A., & van Praag, H. M. (1992). High cholesterol levels in patients with panic disorder. *American Journal of Psychiatry, 149,* 376–378.

Barefoot, J. C. (1993). Keeping conflicting findings in perspective: The case of hostility and health. *Mayo Clinical Proceedings, 68,* 192–193.

Barefoot, J. C., Peterson, B. L., Dahlstrom, W. G., Siegler, I. C., Anderson, N. B., & Williams, R. B. (1991). Hostility patterns and health implications: Correlates of Cook–Medley Hostility Scale scores in a national survey. *Health Psychology, 10,* 18–24.

Beck, A. T., Ward, C. H., Mendelson, M., Mock, J., & Erbaugh, J. (1961). An inventory measuring depression. *Archives of General Psychiatry, 4,* 53–63.

Boomsma, D. I., Kempen, H. J. M., Gevers-Leuven, J. A., Havekes, L., Knijff, P. de, & Frants, R. R. (1996). Genetic analysis of sex and generation differences in plasma lipid, lipoprotein and apolipoprotein levels in adolescent twins and their parents. *Genetic Epidemiology, 13,* 49–60.

Booth-Kewley, S., & Friedman, H. S. (1987). Psychological predictors of heart disease: A quantitative review. *Psychological Bulletin, 101,* 343–362.

Carmelli, D., Rosenman, R. H., & Swan, G. E. (1988). The Cook–Medley Ho scale: A heritability analysis in adult male twins. *Psychosomatic Medicine, 50,* 165–170.

Chesney, M. A., Black, G. W., Chadwick, J. H., & Rosenman, R. H. (1981). Psychological correlates of the Type A behavior pattern. *Journal of Behavioral Medicine, 4,* 217–229.

Davey Smith, G., Shipley, M. J., Marmot, M. G., & Patel, C. (1990). Lowering cholesterol concentrations and mortality. *British Medical Journal, 301,* 552.

DeAlberto, M. J., Ducimetiere, P., Mainard, F., & Alperovitch, A. (1993). Serum lipids and depression. *The Lancet, 341,* 435.

Dembroski, T. M., & Costa, P. T. (1987). Coronary-prone behavior: Components of the Type A pattern and hostility. *Journal of Personality, 55,* 211–235.

Dembroski, T. M., MacDougall, J. M., Costa, P. T., & Grandits, G. A. (1989). Components of hostility as predictors of sudden death and myocardial infarction in the Multiple Risk Factor Intervention Trial. *Psychosomatic Medicine, 51,* 514–522.

Derogatis, L. R. (1977). *SCL-90-R (revised) version manual I.* Baltimore, MD: Johns Hopkins University Press.

Dujovne, V. F., & Houston, B. K. (1991). Hostility-related variables and plasma lipid levels. *Journal of Behavioral Medicine, 14,* 555–565.

Fowkes, F. G. R., Leng, G. C., Donnan, P. T., Deary, I. J., Riemersma, R. A., & Housley, E. (1992). Serum cholesterol, triglycerides and aggression in the general population. *The Lancet, 340,* 995–998.

Freedman, D. S., Byers, T., Barrett, D. H., Stroup, N. E., Eaker, E., & Monroe-Blum, H. (1995). Plasma lipid levels and psychological characteristics in men. *American Journal of Epidemiology, 141,* 507–517.

Friedman, E. H., Hellerstein, H. K., Eastwood, G. L., & Jones, S. E. (1968). Behavior patterns and serum cholesterol in two groups of normal males. *The American Journal of Medical Sciences, 255,* 237–244.

Friedman, M., & Rosenman, R. H. (1959). Association of specific overt behavior pattern with blood and cardiovascular findings. *Journal of the American Medical Association, 169,* 1286–1296.

Friedman, M. A., & Brownell, K. D. (1995). Psychological correlates of obesity: Moving to the next research generation. *Psychological Bulletin, 117,* 3–20.

Glueck, C. J., Tieger, M., Kunkel, R., Tracy, T., Speirs, J., Streicher, P., & Illig, E. (1993). Improvements in symptoms of depression and an index of life stressors accompany treatment of severe hypertriglyceridemia. *Biological Psychiatry, 34,* 240–252.

Harlan, W. R., Oberman, A., Mitchell, R. E., & Graybiel, A. (1967). Constitutional and environmental factors related to serum lipid and lipoprotein levels. *Annals of Internal Medicine, 66,* 540–555.

Hayward, C., Taylor, C. B., Roth, W. T., King, R., & Agras, W. S. (1989). Plasma lipid levels in patients with panic disorder or agoraphobia. *American Journal of Psychiatry, 146,* 917–919.

Hearn, M. D., Murray, D. M., & Luepker, R. V. (1989). Hostility, coronary heart disease, and total mortality: A 33-year follow-up study of university students. *Journal of Behavioral Medicine, 12,* 105–121.

Houston, B. K., & Vavak, C. (1991). Cynical hostility: Developmental factors, psychosocial correlates, and health behaviors. *Health Psychology, 10,* 9–17.

Jenkins, C. D., Rosenman, R. H., & Friedman, M. (1966). Components of the coronary-prone behavior pattern: Their relation to silent myocardial infarction and blood lipids. *Journal of Chronic Diseases, 19,* 599–609.

Jenkins, C. D., Zyzanski, S. J., & Rosenman, R. H. (1971). Progress toward validation of a computer-scored test for the type A coronary-prone behavior pattern. *Psychosomatic Medicine, 73,* 193–202.

Johnson, E. H., Collier, P., Nazzaro, P., & Gilbert, D. C. (1992). Psychological and physiological predictors of lipids in Black males. *Journal of Behavioral Medicine, 15,* 285–298.

Johnston, V. L., Rogers, B. J., & Russell Searight, H. (1991). The relationship between overt hostility, covert hostility, and depression. *Journal of Social Behavior and Personality, 6,* 85–92.

Keith, R. A., Lown, B., & Stare, F. J. (1965). Coronary heart disease and behavior patterns. *Psychosomatic Medicine, 27,* 424–434.

Kop, W. J., Appels, A. P. W. M., Mendes de Leon, C. F., de Swart, H. B., & Bär, F. W. (1994). Vital exhaustion predicts new cardiac events after successful coronary angioplasty. *Psychosomatic Medicine, 56,* 281–287.

Kornitzer, M., Kittel, F., Dramaix, M., & de Backer, G. (1983). Psychosocial variables in relation with coronary risk status. In T. M. Dembroski, T. H. Schmidt, & G. Blumchen (Eds.), *Biobehavioral bases of coronary heart disease* (pp. 459–472). Basel, Switzerland: Karger.

Koskenvuo, M., Kaprio, J., Rose, R. J., Kesnaiemi, A., Sarnaa, S., Heikkila, K., & Langinvanio, H. (1988). Hostility as a risk factor for mortality and ischemic heart disease in men. *Psychosomatic Medicine, 50,* 330–340.

Lang, S., & Haits, G. (1968). Blutserum Cholesterinwerte bei Depression [Serum-cholesterol levels and depression]. *Das Deutsche Gesundheitswesen, 23,* 82–84.

Lundberg, U., Hedman, M., Melin, B., & Frankenhaeuser, M. (1989). Type A behavior in healthy males and females as related to physiological reactivity and blood lipids. *Psychosomatic Medicine, 51,* 113–122.

Maruta, T., Hamburgen, M. E., Jennings, C. A., Offord, K. P., Colligan, R. C., Frye, R. L., & Malichoc, M. (1993). Keeping hostility in perspective: Coronary heart disease and the Hostility Scale on the Minnesota Multiphasic Personality Inventory. *Mayo Clinic Proceedings, 68*, 109–114.

Matthews, K. A. (1988). Coronary heart disease and Type A behaviors: Update and alternative to the Booth-Kewley and Friedman (1987) review. *Psychological Bulletin, 104*, 373–380.

McCranie, E. W., Watkins, L. O., & Brandsma, J. M. (1989). Hostility, coronary heart disease (CHD) incidence, and total mortality: Lack of association in a 25 year follow-up study of 478 physicians. *Journal of Behavioral Medicine, 9*, 119–125.

Megargee, E. I. (1985). The dynamics of aggression and their application to cardiovascular disorders. In M. A. Chesney & R. H. Rosenman (Eds.), *Anger and hostility in cardiovascular and behavioral disorders* (pp. 31–57). Washington, DC: Hemisphere.

Morgan, R. E., Palinkas, L. A., Barrett-Connor, E. L., & Wingard, D. L. (1993). Plasma cholesterol and depressive symptoms in older men. *The Lancet, 341*, 75–79.

Niaura, R., Herbert, P. N., McMahon, N., & Sommerville, L. (1992). Repressive coping and blood lipids in men and women. *Psychosomatic Medicine, 54*, 698–706.

Niaura, R., Stoney, C. M., & Herbert, P. N. (1992). Lipids in psychological research: The last decade. *Biological Psychology, 34*, 1–43.

Oxenkrug, G. F., Branconnier, R. J., Harto-Truax, N., & Cole, J. O. (1983). Is serum cholesterol a biological marker for major depressive disorder? *American Journal of Psychiatry, 140*, 920–921.

Ragland, D. R., & Brand, R. J. (1988). Type A behavior and mortality from coronary heart disease. *New England Journal of Medicine, 318*, 65–68.

Raikkonen, K., Keltikangas-Jarvinen, L., & Hautanen, A. (1994). The role of psychological coronary risk factors in insulin and glucose metabolism. *Journal of Psychosomatic Research, 38*, 705–713.

Rosenman, R. H., Brand, R. J., Jenkins, C. D., Friedman, M., Straus, R., & Wurm, M. (1975). Coronary heart disease in the Western Collaborative Group Study: Final follow-up experience of 8 1/2 years. *Journal of the American Medical Association, 233*, 872–877.

Rosenman, R. H., & Friedman, M. (1961). Association of specific overt behavior pattern in women with blood and cardiovascular findings. *Circulation, 24*, 1173–1184.

Scherwitz, L. W., Perkins, L. L., Chesney, M. A., Hughes, G. H., Sidney, S., & Manolio, T. A. (1992). Hostility and health behaviors in young adults: The CARDIA study. *American Journal of Epidemiology, 136*, 136–145.

Shekelle, R. B., Gale, M., Ostfeld, A. M., & Paul, O. (1983). Hostility, risk of coronary heart disease, and mortality. *Psychosomatic Medicine, 45*, 109–114.

Shekelle, R. B., Hulley, S. B., Neaton, J. D., Billings, J. H., Borhani, N. O., Gerace, T. A., Jacobs, D. R., Lasser, N. L., Mittlemark, M. B., & Stamler, J. (1985). The MRFIT behavior pattern study: II. Type A behavior and incidence of coronary heart disease. *American Journal of Epidemiology, 122*, 559–570.

Siegel, J. M. (1984). Anger and cardiovascular risk in adolescents. *Health Psychology, 3*, 293–313.

Siegel, J. M. (1986). The Multidimensional Anger Inventory. *Journal of Personality and Social Psychology, 51*, 191–200.

Siegler, I. C., Peterson, B. L., Barefoot, J. C., & Williams, R. B. (1992). Hostility during late adolescence predicts coronary risk factors at mid-life. *American Journal of Epidemiology, 136*, 146–154.

Siegman, A. W., Dembroski, T. M., & Ringel, N. (1987). Components of hostility and the severity of coronary artery disease. *Psychosomatic Medicine, 49*, 127–135.

Sloane, R. B., Inglis, J., & Payne, R. W. (1962). Personal traits and maternal attitudes in relation to blood lipid levels. *Psychosomatic Medicine, 24*, 279–283.

Smith, T. W. (1992). Hostility and health: Current status of a psychosomatic hypothesis. *Health Psychology, 11*, 139–150.

Strandberg, T. E. (1993). Serum lipids and depression. *The Lancet, 341*, 433.

Tancer, M. E., Stein, M. B., Moul, D. E., & Uhde, T. W. (1990). Normal serum cholesterol in panic disorder. *Biological Psychiatry, 27*, 99–101.

van der Plues, H. M., Spielberger, C. D., & Defares, P. B. (1980). *Manual for the Dutch version of the State–Trait Anxiety Inventory*. The Netherlands: Swots & Zeitlinger.

van Doornen, L. J. P. (1980). The coronary risk personality: Psychological and psychophysiological aspects. *Psychotherapy and Psychosomatics, 34*, 204–215.

van Doornen, L. J. P., & Orlebeke, J. F. (1982). Stress, personality and serum cholesterol level. *Journal of Human Stress, 8*, 24–29.

van Doornen, L. J. P., Snieder, H., & Boomsma, D. I. (1996). *The relation between lipids, lipoproteins and personality variables in middle-aged subjects*. Manuscript in preparation.

van Doornen, L. J. P., & van Blokland, R. W. (1987). Serum cholesterol: Sex-specific psychological correlates during rest and stress. *Journal of Psychosomatic Research, 31*, 239–249.

van Doornen, L. J. P., & van Blokland, R. W. (1989). The relation of Type A behavior and vital exhaustion with physiological reactions to real life stress. *Journal of Psychosomatic Research, 33*, 715–725.

Ward, K. D., Sparrow, D., Landsberg, L., Young, J. B., Vokonas, P. S., & Weiss, S. T. (1994). The relationship of epinephrine excretion to serum lipid levels: The Normative Aging Study. *Metabolism, 43*, 509–513.

Weidner, G., Connor, S. L., Hollis, J. F., & Connor, W. E. (1992). Improvements in hostility and depression in relation dietary change and cholesterol lowering: The Family Heart Study. *Annals of Internal Medicine, 117*, 820–823.

Weidner, G., Sexton, G., McLellarn, R., Connor, S. L., & Matarazzo, J. D. (1987). The role of Type A behavior and hostility in an elevation of plasma lipids in adult women and men. *Psychosomatic Medicine, 49*, 136–145.

Yates, W. R., & Wallace, R. (1987). Cardiovascular risk factors in affective disorder. *Journal of Affective Disorders, 12*, 129–134.

6

Pathophysiologic Relationships and Linkage Among Triglycerides, Hypocholesterolemia, and Depression

Charles J. Glueck, Robert Kunkel, and Murray Tieger

Over the past decade, depressive symptoms have frequently been observed before treatment, in patients with severe primary and familial hypertriglyceridemia (Fallat & Glueck, 1975; Glueck, Tieger, et al., 1993). When triglycerides are normalized, there is usually concomitant and marked improvement in depressive symptoms (Glueck et al., 1993). We have hypothesized, congruent with the postulations of other investigators (Avellone et al., 1988; Meyer et al., 1987; Meyer & Waltz, 1959; Rogers et al., 1986; Swank, 1956), that symptoms of depression in patients with familial hypertriglyceridemia (Fallat & Glueck, 1975; Glueck & Lang, 1995) are pathophysiologically related to increased blood viscosity and to reduced cerebral blood flow and perfusion (Glueck, Tieger, et al., 1993; see Figure 1). The present chapter presents data that supports the validity of this hypothesized link between hypertriglyceridemia and depression. We begin by defining hypertriglyceridemia and hypocholesterolemia. We then examine the link between hypocholesterolemia, cholesterol-lowering therapy, and non-illness-related mortality (i.e., mortality related to accidents, violence, or suicide) and review hypertriglyceridemia and hypocholesterolemia in selected populations. Finally, we describe familial hypobetalipoproteinemia (i.e., familial hypocholesterolemia) and summarize our prospective study of the impact of triglyceride lowering with diet and medication on depressive symptoms.

The National Institutes of Health Consensus Development Panels on Hypertriglyceridemia (Consensus Conference, 1987; Consensus Development Conference, 1992) identified plasma triglyceride levels >500 mg/dl as high, warranting the label *hypertriglyceridemia*. A trial of drug therapy is indicated in patients when severe hypertriglyceridemia (triglycerides ≥500 mg/dl) persists after correction of any causes of secondary hypertri-

---

This work was supported by Jewish Hospital Medical Research Council Grant 790. This research was approved by the Jewish Hospital Research Committee; all subjects participated with a signed informed consent.

glyceridemia and after maintenance of a very low fat diet. The medical goals of triglyceride lowering by diet and drugs (with concurrent elevation of high density lipoprotein [HDL] cholesterol) are to reduce the risk of triglyceride-associated pancreatitis, premature myocardial infarction, and stroke (Consensus Conference, 1987; Consensus Development Conference, 1992; Glueck & Lang, 1995).

Hypertriglyceridemia is a known determinant of high plasminogen activator inhibitor (PAI; the major inhibitor of fibrinolysis) and, hence, is associated with hypofibrinolysis. Often (Mussoni et al., 1991), but not always (Glueck, Tieger, et al., 1993), triglyceride lowering is associated with reduction of PAI, with a consequent increase in fibrinolysis and (probably) improved organ perfusion. Hypertriglyceridemia also is associated with increased serum viscosity, with low-HDL cholesterol, and with cerebrovascular atherosclerosis. We postulate that the high PAI, high viscosity, and low-HDL cholesterol may lead to reduced cerebrovascular blood flow and segmental reductions of cerebrovascular oxygenation with localized hypoxia, leading to symptoms of depression. Our construct of a hypertriglyceridemia-driven metabolic cause of symptoms of depression is also based on data that reveal amelioration of symptoms of depression after triglyceride lowering. We have shown in a controlled clinical trial (Glueck, Tieger, et al., 1993) that triglyceride lowering is significantly associated with reductions in symptoms of depression. With this hypothesis in mind, (Figures 1 and 2), we summarize below the evidence for a putative link between hypertriglyceridemia and symptoms of depression, and, from that, suicidality.

Hypocholesterolemia has typically been defined in epidemiologic studies as plasma cholesterol levels of <160 mg/dl (Harris et al., 1992; Jacobs

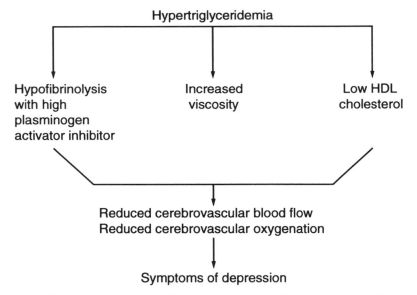

Figure 1. Hypothesis: Reversible associations of hypertriglyceridemia with symptoms of depression.

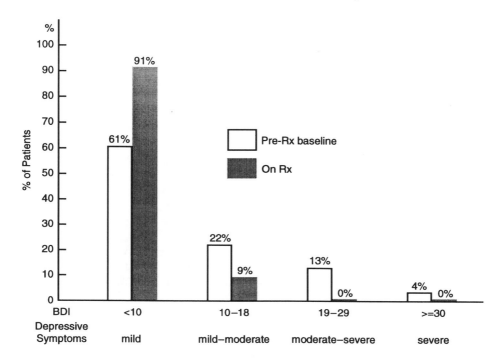

Figure 2. Shift ($\chi^2 = 5.6$, $p = .016$) in the Beck Depression Index Score toward normal during triglyceride-lowering therapy compared with pretreatment baseline. Percent of 23 hypertriglyceridemic patients having depressive symptoms prior to and on triglyceride lowering therapy.

et al., 1992; Johnson et al., 1993; Pekkanen, Nissinen, Punsar, & Karvonen, 1989). In recent studies from a Cincinnati urban supermarket screening and from the National Health and Nutrition Examination Survey (NHANES II; Gartside & Glueck, 1993), 2.5% and 0.7% of participants, respectively, had plasma cholesterol levels of <120 mg/dl; 4.4% and 2.6%, respectively, had levels between 120 and 139 mg/dl; and 13.3% and 6.7%, respectively, had levels between 140 and 159 mg/dl (Gartside & Glueck, 1993; Glueck, Tieger, et al., 1994). Hence, a cutpoint of 160 mg/dl would incorporate 10% of the NHANES II population and 19.8% of urban supermarket screenees in Cincinnati (Glueck, Tieger, et al., 1994).

Hypocholesterolemia, Cholesterol-Lowering Therapy, and Non-Illness-Related Mortality

When assessing associations between low serum cholesterol concentrations and suicide (Neaton et al., 1992) and between pharmacologic cholesterol lowering and suicide (Muldoon, Manuck, & Matthews, 1990; Muldoon et al., 1993; Scandinavian Simvastatin Survival Study Group, 1994), it is important to differentiate between low plasma cholesterol (<160 mg/dl) in epidemiologic studies and potentially increased accident, suicide, and violence mortality in controlled clinical trials of cholesterol lowering (Muldoon et al., 1993). Plasma cholesterol levels achieved in cholesterol-lowering trials (Muldoon et al., 1993; Scandinavian Simvastatin Survival Study Group, 1994) are usually >200 mg/dl and typically are 50–100 mg/dl higher than the low cholesterol levels (<160 mg/dl) associated with increased suicide mortality in epidemiologic studies (Neaton et al., 1992).

In an observational 12-year follow-up of 350,977 men age 35–57 years, who had been screened for the Multiple Risk Factor Intervention Trial (MRFIT), suicide mortality was significantly inversely associated with serum cholesterol concentrations (Neaton et al., 1992). The risk ratio for men with serum cholesterol concentrations ≥160 mg/dl versus those <160 was .62 (Neaton et al., 1992). Neaton et al. speculated that long-term alcohol intake may have been involved in this association and that "poor dietary habits as a consequence of depression or chronic illness may explain the results on suicide" (p. 1498). In the Whitehall 18-year epidemiologic observational follow-up of 17,718 male civil service workers (Davey Smith, Shipley, Marmot, & Rose, 1992), there was no association of serum cholesterol concentrations with violent deaths. Davey Smith et al. (1992) concluded that socioeconomic factors and health status at the time of examination largely accounted for inverse relations between cholesterol concentrations and non-cardiovascular-related mortality: "Participants with low cholesterol possess other characteristics that place them at an elevated risk of death" (p. 70). The epidemiological and controlled clinical trial observations of an inverse association of serum cholesterol concentrations with suicide–violent death have not been consistent or replicated broadly (Farchi, Menotti, & Canti, 1987; Frank, Reed, Grove, & Benfante, 1992; Harris et al., 1992; Isles, Hole, Gillis, Hawthorne, & Leven, 1989; Neaton et al., 1992; Pekkanen, Nissinen, Punsar, & Karvonen, 1989; Roussouw, Lewis, & Rifkind, 1990; Stemmerman, Chyou, Kagan, Nomura, & Yano, 1992; Virkkunen, 1983; World Health Organization European Collaborative Group, 1986; Yusuf, Wittes, & Friedman, 1988). Although Strandberg et al. (1991) observed an excess of deaths from violence and suicide in participants in a multifactor-treatment group, there was no association between cholesterol concentrations and risk of death from violence and suicide.

In a meta-analysis of cholesterol-lowering trials, Muldoon et al. (1993); Muldoon et al. (1990); and Muldoon, Manuck, and Matthews (1991) reported a significant increase in deaths from accidents, suicide, or violence in groups receiving treatments to lower plasma cholesterol concentrations relative to control participants. Davey Smith, Song, and Sheldon (1993) carried out a meta-analysis of 35 randomized controlled trials of cholesterol lowering with ≥6 months of follow-up and with at least one death. As noted by Davey Smith et al. (1993), "net benefit in terms of total mortality from cholesterol lowering was seen only for trials including patients at very high risk of coronary heart disease." However, "in a medium risk group no net effect was seen, and in the low risk group there were adverse treatment effects. Raised mortality from causes other than coronary heart disease was seen in trials of drug treatment . . . , but not in the trials of non-drug treatments."

Several major cholesterol-lowering trials have provided no evidence to support the hypothesis that cholesterol lowering resulted in an increased risk of suicide and violent death (Buchwald et al., 1990; Frick et al., 1987; Hjermann, Velve Byre, Holme, & Leren, 1981; Holme, Hjermann, Hegeland, & Leren, 1985; Lipid Research Clinics Program, 1984; Manninen et al., 1988; Multiple Risk Factor Intervention Trial Research Group, 1990; Rose, 1987; Scandinavian Simvastatin Survival Study Group, 1994; Wysowski & Gross, 1990). Most important, in the recent Scandinavian Simvastatin Survival Study (1994), over 5.4 years of follow-up, there was a 30% reduction in all-cause mortality. There was no suggestion of any increase in non-cardiovascular-related mortality, including deaths due to suicide, trauma, or cancer. Moreover, for this whole study, the risk of cardiovascular death plus nonfatal myocardial infarction was reduced by 37%.

Hypertriglyceridemia and Hypocholesterolemia in Children Hospitalized With Psychiatric Disorders

We have been particularly interested in the putatively causal associations of triglycerides with symptoms of depression because we have shown that adults (Glueck, Tieger, et al., 1994) and children with affective disorders and hospitalization for psychiatric diseases have much higher triglycerides than healthy normal controls (Glueck, Kuller, et al., 1994). Recently, we studied 220 children, age 5–18 years, hospitalized with affective, adjustment, disruptive, anxiety, schizophrenic, and organic psychiatric disorders (Glueck, Kuller, et al., 1994). We also assessed relationships of their plasma total cholesterol to suicide attempts and to suicide ideation. The 135 boys and 85 girls with psychiatric hospitalization had higher fasting plasma triglycerides ($p = .0001, .0003$) than those of 732 male and 316 female schoolchild controls. Triglyceride levels, however, did not differ by psychiatric diagnosis groups. Obesity, a known determinant of triglycerides, may have contributed to the hypertriglyceridemia, because children with psychiatric hospitalization were much heavier than were controls. Alcohol, cigarette smoking, and substance abuse, all common in these children and all strong positive correlates of their triglyceride levels, could also have contributed to their hypertriglyceridemia. Of interest in this regard is the report by Fowkes et al. (1992; in adults) of a positive correlation of triglyceride values with hostile acts and domineering attitude. Although group triglyceride values in our pediatric patients with hospitalization for psychiatric disease were sharply skewed upward to values above healthy schoolchildren controls, the children with psychiatric hospitalization did not have severe hypertriglyceridemia (>500 mg/dl; Glueck, Kuller, et al., 1994).

Children having adjustment disorders with concomitant depression had the highest group suicide attempts and ideation and the lowest total cholesterol values, 156 mg/dl. Conversely, children having disruptive behavior with attention deficit hyperactivity disorder or disruptive behavior with oppositional–defiant disorder had a 50% lower suicide index than those with adjustment disorders with concomitant depression; these two groups also had higher total cholesterol levels (172 and 198 mg/dl, respectively) than the adjustment disorder–depression group (156 mg/dl). In both univariate and multivariate analyses, substance abuse was an independent, significant, inverse explanatory variable for plasma cholesterol. We postulated that hypocholesterolemia in children hospitalized because of adjustment disorders with concomitant depression might be a consequence of affective-disorder-mediated behavior change. We also speculated that the associations between low plasma cholesterol, high plasma triglycerides, suicide, and hospitalization for psychiatric disease in children might not reflect cause and effect, but might be epiphenomena.

Hypertriglyceridemia and Hypocholesterolemia in Adults Hospitalized With Affective Disorders

In 203 adults hospitalized because of affective disorders (i.e., depression, bipolar disorder, and schizo–affective disorder), when compared with healthy normal controls, patients had much lower HDL cholesterol and higher triglycerides ($p \leq .03$; Glueck, Tieger, et al., 1994). Six percent of MRFIT screenees had cholesterol concentrations <160 mg/dl, as did 10% of NHANES II participants. However, 20% of our recently studied 203 adults hospitalized because of affective disorders had plasma cholesterol levels <160 mg/dl. In the recent NHANES III study (Johnson et al., 1993), in participants 20–74 years of age, 14% had cholesterol concentrations <160 mg/dl versus 20% of our patients with affective disorders; 4% of NHANES III patients had cholesterol concentrations <140 mg/dl versus 6.9% of patients with affective disorders. When paired with Cincinnati urban supermarket screenees by age and sex, our patients with affective disorders had lower plasma total, HDL, and low density lipoprotein (LDL) cholesterols and higher plasma triglyceride levels.

As did Neaton et al. (1992), we postulated that hypocholesterolemia in patients admitted to a hospital with depression was a consequence of depression mediated under nutrition or alcohol dependence or both (Glueck et al., 1994). We hypothesized (Glueck, Tieger, et al.), like Davey Smith et al. (1992) and Harris et al. (1992), that participants in epidemiologic follow-up studies who had low plasma cholesterol concentrations at entry might have affective disorders, subnutrition, or alcoholism that placed them at increased risk of suicide mortality and low plasma cholesterol.

Subnutrition or malnutrition with attendant weight loss and subsequent hypocholesterolemia may be a component of depression-mediated morbidity (Ashley & Kannel, 1974; Morgan, Palinkas, Barrett-Connor, & Wingard, 1993; Olson, 1975; Tripathy, Lotero, & Bolanos, 1970; Weissenburger, 1986). Depression and low plasma cholesterol concentrations could also be epiphenomena, both indicators of poor health status and prognostic indicators of death (Rudman, Mattson, Feller, & Nagraj, 1989; Verdery & Goldberg, 1991). Recently, Weidner, Connor, Hollies, and Connor (1992) reported that modest reduction of plasma cholesterol concentrations on a low-fat, high-complex carbohydrate diet was associated with reductions in depression and aggressive hostility.

Familial Hypobetalipoproteinemia (Familial Hypocholesterolemia)

We had previously reported that persons who are heterozygous for familial hypobetalipoproteinemia, with lifelong, extraordinarily low plasma cholesterol concentrations (usually <100 mg/dl) live an average of 12 years longer than the remainder of their birth cohort, often becoming octo- and nonagenarians (Glueck, Gartside, Fallat, Sielski, & Steiner, 1976; Glueck et al., 1977). Suicide and violent deaths do not characterize them. This common autosomal-dominant disorder, occurring in 1 in 500 unselected kindreds (Glueck et al., 1976), can be taken as an "experiment of nature," suggesting, congruent with the findings of Neaton et al. (1992), that low total cholesterol concentrations are associated with reduced all-cause mortality.

We have carried out a prospective, long-term, single-blind study, to determine whether and to what degree triglyceride lowering with diet and medication would improve scores on tests of symptoms of depression, indices of life stressors, locus-of-control indices, and tests of cognition in 14 men and 9 women with severe primary hypertriglyceridemia over a 54-week, single-blind treatment period (Glueck, Tieger, et al., 1993). We designed this study within the frame of reference of associations of hypertriglyceridemia with hospitalization for depression and psychiatric disease (Glueck, Tieger, et al., 1994) and with the finding that triglyceride lowering improves scores on dementia-screening tests in elderly patients, probably by reducing elevated serum viscosity and secondary segmental cerebral hypoxia caused by hypertriglyceridemia (Rogers, Meyer, McClintic, & Mortel, 1989).

In 14 men and 9 women with severe primary hypertriglyceridemia, our specific aim (in a 54-week, single-blind treatment period) was to determine whether triglyceride lowering with diet and gemfibrozil (Lopid, 1.2 g) would be accompanied by improvement in symptoms of depression, tests of life stressors, change in locus of control tests, and improved cognition (Glueck, Tieger, et al., 1993). The 23 patients were recruited from a group of 25 consecutive patients referred by their family physicians to our Cholesterol Center for evaluation and therapy of severe hypertriglyceridemia, predominantly familial type V hyperlipoproteinemia (Fallat & Glueck, 1975; Glueck & Lang, 1995). No patients had been referred because of symptoms of depression, reduced cognition, or evidence of hypoxic central nervous system depression. None of the patients had previous diagnoses of stroke, space-occupying cranial lesions, substance abuse, alcoholism, or known organic causes of depression. Because the patients were referred and subsequently recruited for this study solely because of primary hypertriglyceridemia, no attempt was made to exclude those with normal baseline pretreatment scores for the psychiatric tests and the test of cognition (Figure 2). Moreover, no attempt was made to select patients through *Diagnostic and Statistical Manual of Mental Disorders* (American Psychiatric Association, 1987) psychiatric criteria for major depressive disorder.

Study Protocol

The patients were evaluated pretreatment and then serially on triglyceride-lowering therapy every 6 weeks for a total of 9 visits (54 weeks). At the baseline visit, and at each of 8 sequential outpatient visits, detailed psychometric and cognitive tests were performed. At the baseline visit, a National Institutes of Health type V diet was initiated with, where appropriate, caloric restriction for weight reduction. Alcohol intake was forbidden or severely restricted to fewer than three drinks per week. Optimized individualized therapy was designed to lower triglycerides below 250 mg/dl, to reduce the risk of severe abdominal pain, pancreatitis, myocardial infarction, and peripheral neuropathy (Consensus Conference, 1987; Consensus Development Conference, 1992). All patients received the triglyceride-lowering drug Lopid, primarily 1.2 g per day, and 6 patients had omega-3 fatty acids added later during the therapeutic period, as an adjunct to further maximize triglyceride lowering.

Results

During therapy, median fasting plasma triglyceride levels fell 47%, total cholesterol fell 15%, and HDL cholesterol rose 19% (all $ps \leq .001$) (Glueck, Tieger, et al., 1993). Six weeks after initiation of triglyceride-lowering treatment, the Beck Depression Index (BDI) fell 43% ($p < .001$) and remained substantially lower than baseline in each of the subsequent visits ($p \leq .001$). Although the most marked improvement in the BDI occurred after 6 weeks of therapy, there was a progressive decrease in the mean BDI up through 30 weeks. Comparing the pretherapy BDI with the BDI at 30 and 54 weeks of therapy, there was a major shift toward absence or amelioration of depressive symptoms, χ^2 (4, $N = 28$) = 5.9, $p = .016$. The median Hassles score fell after 6 weeks of triglyceride-lowering therapy by 31% ($p \leq .05$) and remained significantly lower than pretreatment baseline throughout the remainder of therapy.

Univariate predictors of percentage change from baseline in psychometric tests. The greater the percentage reduction in triglyceride during therapy from baseline, the greater the percentage fall in the BDI ($r = .47$, $p < .05$). Moreover, the greater the percentage reduction in total cholesterol during therapy from baseline, the greater the percentage reduction in the hassles score ($r = .41$, $p < .05$).

Multivariate predictors of percentage change from baseline in psycho-

metric tests. After 12 weeks of triglyceride-lowering therapy, there were two significant independent determinants of the percentage reduction of the BDI. The greater the mean percentage decrease in triglyceride and the greater the mean percentage increase in blood oxygenation during therapy, the greater the mean percentage decrease in the BDI during therapy.

Discussion

Over a 54-week triglyceride-lowering treatment program, in 23 patients with severe primary hypertriglyceridemia, the number of patients with clinically important symptoms of depression (by the BDI) was significantly reduced. The greater the mean percentage reduction in triglyceride on therapy, the greater was the mean percentage reduction in the BDI, a relationship that was significant by both univariate and multivariate analysis. Concurrent with the decrease in plasma cholesterol and triglycerides on therapy, the BDI and Hassles scores fell ($p < .001$), and there were major reductions in semiquantitative tests of depressive symptoms and in tests of life stressors. Moreover, as oxygen saturation in capillary blood increased, the BDI fell, suggesting (speculatively) a positive role for improved oxygenation in amelioration of tests of symptoms of depression during triglyceride-lowering therapy.

Triglyceride-carrying lipoproteins have a concentration-dependent positive association with plasma viscosity (Seplowitz, Chien, & Smith, 1981). Increased viscosity and disordered blood rheology may be involved in the pathogenesis of ischemic syndromes in hyperlipidemia (Koenig et al., 1992). Triglyceride-lowering therapy improves pathologically reduced hemostatic parameters and improves blood fluidity, thus improving organ perfusion (Koenig et al., 1991, 1992; Rogers et al., 1989). In elderly hypertriglyceridemic participants, significant triglyceride lowering with diet and gemfibrozil has led to significantly higher levels of cerebral perfusion and cognitive performance (Rogers et al., 1989).

We postulated that triglyceride lowering may facilitate correction of metabolic defects such as high serum viscosity (Seplowitz et al., 1981) with attendant reduced red blood cell oxygenation and resultant segmental cerebral hypoxia (Rogers et al., 1989), which may, in aggregate, lead to symptoms of depression or to central nervous system depression (Glueck, Tieger, et al., 1993). Within this frame of reference, the greater the percentage reduction in triglyceride in our recent study, the greater was the percentage fall in the BDI score. Moreover, the greater the mean percentage increase in blood oxygenation during therapy, the greater was the mean percentage reduction in the BDI. We hypothesized that there may be a reversible causal relationship between high triglycerides and symptoms of depression (Glueck, Tieger, et al., 1993).

We speculate that the previous reported associations between increased cardiovascular events and affective disorders (Yates & Wallace, 1987) might be accounted for, in part, by high plasma triglycerides and low HDL cholesterol. We have reported atherogenic high triglycerides, low HDL cholesterol, and affective disorders in our study of 23 patients with severe primary hypertriglyceridemia and low HDL cholesterol (Glueck, Tieger, et al., 1993); in our studies of 203 adults hospitalized because of affective disorders (Glueck, Tieger, et al., 1994); and in our evaluation of 220 children hospitalized for psychiatric diseases (Glueck, Kuller, et al., 1994). Hence, we strongly suggest that when a diagnosis of affective disorders is made, a fasting lipid profile be obtained, so that hypertriglyceridemia and low-HDL cholesterol can be prospectively recognized and treated, with a goal of preventing cardiovascular disease (Glueck & Lang, 1995) and possibly ameliorating depressive symptoms (Glueck, Tieger, et al., 1993).

In our recent studies (e.g., Glueck, Tieger, et al., 1993), diet- and drug-induced reductions in cholesterol and triglyceride were coupled with significant reductions in symptoms of depression and in tests of life stressors and, hence, potentially with reduced suicidal tendencies. Similarly, in a prospective study of a cholesterol-lowering diet, dietary changes that led to reduced plasma cholesterol were associated with reductions in a test of depression and aggressive hostility (Weidner et al., 1992). Major reductions in LDL and total cholesterol with simvastatin and separately with pravastatin were not associated with increased mortality from suicide, trauma, or cancer (Scandinavian Group, 1994; Shepherd et al., 1995). Both the Scandinavian Simvastatin and the West of Scotland (pravastatin) studies revealed significant reductions in all-cause mortality on cholesterol-lowering statin drug therapy, compared with placebo (Scandinavian Group, 1994; Shepherd et al., 1995). We suggest that lipid-modulating therapy either would be neutral, or might reduce, but would not increase deaths from accidents, suicide, or violence.

Future Research Directions and Therapeutic Implications

Working on the assumption that hypocholesterolemia in many patients is secondary to behavior change induced by affective disorders (Glueck, Kuller, et al., 1994; Glueck, Tieger, 1993), it would be important to prospectively study lipid profiles in hypocholesterolemic and normocholesterolemic patients admitted to hospitals because of affective disorders. Aside from measures of height, weight, tricep skinfolds, ratios of waist to hip measurements, and (possibly) measures of body fat by impedance, measures of nutritional status should be obtained. These might include total serum protein levels, including albumin and globulin, complete blood count, serum ferritin, serum homocysteine and methylmalonic acid, and serum folate and B_{12} levels. Additional measures of total, LDL, and HDL cholesterol, as well as triglyceride, apolipoprotein A-I, and apolipoprotein B should be obtained. A detailed history of alcohol intake and substance abuse should be taken. If possible to obtain in detail, a 24-h recall of nutrient intake before admission would be useful for group analysis. It would be useful to prospectively assess the measurements just listed and measurements of nutritional status in these patients with affective disorders at their acute hospital admission, during their hospital stay, and 4 and 8 weeks after discharge. This would help to further determine whether, and to what degree, recovery from depression with attendant improvement in nutrition would be associated with rising plasma cholesterol and falling plasma triglyceride levels.

A study of patients undergoing electroconvulsive therapy (ECT) for intractable depression could prospectively obtain the measurements listed in the previous paragraph, before ECT, during the post-ECT recovery period, and 4 and 8 weeks after discharge, to determine whether amelioration of depression by ECT is associated with changes in measures of nutrition and plasma lipid and lipoprotein cholesterol levels. Also, prospective studies (as above) could be done in children with psychiatric hospital admissions, to further evaluate the associations between nutritional status, lipid and lipoprotein cholesterol disorders, and the severity of psychiatric disease, substance abuse, and alcohol intake. Additional studies could be carried out to confirm our initial observations (Glueck, Tieger, et al., 1993) that triglyceride lowering could be associated with amelioration of depression. Although it would not be ethical (due to the risk of cardiovascular disease and pancreatitis) to carry out a placebo-controlled study of the behavioral ramifications of triglyceride lowering in patients with severe hypertriglyceridemia, additional prospective observational data of non-blinded triglyceride lowering would be valuable. To the extent that normalization of triglycerides leads to an improvement in symptoms of depression and in an index of life stressors (Glueck, Tieger, et al., 1993), it would be worthwhile for those treating patients with depression to diagnose and appropriately treat hypertriglyceridemia, in the hope that improvement of the metabolic status would improve the psychiatric status.

References

American Psychiatric Association. (1987). Diagnostic and statistical manual for mental disorders (3rd ed., rev.). Washington, DC: Author.

Ashley, F. W., & Kannel, W. B. (1974). Relation of weight change in changes in atherogenic traits: The Framingham Study. *Journal of Chronic Diseases, 27,* 104–114.

Avellone, G., DiGarbo, V., Pann, A. V., Cordova, R., Leport, R., & Strano, A. (1988). Changes induced by gemfibrozil on lipidic, cogulative, and fibrinolytic pattern in patients with type IV hyperlipoproteinemia. *International Angiology, 7,* 270–277.

Buchwald, H., Varco, R. L., Matts, J. P., Long, J., Fitch, L., Campbell, G. S., Pearce, M., Yellin, A., Edmiston, A., Smink, R., Sawin, H., Campos, C., Hansen, B., Tuna, N., Karnegis, J., Sanmarco, M., Amplatz, K., Castaneda-Zuniga, W., Hunter, D., Bissett, J., Weber, F., Stevenson, J., Leon, A., & Chalmers, T. (1990). Effect of partial ileal bypass surgery on mortality and morbidity from coronary heart disease in patients with hypercholesterolemia: Report of the Program on the Surgical Control of the Hyperlipidemias (POSCH). *New England Journal of Medicine, 323,* 946–955.

Consensus Conference: Treatment of Hypertriglyceridemia. (1987). *Journal of the American Medical Association, 251,* 1196–1200.

Consensus Development Conference on Triglyceride, High Density Lipoprotein, and Coronary Heart Disease. (1992). *Clinical Courier 10,* 1–8.

Davey Smith, G. D., Shipley, M. J., Marmot, M. G., & Rose, G. (1992). Plasma cholesterol concentration and mortality: The Whitehall Study. *Journal of the American Medical Association, 267,* 70–76.

Davey Smith, G., Song, F., & Sheldon, T. A. (1993). Cholesterol lowering and mortality: The importance of considering initial level of risk. *British Medical Journal, 306,* 1367–1373.

Fallat, R. W., & Glueck, C. J. (1975). Familial and acquired Type V hyperlipoproteinemia. *Atherosclerosis, 23,* 41–62.

Farchi, G., Menotti, A., & Canti, S. (1987). Coronary risk factors and survival probability from coronary and other causes of death. *American Journal of Epidemiology, 126,* 400–408.

Fowkes, F. G. R., Leng, G. C., Donnan, P. T., Deary, I. J., Riemersma, R. A., & Housley, E. (1992). Serum cholesterol, triglycerides, and aggression in the general population. *The Lancet, 340,* 995–998.

Frank, J. W., Reed, D. M., Grove, J. S., & Benfante, R. (1992). Will lowering population levels of serum cholesterol affect total mortality? Expectations from the Honolulu Heart Program. *Journal of Clinical Epidemiology, 45,* 333–346.

Frick, M. H., Elo, O., Haapa, K., Heinonen, O. P., Heinsalmi, P., Help, P., Huttunen, J., Kaitaniemi, P., Koskinen, P., Manninen, V., Mäenpää, H., Mälkönen, M., Mänttäri, M., Norola, S., Pasternack, A., Pikkarainen, J., Romo, M., Sjöblom, T., & Nikkilä, E. (1987). Helsinki Heart Study: Primary-prevention trial with gemfibrozil in middle-aged men with dyslipidemia. *New England Journal of Medicine, 371,* 1237–1245.

Gartside, P. S., & Glueck, C. J. (1993). Relationship of dietary intake to hospital admission for coronary heart and vascular disease: The NHANES II national probability survey. *Journal of the American College of Nutrition, 12,* 676–684.

Glueck, C. J., Gartside, P., Fallat, R. W., Sielski, J., & Steiner, P. M. (1976). Longevity syndromes: Familial hypobeta and familial hyperalpha–lipoproteinemia. *Journal of Laboratory and Clinical Medicine, 88,* 941–957.

Glueck, C. J., Gartside, P. S., Steiner, P. M., Miller, M., Todhunter, T., Haaf, J., Pucke, M., Terrana, M., Fallat, R. W., & Kashyap, M. L. (1977). Hyperalpha- and hypobeta-lipoproteinemia in Octogenarian Kindreds. *Atherosclerosis, 27,* 387–406.

Glueck, C. J., Glueck, H. I., Tracy, T., Speirs, J., McCray, C., & Stroop, D. (1993). Relationship between Lp(a), lipids, apolipoproteins, and fibrinolytic activity in 191 hyperlipidemic patients. *Metabolism, 42,* 236–246.

Glueck, C. J., Kuller, F. E., Hamer, T., Rodriguez, R., Sosa, F., Sieve-Smith, L., & Morrison, J. A. (1994). Hypocholesterolemia, hypertriglyceridemia, suicide, and suicide ideation in children hospitalized for psychiatric diseases. *Pediatric Research, 35,* 602–610.

Glueck, C. J., & Lang, J. E. (1995). Lipoprotein disorders. In W. B. Abrams, M. H. Beers, & R. B. Berkow (Eds.), *The Merck manual of geriatrics* (pp. 1023–1052). Whitehouse Station, NJ: Merck.

Glueck, C. J., Rorick, M. H., Schmerler, M., Anthony, J. J., Feibel, J. H., Bishir, M., Glueck, H. I., Stroop, D., Hamer, A. T., & Tracy, T. (1995). Hypofibrinolytic and atherogenic risk factors for stroke. *Journal of Laboratory and Clinical Medicine, 125,* 319–325.

Glueck, C. J., Tieger, M., Kunkel, R., Hamer, T., Tracy, T., & Speirs, J. (1994). Hypocholesterolemia and affective disorders. *American Journal of Medical Sciences, 308,* 218–225.

Glueck, C. J., Tieger, M., Kunkel, R., Tracy, T., Speirs, J., Streicher, P., & Illig, E. (1993). Improvement in symptoms of depression and in an index of life stressors accompany treatment of severe hypertriglyceridemia. *Biological Psychiatry, 34,* 240–252.

Harris, T., Feldman, J. J., Kleinman, J. C., Ettinger, W. H., Jr., Makuc, P. M., & Schatzkin, A. G. (1992). The low cholesterol–mortality association in a national cohort. *Journal of Clinical Epidemiology, 45,* 595–601.

Hjermann, I., Velve Byre, K., Holme, I., & Leren, P. (1981). Effect of diet and smoking intervention on the incidence of coronary heart disease: Report from Oslo Study Group of a randomized trial in healthy men. *The Lancet, 2,* 1303–1310.

Holme, I., Hjermann, I., Hegeleland, A., & Leren, P. (1985). The Oslo Study: Diet and anti-smoking advice. Additional results from a 5-year primary prevention trial in middle-aged men. *Preventive Medicine, 14,* 279–292.

Isles, C. G., Hole, D. J., Gillis, C. R., Hawthorne, V. M., & Leven, A. F. (1989). Plasma cholesterol, coronary heart disease, and cancer in the Renfrew and Paisley survey. *British Medical Journal, 298*, 920–924.

Jacobs, D., Blackburn, H., Higgins, M., Reed, D., Iso, H., McMillian, G., Neaton, J., Nelson, J., Potter, J., Rifkind, B., Rosseau, J., Shekelle, R., & Yusuf, S. (1992). Report of the conference on low blood cholesterol: Mortality associations. *Circulation, 86*, 1046–1060.

Johnson, C. L., Rifkind, B. M., Sempos, C. T., et al. (1993). Declining serum total cholesterol among United States adults. *Journal of the American Medical Association, 269*, 3002–3008.

Koenig, W., Hehr, R., Ditschuneit, H., Staub, J. P., Rosenthal, J., & Hombach, V. (1991). Lovastatin improves blood rheology in primary hypercholesterolemia [Abstract]. *European Heart Journal, 12*, 111.

Koenig, W., Sund, M., Ernst, E., Mraz, W., Hombach, V., & Keil, U. (1992). Association between rheology and components of lipoproteins in human blood. *Circulation, 85*, 2197–2204.

Lipid Research Clinics Program. (1984). The Lipid Research Clinics Coronary Primary Prevention Trial Results: 1. Reduction in incidence of coronary heart disease. *Journal of the American Medical Association, 251*, 351–364.

Manninen, V., Elo, M. O., Frick, M. H., Haapa, K., Heinonen, O., Heinsalmi, P., Helo, P., Huttunen, J., Kaitaniemi, P., Koskinen, P., Mäenpää Mälkönen, M., Mänttäri, M., Norola, S., Pasternack, A., Pikkarainen, J., Romo, M., Sjöblom, T., & Nikkilä, E. (1988). Lipid alterations and decline in the incidence of coronary heart disease in the Helsinki Heart Study. *Journal of the American Medical Association, 260*, 641–651.

Meyer, J. S., Rogers, R. L., Mortel, K. F., et al. (1987). Hyperlipidemia is a risk factor for reduced cerebral perfusion and stroke. *Archives of Neurology, 44*, 418–422.

Meyer, J. S., & Waltz, A. G. (1959). Effects of changes in composition of plasma on blood flow: 1. Lipid and lipid fractions. *Neurology, 9*, 728–740.

Morgan, R. E., Palinkas, L. A., Barrett-Connor, E. L., & Wingard, D. L. (1993). Plasma cholesterol and depressive symptoms in older men. *The Lancet, 341*, 75–79.

Muldoon, M. F., Manuck, S. B., & Matthews, K. A. (1990). Effects of cholesterol lowering on mortality: A quantitative review of primary prevention trials. *British Medical Journal, 301*, 309–314.

Muldoon, M. F., Manuck, S. B., & Matthews, K. A. (1991). Does cholesterol lowering increase non-illness-related mortality? *Archives of Internal Medicine, 151*, 1453.

Muldoon, M., Rossouw, J. E., Manuck, S. B., Glueck, C. J., Kaplan, J. R., & Kaufmann, P. G. (1993). Low or lowered cholesterol and risk of death from suicide and trauma. *Metabolism, 42*, 45–56.

Multiple Risk Factor Intervention Trial Research Group. (1990). Mortality rates after 10.5 years for participants in the Multiple Risk Factor Intervention Trial: Findings related to a prior hypothesis of the trial. *Journal of the American Medical Association, 263*, 1795–1801.

Mussoni, L., Manucci, L., Camera, M., et al. (1991). Hyperlipidemias and the fibrinolytic system. *Atherosclerosis Reviews, 22*, 125–129.

Neaton, J. D., Blackburn, H., Jacobs, D., Kuller, L., Lee, D., Sherwin, R., Shih, J., Stamler, J., & Wentworth, D. (1992). Serum cholesterol level and mortality findings for men screened in the Multiple Risk Factor Intervention Trial. *Archives of Internal Medicine, 152*, 1490–1500.

Olson, R. E. (1975). Protein-calorie malnutrition. In R. E. Olson (Ed.), *Nutrition and clinical nutrition* (pp. 275–297). New York: Academic Press.

Pekkanen, J., Nissinen, A., Punsar, S., & Karvonen, M. N. (1989). Serum cholesterol and risk of accidental or violent death in a 25-year follow-up: The Finnish cohorts of the Seven Countries Study. *Archives of Internal Medicine, 149*, 1589–1591.

Rogers, R. L., Meyer, J. S., McClintic, K., & Mortel, K. F. (1989). Reducing hypertriglyceridemia in elderly patients with cerebrovascular disease stabilizes or improves cognition and cerebral perfusion. *Angiology, 40*, 260–269.

Rogers, R. L., Meyer, J. S., Mortel, K. F., et al. (1986). Decreased cerebral blood flow precedes multi-infarct dementia, but follows senile dementia of Alzheimer's type. *Neurology, 36*, 1–6.

Rose, G. (1987). European Collaborative Trial of Multifactorial Prevention of Coronary Heart Disease. *The Lancet, 1*, 685.

Rossouw, J. E., Lewis, B., & Rifkind, B. M. (1990). The value of lowering cholesterol after myocardial infarction. *New England Journal of Medicine, 323*, 1112–1119.

Rudman, D., Mattson, D. E., Feller, A. G., & Nagraj, H. S. (1989). A mortality risk index for men in a Veterans Administration extended care facility. *Journal of Parenteral and Enteral Nutrition, 13*, 189–195.

Scandinavian Simvastatin Survival Study Group. (1994). Randomized trial of cholesterol lowering in 4,444 patients with coronary heart disease: The Scandinavian Simvastatin Survival Study. *The Lancet, 344*, 1383–1389.

Seplowitz, A. H., Chien, S., & Smith, F. R. (1981). Effects of lipoproteins on plasma viscosity. *Atherosclerosis, 38*, 89–95.

Shepherd, J., Cobb, S. M., Ford, I., Isles, D., Lorimer, A. R., MacFarlane P. W., McKillop, J. H., & Packard, C. J., for the West of Scotland Coronary Prevention Study Group. (1995). Prevention of coronary heart disease with pravastatin in men with hypercholesterolemia. *New England Journal of Medicine, 333*, 1301–1307.

Stemmerman, G. N., Chyou, P. H., Kagan, A., Nomura, A. M., & Yano, K. (1992). Serum cholesterol and mortality among Japanese-American men: The Honolulu (Hawaii) Heart Program. *Archives of Internal Medicine, 151*, 969–972.

Strandberg, T. E., Salomaa, V. V., Naukkarinen, V. A., Vanhanen, H. T., Sarno, S. J., & Miettinen, T. A. (1991). Long-term mortality after 5-year multifactor primary prevention of cardiovascular diseases in middle-aged men. *Journal of the American Medical Association, 266*, 1225–1229.

Swank, R. L. (1956). Effects of fats on blood viscosity in dogs. *Circulation Research, 4*, 579–585.

Tripathy, K., Lotero, H., & Bolanos, O. (1970). Role of dietary protein upon serum cholesterol level in malnourished participants. *American Journal of Clinical Nutrition, 23*, 1160–1168.

Verdery, R. B., & Goldberg, A. P. (1991). Hypocholesterolemia as a predictor of death: A prospective study of 224 nursing home residents. *Journal of Gerontology, 46*, 84–90.

Virkkunen, M. (1983). Serum cholesterol levels in homicidal offenders: A low cholesterol level is connected with a habitually violent tendency under the influence of alcohol. *Neuropsychobiology, 10*, 65–69.

Weidner, G., Connor, S. L., Hollies, J. F., & Connor, W. E. (1992). Improvements in hostility and depression in relation to dietary change and cholesterol lowering. *Annals of Internal Medicine, 117*, 820–823.

Weissenburger, J. (1986). Weight change in depression. *Psychiatry Research, 17*, 275–283.

World Health Organization. (1991). Mental disorders. In *Manual of the International Statistical Classification of Diseases, Injuries, and Causes of Death* (4th ed., 9th rev.). Geneva, Switzerland: Author.

World Health Organization European Collaborative Group. (1986). European collaborative trial of multifactorial prevention of coronary heart disease: Final report on the 6-year results. *The Lancet, 1*, 869–872.

Wysowski, D. K., & Gross, T. P. (1990). Deaths due to accidents and violence in two recent trials of cholesterol-lowering drugs. *Archives of Internal Medicine, 150*, 2169–2172.

Yates, W. R., & Wallace, R. (1987). Cardiovascular risk factors in affective disorder. *Journal of Affective Disorders, 12*, 129–134.

Yusuf, S., Wittes, J., & Friedman, L. (1988). Overview of results of randomized clinical trials in heart disease: II. Unstable angina, heart failure, primary prevention with aspirin, and risk factor modification. *Journal of the American Medical Association, 260*, 2259–2263.

7

Cholesterol Lowering and Emotional Distress: Current Status and Future Directions

Steven M. Schwartz and Mark W. Ketterer

The population of patients suffering from cardiovascular disease (CVD) continues to rise and remains a significant contributor to overall mortality and escalating health care costs in the United States (Weinstein et al., 1987) and abroad (Jacobs et al., 1992). The role of serum cholesterol in the natural history of CVD has essentially been established (Grundy, 1990), and as a result, a good deal of clinical practice and public policy efforts has been directed at reducing serum cholesterol as both therapeutic and preventive interventions. These efforts have paid off, in that treatment data do support the efficacy of lowered serum cholesterol in slowing the progression of CVD and reducing CVD mortality (Buchwald et al., 1990; Frick et al., 1987; Goldman, 1992; Grundy, 1990; Lipid Research Clinics Program, 1984; Oliver, 1991). General acceptance of the therapeutic effects of reduced serum cholesterol is evidenced by the dramatic increase in prescriptions for antilipidemic drugs in the last 10 years (Davey Smith, Song, & Sheldon, 1993).

In contrast to the benefits noted above, a number of studies have indicated that although fatal and nonfatal cardiovascular events decline in cholesterol-treated samples, overall mortality is not significantly reduced (Cucherat & Boissel, 1993; Davey Smith et al., 1993; Dayton, Pearce, Hashmoto, Dixon, & Tomiyasu, 1969; Jacobs et al., 1992; Frick et al., 1987; Lindberg, Rastam, Gullberg, & Eklund, 1992; Lipid Research Clinics Program, 1984; Multiple Risk Factor Intervention Trial Research Group, 1992). The concomitant increase in non-CVD-related deaths responsible for these findings has been explained away as resulting from random or chance factors (Yusuf, Wittes, & Friedman, 1988). Nevertheless, these curious and unpredicted findings prompted Muldoon, Manuck, and Matthews (1990) to conduct a meta-analysis of six primary hypercholesterolemia prevention studies that used random assignment as part of their methodology and mortality as an outcome measure. Their frequently cited and controversial study evaluated nearly 25,000 male patients, some of whom were undergoing either dietary or pharmacological lipid lowering. Muldoon et al. (1990) were able to confirm that total mortality was not

113

reduced, despite the reduction in mortality secondary to CVD. Surprisingly, deaths due to CVD were offset by a concomitant increase in non-illness-related deaths (i.e., suicide, homicide, and accidents) and cancer. Oliver (1991) concluded that the consistency of the findings across studies was unlikely to be the result of chance factors, and this relationship was found in a number of subsequent studies (Cucherat & Boissel, 1993; Davey Smith et al., 1993; Jacobs et al., 1992; Lindberg et al., 1992; Modai, Valevski, Dror, & Weizman, 1994; Multiple Risk Factor Intervention Trial Research Group, 1992).

These findings were acknowledged also by Jacobs et al. (1992) and the National Heart, Lung, and Blood Institute Conference. Jacobs et al. used hazard regression modeling in their evaluation of 19 cohort studies. They, too, found increased risk for non-illness-related deaths in patients with low levels of total serum cholesterol, independent of other possible mediating variables, such as blood pressure, cigarette smoking, body mass index, alcohol usage, and age. What makes the Jacobs et al. findings particularly powerful and disturbing is the consistency of results across different cultural populations and geographic locations (e.g., Japan, the United States, and Europe).

The relationship between serum cholesterol and non-illness-related deaths remains controversial (Hawthon, Cowen, Owens, Bond, & Elliott, 1993), and contrary data do exist (Chen et al., 1991; Farchi, Menotti, & Conti, 1987; Gould, Rossouw, Santanello, Heyse, & Furber, 1995; Iribarren, Reed, Wergowske, Burchfiel, & Dwyer, 1995; Multiple Risk Factor Intervention Trial Research Group, 1992; Pekkanen, Nissinen, Punsar, & Karvonen, 1989; Scandinavian Simvastatin Survival Study Group, 1994; Smith, Shipley, Marmot, & Rose, 1992; Vartiainen et al., 1994; Weidner, Connor, Hollis, & Conner, 1992). For example, the Scandinavian Simvastatin Survival Study Group found overall reductions in mortality for patients undergoing antilipidemic therapy. However, this study did not measure emotional states, which may serve as vulnerability factors in non-illness-related deaths (e.g., depression or anger), in a standardized way. They also excluded patients who might be susceptible to violent deaths, such as those reporting a history of alcohol or drug abuse or of psychiatric treatment; patients who appeared to be poor compliance risks; and patients who failed to comply with a prerandomization trial. These are variables that may plausibly mark patients who are more susceptible to any depressogenic effect of antilipidemic therapies. This chapter reviews the relationships between lipid lowering and emotional distress and explores the many unanswered questions concerning causation. Future directions for research are discussed, along with suggestions for a treatment approach for cholesterol management that takes the patient's level of emotional distress into consideration.

Lipid Lowering and Emotional Distress

Non-illness-related deaths are generally crude, clinical-dependent measures of emotional distress. If non-illness-related deaths represent a rather dramatic endpoint of an iatrogenic process involving lowered serum cholesterol, then antilipidemic therapy should also be associated with common risk factors for these non-illness-related deaths, such as negative emotional states (Murphy et al., 1989). Indeed, many patients undergoing antilipidemic treatment may be suffering emotionally but never actually manifest suicidal ideation or behavior or aggressive acting out.

Morgan, Palinkas, Barrett-Connor, and Wingard (1993) studied depressive symptomatology in men (50–89 years of age) and its relationship to spontaneous (untreated) serum cholesterol levels. Morgan et al. reported that men age 70 and above, with spontaneously low serum cholesterol, were three times more likely to report significant depression, as measured by the Beck Depression Inventory (BDI; Beck, Ward, Mendelsohn, Mock, & Erbaugh, 1961). This result was independent of health status, medication usage, degree of exercise, or weight loss. Although this study prompted heated debate, more recent studies, by Sullivan, Joyce, Bulik, Mulder, and Oakley-Browne (1994) and Golier, Marzuk, Andrew, Weiner, and Tardiff (1995), support its results. For example, Golier et al. assessed 650 patients, consecutively admitted to a psychiatric hospital, for depression and past history of suicide attempts and their relationship to spontaneous cholesterol levels. Golier et al. found that men in the lower cholesterol quartile were twice as likely to have a history of serious suicide attempts, as operationalized by the Medical Lethality Rating Scale. This finding held up even after accounting for other risk factors such as age, race, socioeconomic status, alcohol and drug use, and degree of depression. Interestingly, Irvine and Logan (1994) found that hypercholesterolemic male factory workers scored higher on measures of mental health. Although these relationships do not necessarily imply causation, they are remarkably consistent with the body of mounting evidence that implicates therapeutic cholesterol reduction in development of negative affective states and non-illness-related death.

Contrary findings were reported by Weidner et al. (1992), who studied emotional distress in 305 patients undergoing dietary intervention to reduce serum cholesterol as part of the Family Heart Study. They did not find that patients undergoing dietary cholesterol interventions experienced a negative change in their emotional status. Weidner et al. found improved emotional states in patients who complied with the dietary intervention. However, the dietary effects on cholesterol levels were minimal (reduction of 1% in plasma cholesterol). Their results must further be tempered by the fact that their groups were self-selected based on their willingness to comply with the treatment program. Patient compliance can be associated with protective psychological states (Meichenbaum & Turk, 1987). Therefore, group differences found by Weidner et al. may actually reflect differences in emotional status associated with willingness to comply with treatment rather than any effect of antilipidemic therapy. These contradictory data serve to illustrate the need for further study of possible mediating variables.

Emotional State of Angiographic Patients
Undergoing Therapy

The ability to demonstrate a relationship between lowered serum cholesterol and emotional distress would not only provide further causal support
for the existing body of literature but also suggest the need for early involvement of psychiatric–psychological evaluation and preventative treatment in at-risk patients. With this in mind, Ketterer et al. (1994) evaluated the emotional status of 174 male patients undergoing coronary
angiography, 16 of whom were taking antilipidemic agents. Measures of
emotional distress consisted of the Framingham Type A Scale (Haynes,
Levine, Scotch, Feinleib, & Kannel, 1978), the Cook–Medley Hostility
Scale (Cook & Medley, 1954), and the Ketterer Stress Symptom Frequency
Checklist (KSSFC; Ketterer, Lovallo, & Lumley, 1993). The latter instrument was developed by the principal investigator as a measure of emotional status consistent with aspects of the Type A behavior pattern that
are most strongly associated with CVD (aggravation, irritation, anger, and
impatience). Patients were also screened for gross cognitive dysfunction
and interviewed for information regarding basic demographic data and
quality of their marital relationship (see Table 1). Their results indicated
that patients undergoing antilipidemic therapy did indeed report more
depressive symptomatology than untreated patients (see Table 2). Overall,
a greater percentage of patients in the lipid-lowering group were suffering
from a severe depression (25% vs. 8%). Although not statistically significant, trends were also found for increased anxiety–worry and suicidal ideation in patients taking lipid-lowering agents. These findings held up even
after accounting for possible mediating variables such as degree of disease,

Table 1. Between-Groups Means for Potential Confounding Variables

Confound	Antilipidemic Agent		*p*
	Yes	No	
Age	56.3	58.2	.491
Education	13.4	13.7	.723
Alcohol use per day	0.4	0.6	.654
Packyears of cigarette smoking	30.3	44.3	.224
Weekly hours of exercise	4.0	2.3	.143
Fights with spouse per year	69.9	97.8	.377
Severity of CVD	81.3	68.4	.434
History of divorce	37.5	29.1	.681
History of hypertension	56.3	48.1	.720
Prior myocardial infarction	25.0	29.1	.955
Prescription of beta blockers	43.8	32.1	.344
n	16	158	

Note: CVD = Cardiovascular disease. Age and education are in years. Severity of CVD,
  history of divorce, history of hypertension, prior myocardial infarction, and prescription
  of beta blockers are in percentages.
Data are from Ketterer et al. (1994).

Table 2. Between-Groups Means for Measures of Emotional Distress

Dependent variable	Antilipidemic agent		
	Yes	No	*p*
KSSFC	4.6	3.9	.460
Depression	3.7	2.4	.050
Anxiety	7.6	5.2	.074
Suicidal ideation	0.6	0.2	.086
Framingham Type A Scale	5.1	5.2	.849
Cook−Medley Hostility Scale	19.5	18.9	.826
Sleep latency (minutes)	7.8	16.7	.050
Nighttime Awakenings (frequency)	1.2	1.1	.909
Structured interview (interviewer rating)	2.3	2.0	.152
Hostility	2.3	2.7	.114
n	16	158	

Note: KSSFC = Ketterer Stress Symptom Frequency Checklist (Ketterer, Lovallo, & Lumley, 1993). KSSFC scales are Likert-type ratings of frequency of a given symptom. Framingham Type A Scale is from Haynes, Levine, Scotch, and Medley (1954). Cook−Medley Hostility Scale is from Cook and Medley (1954; figures represent number of items answered in the direction of hostile).
Data are from Ketterer et al. (1994).

alcohol and cigarette use, education, amount of exercise, and marital conflict. Specific items on the KSSFC that strongly differentiated the two groups were "feeling that they should be punished" (guilt) and "tearfulness." Guilt is generally considered one of several critical risk factors for suicidal behavior. Therefore, these findings provide further support that antilipidemic therapy may have a negative iatrogenic impact on emotional status, which is conceptually consistent with other studies measuring negative emotional states (Golier et al., 1995; Hillbrand & Foster, 1993; Hillbrand, Spitz, & Foster, 1995; Morgan et al., 1993; Virkkunen, 1979, 1983) and with the mortality studies (Jacobs et al., 1992; Muldoon et al., 1990).

Unanswered Questions and Areas for Future Research

Many questions remain unanswered (Hawthon et al., 1993; Muldoon et al., 1993). For example, some data suggest that there may be gender differences in vulnerability to lowered cholesterol and emotional distress, indicating that men may be more susceptible to negative changes in emotional status (Golier et al., 1995; Lindberg et al., 1992; Muldoon et al., 1993). The implication is that hormonal differences may be responsible. Therefore, vulnerability and gender may also vary with age, so that older (e.g., postmenopausal) women are more vulnerable than younger women (Brindley, McCann, Niaura, Stoney, & Suarez, 1993).

Other relationships also require empirical testing. For example, is the relationship between lowered serum cholesterol mediated by substance abuse? Does the consequent negative affective state provide patients with a motivation toward self-medicating? The use of substances, particularly alcohol, has a disinhibiting effect that may produce impulsive and self-destructive acting out in at-risk individuals. Low serum cholesterol has been associated with alcohol-related diseases as well (Multiple Risk Factor Intervention Trial Research Group, 1992). The specific nature of cholesterol's relationship to alcohol usage requires considerable further study.

There is little information on the natural history or time course of depressogenesis from antilipidemic treatment. What level of cholesterol reduction and what rate of reduction are most predictive of adverse emotional sequelae? Over what period of time does this depressogenic effect develop? Jacobs et al. (1992) and Multiple Risk Factor Intervention Trial Research Group (1992) results seem to suggest that those patients with total cholesterol levels below 160 mg/dl may be at greater risk for non-illness-related deaths. How important is the differential effect on cholesterol subfractions to developing negative emotional states? Establishment of a critical value, or window, for serum cholesterol would have clinical utility in directing practitioners to aim their therapeutic interventions at optimal rather than maximal cholesterol reduction.

By what biological mechanism might reduced cholesterol affect mood? What role does stress play in lipid metabolism, and how does this relate to the progression of CVD (Brindley et al., 1993)? Penttinen (1995) recently proposed a hypothesis involving the relationship of interleukin-2 with cholesterol and negative emotional states. Engelberg (1992) offered a theoretical explanation for lipid mediation of serotonergic functioning. His theory concerns the integral role of cholesterol in the permeability and microviscosity of cell membranes. This theory draws on animal studies demonstrating both behavioral changes (Kaplan & Manuck, 1990) and biological–synaptic changes (Heron, Shinitzky, Hershkowitz, & Samuel, 1980) associated with serum cholesterol in monkeys and mice, respectively. If true, then are serotonergic systems alone vulnerable, or are other neurotransmitter systems (e.g., norepinephrine or dopamine) also at risk? Penttinen's theory implies that other neurotransmitter systems may also be at risk. Can the depressogenic mood disturbance be reversed by simply discontinuing antilipidemic treatment? Do current treatment modalities for depression, particularly the selective serotonin reuptake inhibitor class of antidepressants, affect lipid-lowering mood disorder while allowing for the beneficial therapeutic effects of lowered serum cholesterol? Selective serotonin reuptake inhibitor class antidepressants are particularly well suited to this line of investigation because of their specificity of action and preferable side effects profile. Specifically, their low incidence of anticholinergic and cardiovascular effects, which could be harmful or fatal to those suffering from CVD, make them ideal for this medical population.

In addition, previous research on emotional distress has been hampered by inconsistent operational definitions for the various mood-state-dependent measures. Although not unique to this literature, the use of standardized structured interviews, such as the Structured Clinical Interview for *DSM–III–R* (Spitzer et al., 1993), would surely improve diagnostic standardization across studies. Freedman et al. (1995) have done exactly this using the Diagnostic Interview Schedule (Robbin, Helzer, Croughan, & Radcliff, 1981) and the Minnesota Multiphasic Personality Inventory. However, structured interviews may also possess inherent limitations when applied to a medically ill sample (Cavanaugh, 1995; Clark, Cavanaugh, & Gibbons, 1983; Moffic & Paykel, 1975), such as those suffering from CVD. Cavanaugh highlighted these limitations and offered reasonable suggestions for diagnosis of depression in the medically ill on the basis of *Diagnostic and Statistical Manual of Mental Disorders* (American Psychiatric Association, 1994) criteria. Her approach attempts to account for some of the confounding factors present in medically ill populations, and these concerns should be addressed where appropriate.

Implications for Treatment

These types of questions and problems do not mitigate the ever tightening circle of empirical data surrounding the deleterious effects of lowered cholesterol levels. This should not be taken to imply a moratorium on antilipidemic drugs, as Davey Smith and Pekkanen (1992) suggested, but rather that practitioners should weigh the costs and benefits of undertaking this treatment regimen, with the possible depressogenic effect included as a formal part of the clinical decision-making process. Morgan et al. (1993) believe that evaluation of depressive symptomatology should be made a standard part of future clinical trials on cholesterol lowering. Davey Smith et al. (1993) suggested that severity of CVD risk factors, associated with increased morbidity and mortality, and alternative treatments (e.g., exercise and weight reduction) also be considered as part of practitioner decision-making process, so that patients at relatively low risk for serious CVD-related events (e.g., myocardial infarction) would not be considered for antilipidemic intervention. These considerations should be of particular concern to practitioners when other risk factors, such as past history of depression or substance abuse, are present.

This body of work suggests also that cardiologists and other practitioners prescribing antilipidemic drugs should regularly evaluate their patients for depressive symptomatology. Evaluation of emotional distress should be part of the standard of care, irrespective of lipid lowering per se, given that another, separate body of literature has indicated that depression is related to 6- and 18-month survival rates (Frasure-Smith, Lesperance, & Talajic, 1993, 1995). Assessment of depression can be as simple as asking a few critical questions during a standard clinic visit or having patients complete one of the several psychometrically sound and clinically straightforward assessment tools (e.g., BDI, Hamilton Rating Scale for Depression, Zung Self-Rating Depression Scale, and Geriatric Depression Scale). The Geriatric Depression Scale is particularly appropriate for aged patients. The BDI is the most widely used of these self-report measures. The BDI has well-established prognostic utility with post-myocardial infarction patients (Frasure-Smith et al., 1993, 1995), and its 13-item short form is particularly well suited to medical settings (Beck & Beck, 1972). Existing data on the full BDI indicate that scores greater than 10 should be referred for further evaluation and possible treatment by a psychologist or psychiatrist.

Conclusion

As medicine has evolved, knowledge has increased about the underlying biomechanisms by which many common disease entities develop. This knowledge often offers seemingly straightforward treatment solutions that can arrest or reverse the progression of the disease process at the organ and cellular level. Therefore, practitioners focus on medicine's ability to impact highly specific biomedical events. Inherent in this development is a reductionistic mindset, which has many advantages but also carries with it several disadvantages as well (Engel, 1977). For example, common treatments for cancer (i.e., radiation therapy and chemotherapy) operate by what essentially amounts to differential poisoning of bodily tissues, with the assumption that cancer cells will be more vulnerable. Generally, patient and doctor know and accept the health trade-off (e.g., hair loss, nausea, vomiting, and weight loss vs. prolonged life). However, the consequence of too reductionistic an approach at the expense of quality-of-life variables can be illustrated by Payer (1988). She describes the enthusiasm reported by some American oncologists for their finding that intensive chemotherapy was able to extend the life of elderly cancer patients for several months. However, these oncologists completely ignored the intense hyperemesis, which resulted in several more months only of misery. Virtually no quality of life was preserved.

This does not imply iniquity on the part of the medical profession but rather is a natural consequence of the ever expanding biomedical database and developing medical technology. Nevertheless, Engel's (1977) seminal paper critiqued the medical culture for its limited view of illness development and treatment and warned that correction of biomedical dysfunction does not necessarily restore the patient back to health. This advice is perhaps even more relevant today. Health is a multifaceted organismic state that is only partially accounted for by proper functioning of integrated organ and cellular systems. Therefore, medical treatments need to be evaluated not only by their ability to effectively combat specific pathological biologic processes but also by their effect on other biological, psychological, and social aspects of the patient's functioning. Careful consideration of treatment effects on each of these domains improves not only quality of care, but quality of life and cost-effectiveness as well (Dunleavy, 1994). The possible iatrogenic effects of antilipidemic treatments appear to impact the quality of life aside from cardiovascular functioning. How many patients are suffering emotionally in silence, feeling depressed and unwilling to seek treatment, is unknown. However, assessment for depressive mood is not particularly time-consuming and can easily be integrated into everyday practice. In the end, it is as important a part of the healing process as affecting atherosclerotic disease.

References

American Psychiatric Association (1994). *Diagnostic and statistical manual of mental disorders* (4th ed.). Washington, DC: Author.

Beck, A. T., & Beck, R. W. (1972). Screening depressed patients in family practice. *Post Graduate Medicine, 52,* 81–85.

Beck, A. T., Ward, C. H., Mendelsohn, M., Mock, J., & Erbaugh, J. (1961). An inventory for measuring depression. *Archives of General Psychiatry, 4,* 561–571.

Brindley, D. N., McCann, B. S., Niaura, R., Stoney, C. M., & Suarez, E. C. (1993). Stress and lipoprotein metabolism: Modulators and mechanisms. *Metabolism, 42,* 3–15.

Buchwald, H., et al. (1990). Posch group: Effect of partial ileal bypass surgery on mortality and morbidity from coronary heart disease in patients with hypercholesterolemia: Report of the program on the surgical control of hyperlipidemia. *New England Journal of Medicine, 323,* 946–955.

Cavanaugh, S. (1995). Depression in the medically ill: Clinical issues in diagnostic assessment. *Psychosomatics, 36,* 48–59.

Chen, Z., Peto, R., Collins, R., MacMahon, S., Lu, J., & Li, W. (1991). Serum cholesterol concentrations and coronary heart disease in a population with low cholesterol concentrations. *British Medical Journal, 303,* 276–282.

Clark, D., Cavanaugh, S., & Gibbons, R. D. (1983). The core symptoms of depression in medical and psychiatric patients. *Journal of Nervous and Mental Disease, 171,* 705–713.

Cook, W. W., & Medley, D. M. (1954). Proposed hostility and pharisaic-virtue scales for the MMPI. *Journal of Applied Psychology, 38,* 414–418.

Cucherat, M., & Boissel, J. P. (1993). Meta-analysis of results from clinical trials on prevention of coronary heart disease by lipid-lowering interventions. *Clinical Trials and Meta-Analysis, 28,* 109–129.

Davey Smith, G., & Pekkanen, J. (1992). Should there be moratorium on the use of cholesterol lowering drugs? *British Medical Journal, 304,* 431–434.

Davey Smith, G., Song, F., & Sheldon, T. A. (1993). Cholesterol lowering and mortality: The importance of considering initial level of risk. *British Medical Journal, 306,* 1367–1372.

Dayton, S., Pearce, M. L., Hashmoto, S., Dixon, W. J., & Tomiyasu, U. (1969). A controlled clinical trial of a diet high in unsaturated fat in preventing complications of atherosclerosis. *Circulation, 40,* 1–63.

Dunleavy, B. P. (1994, July). Quality of life and outcomes in healthcare management. *Group Practice Managed Healthcare News,* pp. 18, 29.

Engel, G. L. (1977). The need for a new medical model: A challenge for biomedicine. *Science, 196,* 129–132.

Engelberg, H. (1992). Low serum cholesterol and suicide. *The Lancet, 339,* 727–729.

Farchi, G., Menotti, A., & Conti, S. (1987). Coronary risk factors and survival probability from coronary and other causes of death. *American Journal of Epidemiology, 126,* 400–408.

Frasure-Smith, N., Lesperance, F., & Talajic, M. (1993). Depression following myocardial infarction: Impact on 6-month survival. *Journal of the American Medical Association, 270,* 1819–1825.

Frasure-Smith, N., Lesperance, F., & Talajic, M. (1995). Depression and 18-month prognosis after myocardial infarction. *Circulation, 91,* 999–1005.

Freedman, D. S., Byers, T., Barrett, D. H., Stroop, N. E., Eaker, E., & Monroe-Blum, H. (1995). Plasma lipid levels and psychologic characteristics in men. *American Journal of Epidemiology, 141,* 507–517.

Frick, M. H., Elo, M. O., Haapa, K., Heinonen, O. P., et al. (1987). Helsinki Heart Study: Primary prevention trial with gomfibrozil in middle-aged men with dyslipidemia: Safety of treatment, changes in risk factors, and incidence of coronary heart disease. *New England Journal of Medicine, 317,* 1237–1245.

Goldman, L. (1992). Cost-effectiveness strategies in cardiology. In E. Braunwald (Ed.), *Heart disease: A textbook of cardiovascular medicine* (pp. 1694–1707). Philadelphia: W. B. Saunders.

Golier, J. A., Marzuk, P. M., Andrew, C. L., Weiner, C., & Tardiff, K. (1995). Low cholesterol level and attempted suicide. *American Journal of Psychiatry, 152,* 419–423.

Gould, A. L., Rossouw, J. E., Santanello, N. C., Heyse, J. F., & Furber, C. D. (1995). Cholesterol reduction yields clinical benefit: A new look at old data. *Circulation, 91,* 2274–2282.

Grundy, S. M. (1990). Cholesterol and coronary heart disease: Future directions. *Journal of the American Medical Association, 264,* 3053–3059.

Hawthon, K., Cowen, P., Owens, D., Bond, A., & Elliott, M. (1993). Low serum cholesterol and suicide. *British Journal of Psychiatry, 162,* 818–825.

Haynes, S. G., Levine, S., Scotch, N., Feinleib, M., & Kannel, W. B. (1978). The relationship of psychosocial factors to coronary heart disease in the Framingham Study I: Methods and risk factors. *American Journal of Epidemiology, 107,* 362–383.

Heron, D. S., Shinitzky, M., Hershkowitz, M., & Samuel, D. (1980). Lipid fluidity markedly modulates the binding of serotonin to mouse brain membranes. *Proceeding of the National Academy of Sciences, USA, 77,* 7463–7467.

Hillbrand, M., & Foster, H. G. (1993). Serum cholesterol and severity of aggression. *Psychological Reports, 72,* 270.

Hillbrand, M., Spitz, R. T., & Foster, H. G. (1995). Serum cholesterol and aggression in hospitalized male forensic patients. *Journal of Behavioral Medicine, 18,* 33–43.

Iribarren, C., Reed, D. M., Wergowske, G., Burchfiel, C. M., & Dwyer, J. H. (1995). Serum cholesterol level and mortality due to suicide and trauma in the Honolulu Heart Program. *Archives of Internal Medicine, 155,* 695–700.

Irvine, M. J., & Logan, A. G. (1994). Is knowing your cholesterol number harmful? *Journal of Clinical Epidemiology, 47,* 131–145.

Jacobs, D., et al. (1992). Report of the conference on low blood cholesterol and mortality associations. *Circulation, 86,* 1046–1060.

Kaplan, J. R., & Manuck, S. B. (1990). The effects of fat and cholesterol on aggressive behavior in monkeys. *Psychosomatic Medicine, 52,* 226–227.

Ketterer, M. W., Brymer, J., Rhoads, K., Kraft, P., Goldberg, D., & Lovallo, W. A. (1994). Lipid lowering therapy and violent death: Is depression a culprit? *Stress Medicine, 10,* 233–237.

Ketterer, M. W., Lovallo, W. R., & Lumley, M. A. (1993). Quantifying the density of Friedman's pathogenic emotions (AIAI). *International Journal of Psychosomatics, 40,* 22–28.

Lindberg, G., Rastam, L., Gullberg, B., & Eklund, G. A. (1992). Low serum cholesterol concentration and short term mortality from injuries in men and women. *British Medical Journal, 305,* 277–279.

Lipid Research Clinics Program. (1984). The Lipid Research Clinics Coronary Primary Prevention Trial Results: I. Reduction in incidence of coronary heart disease. *Journal of the American Medical Association, 251,* 351–364.

Meichenbaum, D., & Turk, D. C. (1987). *Facilitating treatment adherence: A practitioner's guidebook.* New York: Plenum.

Modai, I., Valevski, A., Dror, S., & Weizman, A. (1994). Serum cholesterol levels and suicidal tendencies in psychiatric inpatients. *Journal of Clinical Psychiatry, 55,* 252–254.

Moffic, H. S., & Paykel, E. S. (1975). Depression in medical inpatients. *British Journal of Psychiatry, 126,* 346–353.

Morgan, R. E., Palinkas, L. A., Barrett-Connor, E. L., & Wingard, D. L. (1993). Plasma cholesterol and depressive symptoms in older men. *The Lancet, 341,* 75–79.

Muldoon, M. F., Manuck, S. B., & Matthews, K. A. (1990). Lowering cholesterol concentrations and mortality: A quantitative review of primary prevention trials. *British Medical Journal, 301,* 309–314.

Muldoon, M. F., Rossouw, J. E., Manuck, S. B., Glueck, C. J., Kaplan, J. R., & Kaufman, P. G. (1993). Low or lowered cholesterol and risk of death from suicide and trauma. *Metabolism, 42*, 45–56.

Multiple Risk Factor Intervention Trial Research Group. (1992). Serum cholesterol level and mortality. *Archives of Internal Medicine, 152*, 1490–1500.

Murphy, J. M., Munson, R. R., Oliver, D. C., Sobol, A. M., Pratt, L. A., & Leighton, A. H. (1989). Mortality risk and psychiatric disorders: Results of a general physicians survey. *Psychiatric Epidemiology, 24*, 134–142.

Oliver, M. F. (1991). Might treatment of hypercholesterolemia increase non-cardiac mortality. *Lancet, 337*, 1529–1531.

Payer, L. (1988). *Medicine and culture*. New York: Penguin Books.

Pekkanen, J., Nissinen, A., Punsar, S., & Karvonen, J. (1989). Serum cholesterol and risk of accidental or violent death in a 25 year follow up—The Finnish cohorts of the Seven Countries Study. *Archives of Internal Medicine, 149*, 1589–1591.

Penttinen, J. (1995). Hypothesis: Low serum cholesterol, suicide, and interleukin-2. *American Journal of Epidemiology, 141*, 716–718.

Robbin, L. N., Helzer, J. E., Croughan, J., & Radcliff, K. (1981). National Institute of Mental Health Diagnostic Interview Schedule. *Archives of General Psychiatry, 38*, 381–389.

Scandinavian Simvastatin Survival Study Group. (1994). Randomized trial of cholesterol lowering in 4444 patients with coronary heart disease: The Scandinavian Simvastatin Survival Study (45). *Lancet, 344*, 1383–1389.

Smith, G. D., Shipley, M. J., Marmot, M. G., & Rose, G. (1992). Plasma cholesterol concentrations and mortality: The Whitehall Study. *Journal of the American Medical Association, 267*, 70–76.

Spitzer, R. L., Williams, J. B. W., Gibbon, M., & First, M. B. (1993). The Structured Clinical Interview for *DSM-III-R* (SCID): I. History, rationale, and description. *Archives of General Psychiatry, 49*, 624–629.

Sullivan, P. F., Joyce, P. R., Bulik, C. M., Mulder, R. T., & Oakley-Browne, M. (1994). Total cholesterol and suicidality in depression. *Biological Psychiatry, 36*, 472–477.

Vartiainen, E., Pushka, P., Pekkanen, J., Tuomilehto, J., Lonnqvist, J., & Ehnholm, C. (1994). Serum cholesterol concentration and mortality from accidents, suicide, and other violent causes. *British Medical Journal, 309*, 445–447.

Virkkunen, M. (1979). Serum cholesterol in antisocial personality. *Neuropsychobiology, 5*, 27–30.

Virkkunen, M. (1983). Serum cholesterol levels in homicidal offenders. *Biological Psychiatry, 10*, 65–69.

Weidner, G., Conner, S. L., Hollis, J. F., & Conner, W. E. (1992). Improvements in hostility and depression in relation to dietary change and cholesterol lowering. *Annals of Internal Medicine, 117*, 820–823.

Weinstein, M. C., Coxson, P. G., Williams, L. W., et al. (1987). Forecasting coronary heart disease, incidence, mortality and cost: The coronary heart disease policy model. *American Journal of Public Health, 77*, 1417.

Yusuf, S., Wittes, J., & Friedman, L. (1988). Overview of results of randomized clinical trials in heart disease: II. Unstable angina, heart failure, primary prevention with aspirin, and risk factor modification. *Journal of the American Medical Association, 260*, 2259–2263.

Part III

Lipids and Brain Function

8

Molecular Mechanisms Underlying the Effects of Cholesterol on Neuronal Cell Membrane Function and Drug–Membrane Interactions

R. Preston Mason, Robert T. Rubin,
Pamela E. Mason, and Thomas N. Tulenko

Overview

Our interest in the physiological role of cholesterol in neuronal cell activity and human behavior has been stimulated by observations that a significant and unexpected increase in nonmedical deaths occurs among individuals prescribed cholesterol-lowering drugs. In several clinical trials of these drugs, the increase in nonmedical deaths could be attributed to violence or traumatic events. These surprising results have led to concern and even skepticism about the value of pharmacological cholesterol-lowering therapy. They also have raised important questions about the physiological role of cholesterol in basic functions of the central nervous system, including the activity of neurotransmitters, such as serotonin, that have been implicated in aggressive and violent behavior. In this chapter, we review the role of cholesterol in regulating the structure and function of the neuronal plasma (cell) membrane, including synaptic neurotransmitter receptors, and the effect of cholesterol on drug interactions with the cell membrane.

Function and Structure of the Neuronal Plasma Membrane

The neuronal plasma membrane is a highly specialized structure that regulates and maintains the internal milieu of the cell. The plasma membrane lipid bilayer provides a complex, amphipathic (both hydrophilic and hydrophobic) chemical environment for protein molecules that mediate cell function. Some membrane proteins serve as receptors to which ligands such as neurotransmitters bind to initiate their effects on the cell.

We thank Dr. Barbara Good for assistance in writing this chapter.

Certain protein receptors modulate the flow of ions such as potassium and calcium into and out of the cell, and other protein receptors are involved in signal transduction, promoting the synthesis of second messengers such as cyclic adenosine 5'-monophosphate (cAMP), which diffuse within the cytoplasm to target receptors that modulate specific cellular functions. Proteins in the plasma membrane also interact with cytoskeletal fibers within the cell and components of the extracellular matrix, to maintain the shape of the cell.

Despite variations in membrane lipid content, the basic structural unit of all cell plasma membranes is the lipid bilayer. Analogous to a liquid-crystalline display in which molecules are aligned by an electric field, the lipid molecules that constitute the membrane (phospholipids and unesterified cholesterol) are oriented in a bilayer because of their amphipathic chemical properties. Hydrophilic headgroups of the phospholipid molecules are in contact with the water phase at the two surfaces of the membrane, whereas the hydrophobic acyl chains point toward the center of the membrane and interact with neighboring acyl chains. Cholesterol is a critical and major constituent of all plasma membranes, as detailed below.

The structure and molecular dynamics of the membrane lipid bilayer have been extensively examined by various biophysical techniques, including nuclear magnetic resonance spectroscopy and small-angle X-ray diffraction. These approaches have demonstrated that varying the concentration of cholesterol in the cell membrane has significant effects on the basic architecture and organization of the lipid bilayer. The cholesterol molecule is a highly planar steroid and is oriented in the bilayer so that the long axis of the steroid nucleus is parallel to the phospholipid acyl chains (Franks, 1976; Huang, 1977), as shown in Figure 1. The lipophilic cholesterol molecule reduces the rotational and diffusional dynamics of neighboring phospholipid acyl chains (Stockton & Smith, 1976; Yeagle, 1991); that is, it stiffens them. This modulation of membrane lipids by cholesterol can either increase or decrease membrane width, depending on length and extent of hydrogenation of the phospholipid acyl chains (Mason, Moisey, & Shajenko, 1992; McIntosh, 1978). For example, X-ray diffraction analysis has shown that the molecular structure of neural membranes from human brain tissue is highly dependent on cholesterol content and is altered as a function of degenerative disease (Mason, Shoemaker, Shajenko, Chambers, & Herbette, 1992).

Role of the Synaptic Junction in Neuron–Other Cell Communication

Neurons communicate with other cells, including other neurons, muscle cells, and gland cells, primarily at molecular junctions called synapses. Synaptic signaling between neurons and other cells involves chemical neurotransmitters, which are stored in small, membrane-bound vesicles in the axon terminal of the presynaptic cell. The release of neurotransmitters is

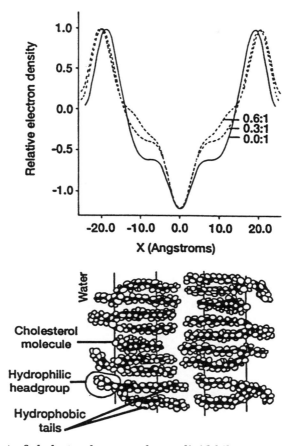

Figure 1. Effect of cholesterol on membrane lipid bilayer structure. The upper part of the figure displays electron density profiles generated from X-ray diffraction data, which demonstrate a strong, concentration-dependent effect on membrane structure. The profiles (electron density vs. distance across the membrane bilayer) are superimposed for samples prepared in the absence of cholesterol and the presence of cholesterol at 0.3:1 and 0.6:1 cholesterol:phospholipid mole ratios. The two maxima of electron density near the edges of the profile correspond to the electron-dense phosphate headgroups, and the electron-density minimum at the center of the profile corresponds to the membrane bilayer center. The profiles were placed on the same scale to match the peaks of electron density with the electron-density minima. The lower part of the figure portrays the cartoon of a space-filled phospholipid–cholesterol membrane bilayer corresponding to the electron-density profiles. The long axis of the cholesterol molecule is aligned parallel to the phospholipid acyl chains. Successive addition of cholesterol to the membrane produced a broad increase in electron density within the hydrocarbon core, in a region approximately 11 Å in width, about the length of cholesterol's steroid nucleus. There also was outward displacement of the phosphate headgroups by cholesterol. From "Cholesterol Alters the Binding of Ca^{+2} Channel Blockers to the Membrane Lipid Bilayer," by R. P. Mason et al., 1992, *Molecular Pharmacology, 41*, p. 317. Copyright 1992 by American Society for Pharmacology and Experimental Therapeutics. Reprinted with permission.

initiated by the arrival of an action potential at the axon terminal, which results in an increase in cytosolic calcium concentration that triggers exocytosis of the synaptic vesicles and the release of transmitters from the presynaptic membrane. The chemical transmitter then diffuses rapidly across the synaptic cleft to the postsynaptic cell membrane, where it binds to specific receptors. As mentioned above, the binding of neurotransmitters such as serotonin, norepinephrine, and acetylcholine to specific membrane-bound protein receptors either effects a change in the permeability of the postsynaptic membrane to ions such as potassium and calcium or triggers the second-messenger cascade.

Chemical synapses may be either excitatory or inhibitory, depending on their effect on postsynaptic membrane polarization. If the presynaptic neurotransmitter release causes a localized change in ion transport in the postsynaptic membrane that results in depolarization, the synapse is considered to be excitatory. Glutamate is the major excitatory neurotransmitter in the central nervous system. Conversely, a change in ion permeability that reduces the propagation of an action potential in the postsynaptic cell is considered an inhibitory synapse, the result of hyperpolarization of the postsynaptic membrane. The derivative of glutamate, γ-aminobutyric acid (GABA), is a major inhibitory amino acid in the CNS.

Many neurotransmitter receptors are coupled to membrane-bound signal transduction proteins known as G proteins, so named because of their ability to bind guanosine diphosphate and triphosphate. In some cases, G proteins modulate ion channel activity; in other cases, they activate adenylate cyclase or phospholipase C, an early event in the cascade of intracellular regulatory processes. The interaction of neurotransmitter receptors with G proteins occurs in the synaptic membrane lipid bilayer. Changes in brain synaptic membrane lipid composition, especially cholesterol content, have been associated with perturbations in both membrane lipid bilayer structure and G protein activity as a function of aging in rats (Kelly et al., 1995). These findings support the hypothesis that fundamental changes in membrane structure effected by cholesterol may contribute to alterations in signal transduction in the brain.

In addition to operating through a G-protein mechanism for ion channel activation in the postsynaptic membrane, some neurotransmitter receptors are themselves ligand-dependent ion channels. Binding of the neurotransmitter to its receptor induces a direct conformational change in the protein that permits the transmembrane flux of certain ions into the cell. Ligand-dependent ion channels include the excitatory nicotinic acetylcholine receptor, which serves as a channel for sodium and potassium ions, and the receptors for the inhibitory neurotransmitters GABA and glycine, which act as channels for chloride ions. The structure of ligand-dependent ion channels includes multiple transmembrane α-helices that span the hydrocarbon core of the membrane lipid bilayer. Here, too, alterations in the three-dimensional architecture of the synaptic plasma membrane, as a result of lipid composition changes, including cholesterol content, may have significant effects on both neurotransmitter ligand affinity and conductance properties of these ion channels. For example, membrane-bound

cholesterol is necessary for maintaining the function of the nicotinic cholinergic receptor (Fong & McNamee, 1987).

Cholesterol: A Key Component of the Plasma Membrane

Cholesterol is an abundant lipid component of all plasma membranes (Mason, Shoemaker, et al., 1992; Svennerholm, Bostrom, Helander, & Jungbjer, 1991). The concentration of cholesterol in the membrane, expressed
as the free cholesterol:phospholipid mole ratio, varies between 0.4–0.6:1.
Cholesterol concentration correlates directly with membrane viscosity and
is influenced by cholesterol content of the extracellular environment, including serum cholesterol. Cholesterol-feeding studies in rabbits have
demonstrated a strong, direct relationship between serum cholesterol levels and the ratio of cholesterol to phospholipid in arterial smooth muscle
cells (Chen, Mason, & Tulenko, 1995). The elevated membrane cholesterol
produced marked changes in the basic structure and organization of the
membrane lipid bilayer, as assessed directly by small-angle X-ray diffraction, including an increase in membrane bilayer width. After prolonged
cholesterol feeding, there was evidence for an immiscible microdomain of
cholesterol in the isolated arterial smooth muscle plasma membrane, associated with an elevated membrane cholesterol content (>0.9:1 choles-
terol:phospholipid mole ratio). In cell-culture experiments, the plasma
membrane free cholesterol:phospholipid mole ratio can be reproducibly
modified with cholesterol-enriched liposomes (Gleason, Medow, & Tulenko,
1991; Kutryk & Pierce, 1988; Phillips, Johnson, & Rothblat, 1987). Cholesterol is rapidly transferred, in a concentration-dependent manner, from
high-cholesterol-containing liposomes to the cell plasma membrane, and
in the opposite direction when the concentration gradient is reversed.

The presentation of cholesterol to cells in the body, including neural
tissue, occurs through binding of cholesterol-carrying low density lipoprotein (LDL) to receptors on the cell plasma membrane. The lowering of
extracellular cholesterol increases cell-surface LDL receptor number,
which leads to increased transport of cholesterol into cells, where it is
redistributed between cell and nuclear membranes, stored as cholesteryl
ester, or exported from the cell (Brown & Goldstein, 1986). Low density
lipoprotein receptors are expressed on neural cells throughout the CNS
(Hoffman, Russell, Goldstein, & Brown, 1987; Pitas, Boyles, Lee, Hui, &
Weisgraber, 1987; Swanson, Simmons, Hoffmann, Goldstein, & Brown,
1988), suggesting that LDL has an important role in CNS cholesterol metabolism. However, the relationship between serum cholesterol and neural
plasma membrane cholesterol content has not yet been established.

Changes in Neuronal Membrane Cholesterol Content Alter
Neurotransmitter Activity

Alterations in neuronal plasma membrane cholesterol content have been
shown to modulate the activity of neurotransmitter receptors. Both in-

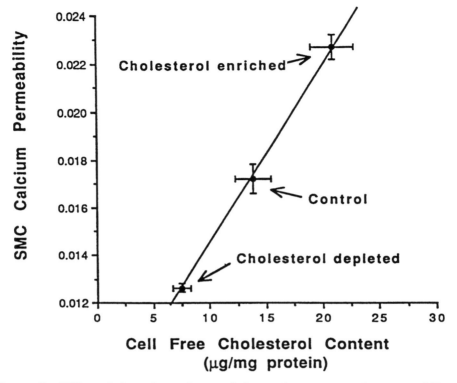

Figure 2.   Effect of altered membrane cholesterol content on the permeability of smooth muscle cells (SMC) to calcium. In these experiments, the cholesterol content of cultured arterial smooth muscle cells was modulated with liposomes. There was a strong, direct relationship between membrane cholesterol content and membrane calcium permeability, indicating that both increases and decreases in cell cholesterol content can alter calcium homeostasis in a peripheral cell. (R = .951, p <.001, n = 6–9).

creases and decreases in mouse brain synaptosomal membrane cholesterol content produce pronounced changes in the binding of endogenous and exogenous ligands to adrenergic, serotonergic, and opiate receptors (Heron, Hershkowitz, Shinitzky, & Samuel, 1980; Heron, Shinitzky, Hershkowitz, & Samuel, 1980; Hershkowitz, Heron, Samuel, & Shinitzky, 1982). The authors of these studies suggest that changes in membrane cholesterol content alter the tertiary conformation of membrane proteins, rendering the specific receptor site more or less exposed to the ligand, depending on the cholesterol content. Alterations in the activity of membrane-bound receptors and ion channels in response to changes in cholesterol content also occur in smooth muscle cells under autonomic nervous system control (Gleason et al., 1991), as shown in Figure 2.

Of particular interest is the effect of cholesterol on the activity of the serotonin receptor, an important receptor in human behavior. Increased serotonergic receptor-mediated calcium uptake and cell function in vascular smooth muscle result from dietary-induced hypercholesterolemia in rabbits (Stepp & Tulenko, 1994). There are many serotonergic terminal field areas in the limbic system, a major area of the brain involved in the modulation of emotion. The serotonin receptor is important for the pharmacological treatment of several psychiatric disorders, including major depression, anxiety disorders, and some psychotic conditions. The ability of cholesterol to modulate serotonin receptor activity therefore may underlie its role in affecting certain psychiatric symptoms and altered behaviors, as discussed in other chapters in this volume.

A recent study (Chang, Reitstetter, Mason, & Gruener, 1995) that used electrophysiology and X-ray diffraction approaches has provided further insight into the biophysical mechanism by which cholesterol modulates the function of membrane-bound proteins in the brain, specifically calcium-activated potassium channels, important ion channels in the depolarization of neuronal plasma membranes. These ion channels were isolated from rat brain homogenates and were reconstituted into planar lipid bilayers of varying cholesterol content. Under these controlled conditions, the conductance properties of the channels could be monitored as a function of cholesterol content. Increasing the cholesterol content resulted in a reduction in both channel mean open time and the probability that the channel was open. Identical lipid bilayer preparations were subjected to small-angle X-ray diffraction analysis, which showed that the increase in cholesterol altered the basic structure of the membrane, including the width of the membrane bilayer and organization of the lipid molecules.

Chang et al. (1995) suggested that these data are in keeping with a model in which cholesterol affects the activity of an integral membrane protein by increasing structural stress (lateral resistance) in the membrane lipid bilayer, favoring the transition from an open to a closed state of the ion channel, independent of direct interactions of cholesterol with the channel. Thus, modulation of the biophysical properties of the membrane by cholesterol appears to represent an important mechanism for regulating the activity of plasma-membrane-bound proteins and neuronal membrane function.

Cholesterol Modulates the Interactions of Drugs That Target Membrane Receptors

By modifying the biophysical properties of the membrane lipid bilayer, cholesterol may alter the interactions of certain lipophilic drugs that target receptors in the cell plasma membrane (Mason, Moisey, & Shajenko, 1992). A two-step molecular pathway for receptor binding has been proposed for 1,4-dihydropyridine calcium-channel blockers, a class of drugs, represented by nifedipine and amlodipine, that is widely used to treat hypertension and angina and is being developed for the treatment of certain neurodegenerative diseases. This membrane pathway, as described by Rhodes, Sarmiento, and Herbette (1985), involves the partitioning of a drug to an energetically favorable site in the membrane, followed by diffusion to an intrabilayer receptor site on the voltage-sensitive calcium

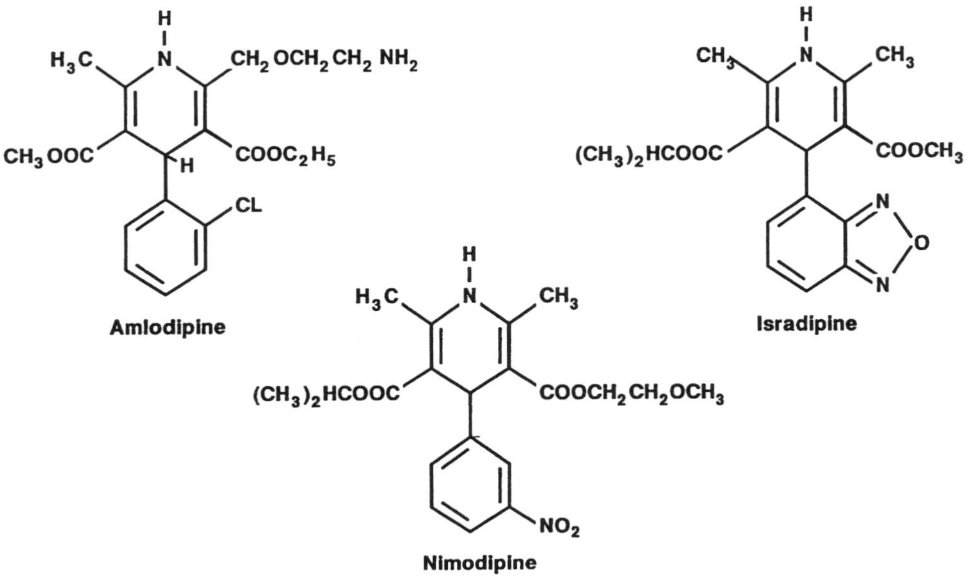

Figure 3. Chemical structure of three 1,4-dihydropyridine calcium channel antagonists, amlodipine, nimodipine, and isradipine.

channel. Subsequent studies have provided experimental support for this receptor-binding mechanism involving the L-type calcium channel (Baindur, Rutledge, & Triggle, 1993; Chester et al., 1987; Herbette, Chester, & Rhodes, 1986; Herbette, Vant Erve, & Rhodes, 1989; Kass & Arena; 1989; Mason, Campbell, Wang, & Herbette, 1989). Changes in the structure and composition of the membrane may alter this drug-binding pathway by modulating the partitioning of the drug into the membrane or rates of lateral diffusion to its receptor site.

We explored the effect of cholesterol content on membrane interactions of the 1,4-dihydropyridine calcium channel blockers amlodipine, nimodipine, and isradipine (structures shown in Figure 3), using liposomes composed of synthetic and native phospholipids (Mason, Moisey, & Shajenko, 1992). There was a highly significant, inverse relationship between membrane cholesterol content and the equilibrium partition coefficients of all three compounds, as shown in Figure 4. A similar effect of cholesterol on membrane binding of these compounds was observed with membranes from various tissues, including brain and skeletal muscle. These data indicate that the concentration of these drugs in the membrane and in equilibrium with an intrabilayer receptor site is highly influenced by the ratio of cholesterol to phospholipid in the plasma membrane. This effect of membrane cholesterol content on drug partition coefficients was reproduced with the glutamate transmitter antagonist, MK-801 (Moring, Niego, Ganley, Trumbore, & Herbette, 1994).

Molecular models of the membrane provide a rationale for the ability of cholesterol to inhibit the nonspecific binding of certain drugs to the membrane. The large steroid nucleus of cholesterol reduces the molecular

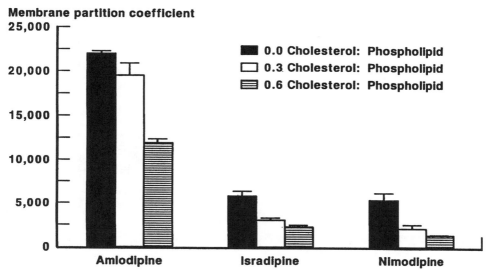

Figure 4. Effect of membrane cholesterol content on nonspecific binding of calcium channel blockers. There was a strong, inverse relationship between membrane cholesterol content and the equilibrium partition coefficients of three 1,4-dihydropyridine calcium channel blockers to liposomes. In these experiments, drug concentration was maintained at 5×10^{-10} M, and phospholipid concentration was 20 μg/ml (pH 7.0, 21 °C). Each value represents the mean standard error of 12 determinations. From "Cholesterol Alters the Binding of Ca^{+2} Channel Blockers to the Membrane Lipid Bilayer," by R. P. Mason et al., 1992, *Molecular Pharmacology, 41*, 315–321. Copyright 1992 by American Society for Pharmacology and Experimental Therapeutics. Adapted with permission.

volume available for drug partitioning over a broad region of the membrane hydrocarbon core adjacent to the phospholipid headgroups. Indeed, studies indicate that the equilibrium location for 1,4-dihydropyridine calcium channel blockers is in a region of the membrane that overlaps the steroid nucleus of cholesterol, as diagramed in Figure 5 (Mason et al., 1989; Mason, Moisey, & Shajenko, 1992). The observation that cholesterol can significantly attenuate the binding of lipophilic calcium channel blockers to the cell membrane may have important pharmacological implications for the treatment of individuals with elevated serum cholesterol. Under pathophysiological conditions in which membrane cholesterol is elevated, such as hypercholesterolemia, concentrations of drugs in the membrane available for receptor binding may be significantly reduced. Conversely, profound reduction of serum cholesterol, as with cholesterol-lowering drugs, may have the opposite effect, perhaps resulting in toxic sequelae.

Conclusion

Free cholesterol is a major constituent of the neuronal plasma membrane and serves to maintain a vital physicochemical environment for

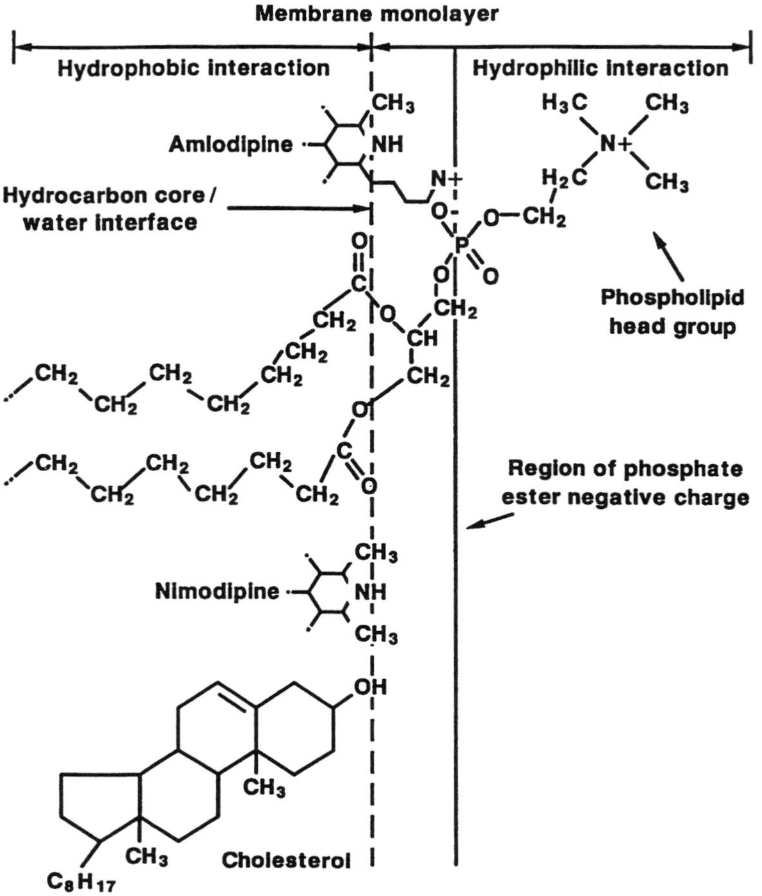

Figure 5. Molecular model of possible cholesterol–phospholipid and drug–phospholipid interactions. This model is based on the results of small-angle X-ray diffraction experiments, which indicate that cholesterol shares an equilibrium location in the membrane that overlaps these lipophilic drug molecules, although the cholesterol molecule is considerably larger. By decreasing the available volume in the membrane, cholesterol reduces the equilibrium binding of calcium channel blockers, as indicated in Figure 2. From "Cholesterol Alters the Binding of Ca^{+2} Channel Blockers to the Membrane Lipid Bilayer," by R. P. Mason et al., 1992, *Molecular Pharmacology*, *41*, 315–321. Copyright 1992 by American Society for Pharmacology and Experimental Therapeutics. Reprinted with permission.

membrane-bound proteins, including neurotransmitter receptors involved in synaptic transmission. Of particular interest is the observation that changes in neuronal membrane cholesterol content have a significant effect on the binding of the neurotransmitter serotonin to its receptor. Such alterations in serotonin neurotransmission may contribute to certain psychiatric symptoms and altered behavior, as reviewed in other chapters of this volume. Manipulation of membrane cholesterol content also has dramatic effects on the activity of lipophilic drugs, such as voltage-sensitive calcium channel blockers, which appear to target receptor binding sites embedded in the membrane lipid bilayer. Collectively, these studies point to an important role for cholesterol in neuropsychopharmacology.

References

Baindur, N., Rutledge, A., & Triggle, D. J. (1993). A homologous series of permanently charged 1,4-dihydropyridines: Novel probes designed to localize drug binding sites on ion channels. *Journal of Medicinal Chemistry, 36,* 3743–3745.

Brown, M. S., & Goldstein, J. L. (1986). A receptor-mediated pathway for cholesterol homeostasis. *Science, 232,* 34–47.

Chang, H. M., Reitstetter, R., Mason, R. P., & Gruener, R. (1995). Attenuation of channel kinetics and conductance by cholesterol: An interpretation using structural stress as a unifying concept. *Journal of Membrane Biology, 143,* 51–63.

Chen, M., Mason, R. P., & Tulenko, T. N. (1995). Atherosclerosis alters composition, structure and function of arterial smooth muscle plasma membranes. *Biochimica et Biophysica Acta, 1272,* 101–112.

Chester, D. W., Herbette, L. G., Mason, R. P., Joslyn, A. F., Triggle, D. J., & Koppel, D.E. (1987). Diffusion of dihydropyridine calcium channel antagonists in cardiac sarcolemmal lipid multibilayers. *Biophysics Journal, 52,* 1021–1030.

Fong, T. M., & McNamee, M. G. (1987). Stabilization of acetylcholine receptor secondary structure by cholesterol and negatively charged lipids. *Biochemistry, 26,* 3871–3880.

Franks, N. P. (1976). Structural analysis of hydrated egg lecithin and cholesterol bilayers. *Journal of Molecular Biology, 100,* 345–358.

Gleason, M. M., Medow, M. S., & Tulenko, T. N. (1991). Excess membrane cholesterol alters calcium movements, cytosolic calcium levels and membrane fluidity in arterial smooth muscle cells. *Circulatory Research, 69,* 216–227.

Herbette, L. G., Chester, D. W., & Rhodes, D. G. (1986). Structural analysis of drug molecules in biological membranes. *Biophysical Journal, 49,* 91–94.

Herbette, L. G., Vant Erve, Y. M. H., & Rhodes, D. G. (1989). Interaction of 1,4-dihydropyridine calcium channel antagonists with biological membranes: Lipid bilayer partitioning could occur before drug binding to receptors. *Journal of Molecular and Cellular Cardiology, 21,* 187–201.

Heron, D. S., Hershkowitz, M., Shinitzky, M., & Samuel, D. (1980). The lipid fluidity of synaptic membranes and the binding of serotonin and opiate ligands. In U. Z. Littauer, Y. Dudai, I. Silman, V. I. Teichberg, & Z. Vogel (Eds.), *Neurotransmitters and their receptors* (pp. 125–138). New York: Wiley.

Heron, D. S., Shinitzky, M., Hershkowitz, M., & Samuel, D. (1980). Lipid fluidity markedly modulates the binding of serotonin to brain membranes. *Proceedings of the National Academy of Sciences, USA, 77,* 7463–7467.

Hershkowitz, M. D., Heron, D., Samuel, D., & Shinitzky, M. (1982). The modulation of protein phosphorylation and receptor binding in synaptic membranes by changes in lipid fluidity: Implications for aging. *Progress in Brain Research, 56,* 419–434.

Hoffman, S. L., Russell, D. W., Goldstein, J. L., & Brown, M. S. (1987). mRNA for low density lipoprotein receptor in brain and spinal cord of immature and mature rabbits. *Proceedings of the National Academy of Sciences, USA, 84,* 6312–6316.

Huang, C. (1977). A structural model for the cholesterol–phosphatidycholine complexes in bilayer membranes. *Lipids, 12,* 348–356.

Kass, R. S., & Arena, J. P. (1989). Influences of pH on calcium channel block by amlodipine, a charged dihydropyridine compound: Implications for location of the dihydropyridine receptor. *Journal of General Physiology, 93,* 1109–1127.

Kelly, J. F., Mason, R. P., Denisova, N. A., Joseph, J. A., Erat, S., & Roth, G. S. (1995). Age-related impairment in striatal muscarinic cholinergic signal transduction is associated with reduced membrane bilayer width measured by small angle X-ray diffraction. *Biochemical Biophysical Research Communications, 213,* 869–874.

Kutryk, M. J. B., & Pierce, G. N. (1988). Stimulation of sodium–calcium exchange by cholesterol incorporation into isolated cardiac sarcolemmal vesicles. *Journal of Biological Chemistry, 263*, 13167–13172.

Mason, R. P., Campbell, S., Wang, S., & Herbette, L. G. (1989). A comparison of bilayer location and binding for the charged 1,4-dihydropyridine calcium channel antagonist amlodipine with uncharged drugs of this class in cardiac and model membranes. *Molecular Pharmacology, 36*, 634–640.

Mason, R. P., Moisey, D. M., & Shajenko, L. (1992). Cholesterol alters the binding of Ca^{+2} channel blockers to the membrane lipid bilayer. *Molecular Pharmacology, 41*, 315–321.

Mason, R. P., Shoemaker, W. J., Shajenko, L., Chambers, T. E., & Herbette, L. G. (1992). Structure changes in Alzheimer's disease brain membranes mediated by alteration in cholesterol. *Neurobiology of Aging, 13*, 413–419.

McIntosh, T. J. (1978). The effect of cholesterol on the structure of phosphatidylcholine bilayers. *Biochimica Biophysica Acta, 513*, 43–58.

Moring, J., Niego, L. A., Ganley, L. M., Trumbore, M. W., & Herbette, L. G. (1994). Interaction of the NMDA receptor noncompetitive antagonist MK-801 with model and native membranes. *Biophysical Journal, 67*, 2376–2386.

Phillips, M. C., Johnson, W. J., & Rothblat, G. H. (1987). Mechanisms and consequences of cellular cholesterol exchange and transfer. *Biochimica et Biophysica Acta, 906*, 223–276.

Pitas, R. E., Boyles, J. K., Lee, S. H., Hui, D., & Weisgraber, K. H. (1987). Lipoproteins and their receptors in the central nervous system: Characterization of the lipoproteins in cerebrospinal fluid and identification of apolipoprotein B,E(LDL) receptors in the brain. *Journal of Biological Chemistry, 262*, 14352–14360.

Rhodes, D. G., Sarmiento, J. G., & Herbette, L. G. (1985). Kinetics of binding of membrane-active drugs to receptor sites: Diffusion-limited rates for a membrane bilayer approach of 1,4-dihydropyridine calcium channel antagonists to their active site. *Molecular Pharmacology, 27*, 612–623.

Stepp, D. S., & Tulenko, T. N. (1994). Alterations in basal and serotonin-stimulated Ca^{+2} movements and vasoconstriction in atherosclerotic aorta. *Arteriosclerosis and Thrombosis, 14*, 1854–1859.

Stockton, G. W., & Smith, I. C. P. (1976). A deuterium nuclear magnetic resonance study of the condensing effect of cholesterol on egg phosphatidylcholine bilayer membranes: I. Perdeuterated fatty acid probes. *Chemistry and Physics of Lipids, 17*, 251–263.

Svennerholm, L., Bostrom, K., Helander, C. G., & Jungbjer, B. (1991). Membrane lipids in the aging of human brain. *Journal of Neurochemistry, 56*, 2051–2059.

Swanson, L. W., Simmons, D. M., Hofmann, S. L., Goldstein, J. L., & Brown, M. S. (1988). Localization of mRNA for low density lipoprotein receptor and a cholesterol synthetic enzyme in rabbit nervous system by in situ hybridization. *Proceedings of the National Academy of Sciences, USA, 85*, 9821–9825.

Yeagle, P. (1987). Cholesterol and cell membranes. In *The membranes of cells* (pp. 120–138). New York: Academic Press.

Yeagle, P. L. (1991). Modulation of membrane function by cholesterol. *Biochimie, 73*, 1303–1310.

9

The Cholesterol–Serotonin Hypothesis: Interrelationships Among Dietary Lipids, Central Serotonergic Activity, and Social Behavior in Monkeys

*Jay R. Kaplan, Stephen B. Manuck,
M. Babette Fontenot, Matthew F. Muldoon,
Carol A. Shively, and J. John Mann*

The National Cholesterol Education Program and other health advocacy groups advise all Americans to restrict their dietary intake of saturated fat and cholesterol as an efficacious and safe way to lower plasma cholesterol concentrations and thus reduce the risk of cardiovascular disease (CVD) (Report of the Expert Panel on Population Strategies for Blood Cholesterol Reduction, 1991; National Cholesterol Education Program Expert Panel, 1988, 1993). However, accumulating evidence suggests that low or lowered cholesterol may be associated with increased non-illness-related mortality (principally suicide and accidents), possibly mediated by adverse changes in behavior and mood (Hulley, Walsh, & Newman, 1992; Lindberg, Rästam, Gullberg, & Eklund, 1992; Morgan, Palinkas, Barrett-Connor, & Wingard, 1993; Muldoon, Manuck, & Matthews, 1990; Virkkunen, 1983). This evidence provided the rationale for an ongoing series of studies in monkeys, designed to explore the hypothesis that alterations in dietary or plasma cholesterol influence behavior and that such effects are mediated by lipid-induced changes in brain chemistry. After a brief presentation of relevant background material, we review the data derived from investigations using monkeys and discuss the public health implications and possible biological and evolutionary significance of the findings.

Background

Population surveys show that naturally occurring low cholesterol concentrations (i.e., below 160–180 mg/dl) are associated with excessive noncardiovascular, noncancer mortality, including mortality due to violence and

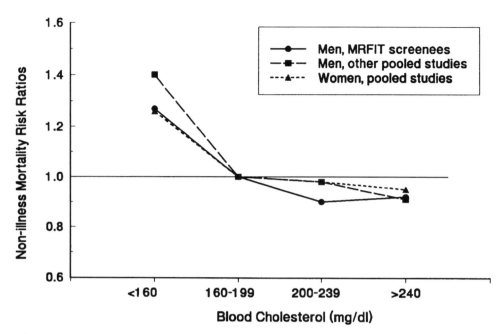

Figure 1. Total cholesterol and age-adjusted mortality rates for 351,000 men originally free of heart disease. CVD = cardiovascular disease. From "Report of the Conference on Low Blood Cholesterol: Mortality associations," by D. Jacobs et al., 1992, *Circulation*, *86*, p. 1053. Copyright 1992 by American Heart Association. Adapted with permission.

injury (Jacobs et al., 1992; Muldoon & Manuck, 1992; Muldoon et al., 1993). One particularly striking example of this phenomenon concerns the age-adjusted death rates during the 12-year follow-up of 351,000 initially healthy men screened for the Multiple Risk Factor Intervention Trial (Jacobs et al., 1992; Neaton et al., 1992). Here, total mortality assumed a U-shaped curve in relation to total cholesterol (TC). That is, increased cardiovascular mortality was associated with higher TC concentrations, whereas low TC was associated with elevations in noncardiovascular mortality (see Figure 1). In this report, deaths from suicide, in particular, rose with lower cholesterol concentrations (Jacobs et al., 1992; Neaton et al., 1992). A relationship between low cholesterol and increased risk of non-illness-related death (especially suicide) was found also in a Swedish cohort of 27,000 men during the first 7 years of follow-up. In contrast, there was no relationship between any type of non-illness-related death and low cholesterol among the 28,000 women in this study (Lindberg et al., 1992).

There was also an association between cholesterol lowering and violence-related mortality in clinical trials involving individuals initially free of CVD (i.e., primary prevention trials). Each of six primary prevention trials provided evidence of a small number of excess deaths from suicide and violence among treated participants. Meta-analysis aggregating across six randomized primary prevention trials, involving either dietary or drug interventions for hypercholesterolemia and encompassing 119,000 person-years of follow-up, revealed a highly significant, 70% increase in mortality due to accidents, violence, and trauma among treated individuals (Muldoon et al., 1990). The increase in non-illness-related deaths offset the benefits of CVD prevention; as a result, total mortality was numerically (though not significantly) greater in the intervention group. Only a recently completed primary prevention trial using pravastatin has not observed any increase in suicide and accidental deaths (Shepherd et al., 1995). However, non-illness-related mortality in the placebo and treatment arms of this study were less than half that of previous primary prevention trials, indicating that the trial enrolled participants at very low risk for non-illness-related mortality.

In addition to the mortality data, there exists a generally unrecognized literature linking low serum cholesterol concentrations to psychiatric and behavioral manifestations of negative affect, violence, and impulsivity. For example, a study assessing CVD risk factors and mood in a cohort of 1,020 White men age 50–89 years reported that Beck Depression Inventory scores correlated significantly and inversely with plasma cholesterol concentrations in men over 70 years old, even after adjustment for age and health status (Morgan et al., 1993).[1] Another study of almost 300 participants found that individuals with an antisocial personality (sociopathy or psychopathy) had significantly lower serum cholesterol concentrations than either a control group characterized by other personality disorders or the mean of a large male population from the same location (Virkkunen, 1979). The same investigator reported lower cholesterol concentrations in antisocial or homicidal offenders with personality disorders who were habitually violent under the influence of alcohol (Virkkunen, 1983). A similar relationship between violence or aggressive conduct disorder and low cholesterol concentrations occurred in a sample of young people with an attention deficit disorder (Virkkunen & Penttinen, 1984). Low serum cholesterol concentrations have been observed also in at least six other subgroups: (a) nonpatients characterized by high impulsivity and poorly internalized social norms (Jenkins, Hames, Zyzanski, Rosenman, & Friedman, 1969); (b) prisoners (Hatch et al., 1966); (c) regressed, withdrawn, and depressed patients (Sletten, Nilsen, Young, & Anderson, 1964); (d) patients hospitalized for violence (Hillbrand, Spitz, & Foster, 1995); (e) people with affective disorder (Kruesi & Rapoport, 1986); and (f) serious suicide attempters (Golier, Marzuk, Leon, Weiner, & Tardiff, 1995). Furthermore, among 174 male patients undergoing coronary angiography, those taking lipid-lowering medications reported more depression than men not taking such treatment (Kettere, Brymer, Rhoads, Kraft, & Goldberg, 1994). Most recently, an evaluation of a random sample of 3,490 men who served in the U.S. Army from 1965 to 1971 indicated that TC was 7

---

[1]The association between hypocholesterolemia and depression does not conflict with evidence that depression is a risk factor for CVD, because the latter relationship is independent of cholesterol concentration. However, among 174 male patients undergoing coronary angiography, those taking lipid-lowering medications reported more depression than men not taking such treatment (Ketterer et al., 1994).

mg/dl lower among men with antisocial personality disorder than among other men in this sample (Freedman et al., 1995).

The foregoing studies suggest that naturally low or clinically reduced serum cholesterol concentrations might increase mortality by elevating the probability of engaging in impulsive, antagonistic, risky, or self-destructive behavior. The biologic mechanism mediating any such effect of cholesterol on behavior and, ultimately, mortality remains undiscovered. However, a number of investigators have speculated that dietary fats or cholesterol might directly influence brain lipids, with subsequent effects on neurotransmitters or their membrane-bound receptors (Engleberg, 1992; Mason, Herbette, & Silverman, 1991; Oliver, 1991; Young, 1993). It is known, for example, that the cholesterol content of surrounding plasma affects the membrane cholesterol to phospholipid mole ratio (a determinant of membrane fluidity and, thus, function) both in vitro (according to a study done on monkeys) and in vivo (according to a study done on rats; McMurchie & Patten, 1988; McMurchie, Patten, Charnock, & McLennan, 1987). Among the neurotransmitters particularly affected by cholesterol may be serotonin, the binding of which can be increased or decreased in vitro by the addition or removal of cholesterol from brain synaptic membranes (Heron, Shinitzky, Hershkowitz, & Samuel, 1980). Brain serotonergic activity also may be reduced after dieting, an effect mediated by low levels of plasma tryptophan (Anderson, Parry-Billings, Newsholme, Fairburn, & Cowen, 1990). In turn, reduced central nervous system (CNS) serotonergic activity characterizes violent offenders and people attempting suicide (Brown et al., 1982; Roy, DeJong, & Linnoila, 1989; Virkkunen, DeJong, Bartko, Goodwin, & Linnoila, 1989; Virkkunen, DeJong, Bartko, & Linnoila, 1989). Furthermore, indices of CNS serotonin correlate negatively with ratings of aggressive behavior, irritability, and hostility (Brown, Goodwin, Ballenger, Goyer, & Major, 1979; Coccaro, 1989; Kruesi et al., 1990; Roy, Adinoff, & Linnoila, 1988).

The Cholesterol–Serotonin Hypothesis

Taken together, the studies cited in the previous section provide a foundation for the hypothesis that low or lowered plasma cholesterol predisposes to violent death and that such a relationship is mediated by alterations in central serotonergic activity. This latter suggestion could be termed the *cholesterol–serotonin hypothesis*, which presumes three associations: (a) an inverse relationship between plasma cholesterol and violent or otherwise negative behavior, (b) a positive association between plasma or dietary cholesterol and central serotonergic activity, and (c) a link between reduced central serotonergic activity and increased violence or aggression. Practical and ethical considerations constrain systematic testing of this hypothesis in human beings. However, a series of studies involving cynomolgus macaques has provided data illustrating the existence of all three of the presumed associations, thus supporting the cholesterol–serotonin hypothesis. These data are reviewed in the following sections.

Cholesterol and Behavior

If there were a causal association between low serum cholesterol concentrations and mortality due to accident, suicide, and violence, it might be expected that consumption of a low-cholesterol diet would be accompanied by behavioral changes entailing, for example, increased aggressiveness, reduced sociality, or both. A number of investigations in our laboratory provide results relevant to testing the hypothesis that social patterns, particularly those involving violent or aggressive acts, are affected by plasma cholesterol concentrations. Cynomolgus macaques (*Macaca fascicularis*; an Asian monkey about half the size of the closely related rhesus monkey) were used in all of these studies, which varied in design and data collection. Note that none of the investigations were originally designed to assess relationships between diet and behavior; rather, these studies were designed to investigate behavioral influences on coronary artery atherosclerosis or to assess the effect of dietary cholesterol on atherosclerosis. Three of these studies involved data collected from monkeys living in stable social units. In two other studies, animals were housed in groups of rotating social membership, a manipulation designed to induce social disruption, so that the relationship between stress and atherosclerosis could be investigated.[2]

Comparison 1. This investigation evaluated the social behavior and plasma lipids of 27 adult male monkeys fed diets either high or low in saturated fat and cholesterol for a period of 22 months (Kaplan, Manuck, & Shively, 1991). All animals lived in stable social groupings of 4 or 5 monkeys each. The animals were subjected to routine behavioral, as well as clinical (plasma lipid), observations while they were fed the experimental diets. There were no behavioral observations that preceded assignment of the animals to their experimental conditions. Animals in the high-fat condition consumed a diet containing approximately 43% of calories from fat and 0.34 mg cholesterol per kilocalorie, the latter equivalent to a human consumption of 680 mg cholesterol per day.[3] Animals in the low-fat condition were fed a diet approximating the American Heart Association recommendations of 30% of calories from fat and 0.05 mg cho-

---

[2]In cynomolgus monkeys, the instability induced by reorganization of membership across social groups is often accompanied by an acute increase in intensity of agonistic behavior, as animals attempt to reestablish their social relationships and hierarchies. This manipulation also is associated with an exacerbation of coronary artery atherosclerosis, particularly among animals that are habitually high ranking (see review in Kaplan, Manuck, Adams, Weingand, & Clarkson, 1987).

[3]Because the metabolic rate of monkeys is considerably higher than that of human beings (a 5-kg macaque will consume almost one third the calories of an 80-kg human being), dietary constituents were added on a caloric rather than weight basis. All human-equivalent cholesterol values were based on a 2,000-calorie-per-day diet.

Table 1. Total Plasma Cholesterol and Body Weight in Each Comparison

| Compari-son | n | Cholesterol | | | | | Weight | | | | |
| | | Low | | High | | | Low | | High | | |
		M	SEM	M	SEM	p	M	SEM	M	SEM	p
1	27	146	10	468	30	.0001	5.7	0.3	5.2	0.2	ns
2	23	182	34	690	168	.0001	6.2	0.2	5.6	0.2	.01
3	17	235	23	623	34	.0001	1.33	0.1	1.33	0.1	ns
4	39	176	30	355	80	.0001	5.8	0.2	6.4	0.3	.11
5	30	156	5	473	16	.0001	5.9	0.2	5.6	0.2	ns

Note: Cholesterol values are in milligrams per deciliter; weights are in kilograms. Low = the low fat and cholesterol condition; high = the high fat and cholesterol condition.

lesterol per kilocalorie (equivalent to a human consumption of 100 mg cholesterol per day). Animals in the two dietary conditions were treated identically in all other respects (e.g., housing, group composition, and handling procedures). Animals in this and all subsequent investigations were fed in their social groupings, with 100 g of diet provided for each monkey, twice per day.

The dietary manipulation had profound effects on plasma concentrations of TC. These data, representing the average of 20 determinations made over the course of the study, are summarized in Table 1. They demonstrate significant differences between the groups. Despite the difference in diet and resulting plasma lipids, there were no statistically significant differences in body weight between the animals in the different dietary conditions.

Social behavior was collected by a technique involving three 15-min focal samples (i.e., a procedure in which animals were observed sequentially for 15 min each, with behavior of the focal animal recorded in detail), per monkey per week (Altmann, 1974). The recorded behavioral events comprised those motor patterns displayed most frequently by cynomolgus monkeys living in small social groups and included episodes of attacking, fleeing, interacting positively (e.g., grooming or maintaining proximity), and being asocial (maintaining a significant distance from other monkeys). The behavioral data from the focal samples were averaged over the entire study and compared across dietary conditions. The difference was significant, although only with respect to a single category of behavior: Animals in the low-fat condition exhibited more aggression involving physical contact (the more extreme, unritualized forms of aggression) than did their counterparts in the high-fat condition, $\chi^2(20) = 11.7$, $p < 0.01$; see Figure 2. This effect was generalized across all three social groups in the low-fat condition, was independent of body weights, and was noted within the first 3 months of the dietary treatment. There were no other behavioral differences between diet conditions. The absence of a statistically significant difference in body weight between the two conditions suggests that the increased aggression of the monkeys in the low-fat condition could not be ascribed to hunger.

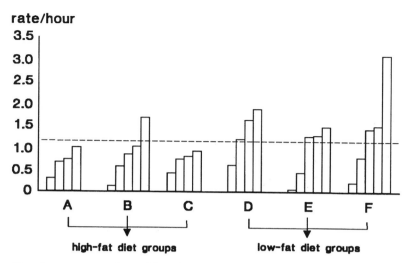

Figure 2. Average number of incidents of contact aggression initiated per hour by each monkey over the course of 22 months; each contiguous set of bars represents one social group. From "The Effects of Fat and Cholesterol on Social Behavior in Monkeys," by J. R. Kaplan et al., 1991, *Psychosomatic Medicine, 53,* p. 638. Copyright 1991 by the American Psychosomatic Society. Adapted with permission.

Comparison 2. A second investigation also involved adult male monkeys housed in social groups of 4 or 5 (Kaplan, Fontenot, Manuck, & Muldoon, 1996). It was the first to present within-subject data based on the social behavior of animals before and after a change from a high-fat diet to one low in fat and cholesterol. The animals described here were part of a larger study designed to evaluate the effects of diet and psychosocial stress on the regression of atherosclerotic lesions. The experiment was done in two phases. In Phase 1, all animals were first housed in stable social groups for 14 months, during which they consumed a diet very high in fat and cholesterol (45% calories from fat, 1.0 mg cholesterol/calorie, equivalent to human consumption of 2,000 mg/cholesterol per day), sufficient to induce the relatively rapid development of atherosclerotic lesions. The 23 animals described here then entered Phase 2, a period of 20 months, during which time they were maintained in stable groups and fed a diet relatively low in fat (30% of calories) and cholesterol (0.05 mg/calorie/day, equivalent to human consumption of 100 mg cholesterol per day).

The dietary manipulation resulted in a substantial reduction in TC concentrations between Phase 1 and Phase 2 (see Table 1). Again, there were no statistically significant differences in body weight between animals in the two conditions. We next compared the social behavior of these animals while they consumed the two diets. The recording of social behavior was somewhat different in this experiment than in Comparison 1. Here, specific behavioral episodes categorized as aggressive, submissive, affiliative, and nonsocial were recorded from each social group using all-occurrence and scan sampling (Altmann, 1974; Bernstein, 1991) rather

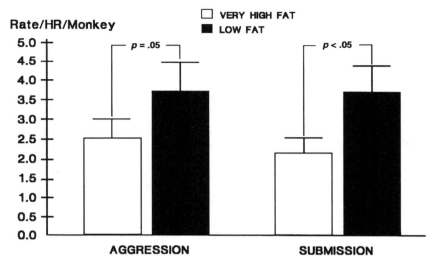

Figure 3.   Comparison of the monthly rates of aggression and submission among monkeys (n = 23) that all lived in stable social groups and first consumed a very high-fat diet (Phase 1) and then a low-fat diet (Phase 2). Error bars are ± standard errors of measurement. HR = heart rate. From "Influence of Dietary Lipids on Agonistic and Affiliative Behavior in *Macaca fascicularis*," by Kaplan et al., 1996, *American Journal of Primatology*, *38*, p. 341. Copyright 1996 by the American Society of Primatologists. Reprinted with permission.

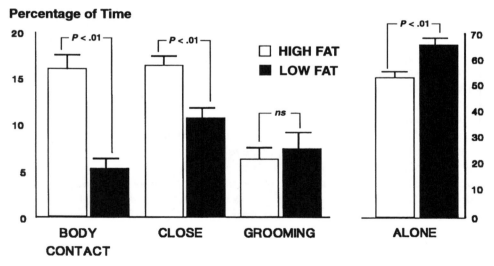

Figure 4.   Comparison of the percentage of time (± *SEM*) in which animals (n = 23) exhibited particular behavioral states. These monkeys lived in stable social groups and first consumed a very high fat diet (Phase 1) and then a low-fat diet (Phase 2). From "Influence of Dietary Lipids on Agonistic and Affiliative Behavior in *Macaca fascicularis*," by Kaplan et al., 1996, *American Journal of Primatology*, *38*, p. 342. Copyright 1996 by the American Society of Primatologists. Adapted with permission.

than focal sampling.[4] Each social group was subjected to three 30-minute all-occurrence and 10 instantaneous scan samples per week. For analysis, fights (attacks and flights) were considered to be actions that occurred nearly instantaneously and were derived from the all-occurrence samples as hourly rates per monkey. These values were then averaged over each phase of the experiment. Behavioral events that occurred over a period of time (e.g., grooming, passive body contact, and being alone [not within touching distance]) were derived from the scan samples as an average percentage of samples (i.e., percentage of time) in which that behavior occurred (Botchin, Kaplan, Manuck, & Mann, 1993; Kaplan et al., 1993). In addition to considering total rates of aggression and submission, we also calculated an index of overt aggression and submission (ratio of intense aggression or submission:total aggression or submission), to reflect the relative mix of the animals' behaviors when they were fighting, regardless of the overall rates of agonism (see also Botchin et al., 1993; Mehlman et al., 1994). To determine the possible effects of a change from consumption of a diet high in saturated fat and cholesterol to one low in these components, the behavioral data were analyzed with a series of t tests for related measures. As shown in Figure 3, the rates of aggression and submission differed significantly between the two dietary conditions, with higher rates observed when animals were consuming the low-fat diet, $t(22) = 2.08$, $p < .05$; $t(22) = 2.10$, $p < .05$, respectively. This increase was generalized across both mild and intense fights, as there was no corresponding difference in the percentage of fights characterized by overt forms of aggression. Figure 4 illustrates further that after animals switched from the Phase 1 (high-fat) diet to the Phase 2 (low-fat) diet, they spent less time in passive body contact, $t(22) = 5.60$, $p < .001$; less time within touching distance, $t(22) = 4.73$, $p < .001$; and more time alone, $t(22) = 5.68$, $p < .001$, than they had previously. Grooming was unchanged.

Note that the animals described here all gained weight over the course of the experiment. Therefore, the monkeys were all significantly heavier during Phase 2 than during Phase 1 (see Table 1); that is, animals were heavier while eating the low-fat diet.

Comparison 3. The study animals in this comparison were 8 female and 9 male, sexually immature cynomolgus macaques born at our facility (Kaplan et al., 1994). These animals were part of a larger investigation of the effects of dietary cholesterol on atherosclerosis. After weaning, at approximately 8 months of age, animals were assigned to either a high- or a low-cholesterol condition, using stratified randomization to balance for age, sex, and parentage. The sex distribution, ages, and preexperimental cholesterol concentrations were comparable between conditions (Table 2).

---

[4]In the all-occurrence samples, observers recorded all occurrences of certain kinds of behaviors initiated by any animal in the group being observed, whereas in the scan samples, the observer recorded a "snapshot" of activities occurring at that time. These sampling techniques differ somewhat from the focal procedure but still can provide accurate estimates of behavioral rates or the percentage of time spent in particular activities (Altmann, 1974).

Table 2. Preexperimental Characteristics of Animals

Characteristic	Low cholesterol	High cholesterol
Age (days)	250 (17)	243 (17)
TC level (mg/dl)	211 (31)	238 (32)
HDL cholesterol (mg/dl)	82 (11)	84 (9)
Sex	4M, 4F	5M, 4F

Note: Comparisons, except for sex, were by one-way Diet × Condition (high vs. low) analysis of variance. Standard error is in parentheses. M = male, F = female. Probability levels were all nonsignificant.

Unlike our other studies, all animals consumed a diet relatively high in fat (40% of calories). The 8 monkeys assigned to the high-cholesterol condition also consumed 0.80 mg cholesterol/kilocal (equivalent to human consumption of 1,600 mg cholesterol per day), whereas 0.03 mg cholesterol/kilocal (equivalent to human consumption of 60 mg per day) was fed to the 9 monkeys in the low-cholesterol condition.

The animals lived in two social groups corresponding to their dietary condition. The behavior of each monkey in each group was observed for 10 min twice per week by technicians who were blind to the diets being used and to the hypotheses being tested. Technicians used a focal-sampling procedure (Altmann, 1974) to record the frequency of acts that were aggressive (e.g., biting, grabbing, hitting, threatening face, or displacement) or submissive (e.g., crouching, fleeing, screaming, grimacing, or lip smacking) and the percentage of time spent in affiliation (passive body contact) or alone (not within touching distance of other animals). Behavioral observations began after the animals had consumed the experimental diets for an average of 4 months; the observations continued for 8 months. Animals ranged in age from 10 to 19 months during this period.

Plasma lipid samples were taken on two occasions during the period of behavioral observations. Analysis of these data revealed that TC differed significantly between monkeys consuming the high- and low-cholesterol diets (see Table 1); in contrast, body weights did not differ significantly between groups. With respect to social behavior, the mean rate of aggression was higher in the group consuming the low-cholesterol diet, $F(1, 12) = 19.3$, $p < .001$ (see Figure 5). Monkeys consuming the low-cholesterol diet also spent less time in body contact, a passive form of affiliation, $F(1, 13) = 19.6$, $p < .01$, and more time alone (i.e., not within touching distance of other individuals), $F(1, 13) = 13.7$, $p < .01$), than animals eating the high-cholesterol diet.

In addition to differences in social behavior, the animals consuming the low-cholesterol diet responded more aggressively when, as individuals, they were placed in a chamber and exposed to slides depicting a threatening monkey or person (technique described in Kyes, Botchin, Kaplan, Manuck, & Mann, 1995). None of the foregoing results were confounded by age or sex differences.

Comparison 4. This study constituted the remainder of the regression experiment described in Comparison 2 (Kaplan et al. 1996). Here, after 14

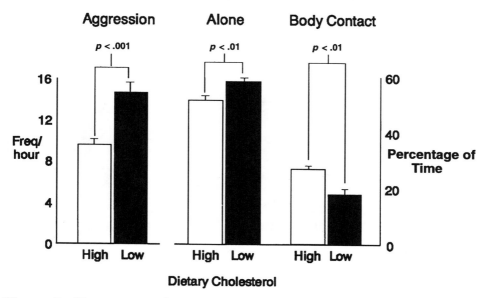

Figure 5.   Frequency per hour ($\pm$ *SEM*) of all aggressive behavior received and percentage of time spent alone and sitting in passive body contact, for monkeys in the low- and high-cholesterol conditions. From "Demonstration of an Association Among Dietary Cholesterol, Central Serotonergic Activity, and Social Behavior in Monkeys," by Kaplan et al., 1994, *Psychosomatic Medicine, 56,* p. 482. Copyright 1994 by the American Psychosomatic Society. Reprinted with permission.

months of living in stable social groups of 4 or 5 monkeys each, during which all animals consumed a diet high in fat and cholesterol (i.e., Phase 1), these adult male monkeys were assigned randomly to one of two conditions for the next 28 months (Phase 2): (a) a diet high in fat and cholesterol and an unstable social environment ($n = 18$) or (b) a diet low in fat and cholesterol and an unstable social environment ($n = 21$). Monkeys in the high-fat condition consumed a diet consistent with the current upper quintile of cholesterol consumption in the United States (0.20 mg cholesterol/kilocalorie—equivalent to human consumption of 400 mg/day—and about 45% of calories from fat). All animals lived in social groups made unstable by monthly reorganization of group memberships. Monkeys in the low-fat condition ate a diet approximating current recommendations of the National Cholesterol Education Program (Report of the Expert Panel on Population Strategies for Blood Cholesterol Reduction, 1991; 0.05 mg cholesterol/kilocalorie—equivalent to human consumption of 100 mg/day—and about 30% of calories from fat). Like the animals consuming the high-fat diet, these monkeys also lived in social groups perturbed by monthly reorganization.

Not surprisingly, the consumption of these two diets resulted in a significant difference in TC between the conditions (see Table 1). As with the monkeys in Comparison 2, data on social behavior were collected by means of all-occurrence and scan sampling. We conducted a series of one-way High-Fat Condition $\times$ Low-Fat Condition analyses of covariance, with be-

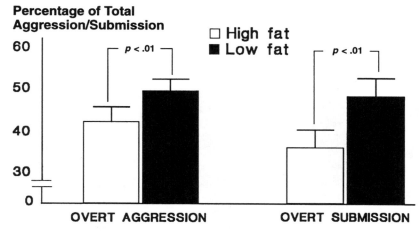

Figure 6. Comparison of overt aggression and submission (as percentages of total aggression or submission) between monkeys consuming either the high-fat ($n = 18$) or the low-fat ($n = 21$) diets and all living in unstable social groupings; data analysis involved covariance of social behavior during Phase 1 (i.e., when all monkeys consumed a very high fat diet and lived in stable social groups). Error bars are ± standard errors of measurement. From "Influence of Dietary Lipids on Agonistic and Affiliative Behavior in *Macaca fascicularis*," by Kaplan et al., 1996, *American Journal of Primatology, 38,* p. 341. Copyright 1996 by the American Society of Primatologists. Reprinted with permission.

havior during Phase 1 as the covariate, to evaluate Phase 2 behavioral differences between the monkeys in the two conditions. Total rates of aggression and submission did not differ between these groups. However, monkeys that consumed the low-fat diet exhibited higher percentages of overt aggression, $F(1, 36) = 15.45$, $p < .001$, and overt submission, $F(1, 36) = 8.21$, $p < .01$, than did their high-fat-condition counterparts (see Figure 6).[5] The monkeys in the two dietary conditions did not differ by any other behavioral characteristics. There was a tendency for animals consuming the high-fat diet to weigh somewhat less than those eating the low-fat diet, but this difference was not significant (see Table 1).

Comparison 5. A final contrast involved the behavior of monkeys fed the same diets as in Comparison 1 but all housed in unstable social groups, as a means of inducing psychosocial stress (Kaplan et al., 1991). Fifteen adult male monkeys were in each dietary condition, and social behavior was observed with a focal-sampling technique. Total cholesterol was significantly elevated among animals consuming the high-fat diet, in comparison with their low-fat counterparts (see Table 1). As in the preceding comparison involving monkeys housed in unstable social groups, the animals consuming the diets low in fat and cholesterol exhibited higher percentages of overt aggression and submission. However, in this instance,

---

[5]Again, "overt" aggression and submission refer to the ratio of severe aggressive (submissive) acts to total acts of aggression (submission).

the differences between conditions approximated only 12% for each behavior, a distinction that did not reach statistical significance.

Assessment. As a group, the foregoing comparisons provide preliminary support for the hypothesis that consumption of cholesterol-lowering diets potentiates aggressive or antisocial patterns of social expression and interaction. In this context, a number of points could be emphasized. First, although causality was not perfectly demonstrated in any of the studies, random assignment of animals to the high and low fat and cholesterol groups supports the suggestion that TC influenced social behavior rather than the reverse. This suggestion is reinforced by the observation that there was an increase in aggression and corresponding decrease in sociability among animals that switched from a diet high in fat and cholesterol to one low in these constituents (Comparison 2). Moreover, behavioral distinctions between dietary conditions were less dependent on absolute levels of cholesterol than on the existence of differences in TC between groups. Thus, significant behavioral distinctions were found when animals with TC levels between 150 and 235 mg/dl (low cholesterol) were compared with those with a TC between 355 and 690 mg/dl (high cholesterol).

Furthermore, the data from Comparison 3 indicate that differences in dietary cholesterol alone can influence social behavior, even when all individuals are also consuming a high-fat diet. The general absence of significant differences in body weight between dietary conditions argues against the possibility that differences in behavior were potentiated by hunger or weight loss rather than variability in TC. In the one instance in which there was a significant difference in body weight between dietary groups (i.e., Comparison 2), it was the low-fat-condition animals that were heavier. It is unlikely that this weight gain can explain the behavioral differences, because it was in the opposite direction than would be predicted for such an effect. Rather, this increase in weight probably represents the effect of chronic exposure to a diet relatively high in calories. Finally, there is no evidence from any of our studies that cholesterol lowering has any effects on cortisol or other stress indices, precluding the argument that the observed behavioral effects are secondary to stress.

Though intriguing, the results of the studies described here must be qualified in several ways. First, one of the five studies failed to reveal a significant behavioral difference between dietary groups, despite a substantial difference in TC. Furthermore, as noted previously, all of the comparisons involve secondary analyses of data derived from investigations conducted for other purposes. As a result, the contrasts are less than ideal, often lacking appropriate control groups or observations. For example, prediet behavioral observations were not available for the monkeys used in Comparisons 1, 3, and 5. Furthermore, except for Comparison 3, dietary conditions varied in the percentage of calories derived from fat, protein, and carbohydrates, as well as the amount of cholesterol. Hence, these other factors cannot be ruled out as contributory to the observed behavioral differences.

Additionally, the monkeys used in Comparisons 4 and 5 were distinguished by a social manipulation (repeated group reorganization) as well as a dietary distinction. The social manipulation itself may have altered behavior and thus could have confounded some dietary effects, perhaps explaining why there were no statistically significant behavioral differences among monkeys used in Comparison 5. Even the interpretation of the finding that monkeys changed their behavior after switching from a high-fat to a low-fat diet is somewhat clouded by the absence of suitable controls (i.e., animals that lived in stable social groups and continued to eat the high-fat diet).

These and other shortcomings that may be identified with respect to the foregoing investigations render the results preliminary rather than conclusive. A fully convincing demonstration that TC or dietary cholesterol influence behavior awaits the completion of prospective studies involving within-participant manipulation of cholesterol by diet and cholesterol-lowering drugs. Such studies are currently under way. Finally, some investigators suggest that the type and amount of fatty acids consumed, not cholesterol per se, mediate the effects of diet on behavior and non-illness-related mortality (Hibbein & Salem, 1995). These observations argue against this suggestion: (a) The randomized primary prevention trials did not manipulate fatty acid intake; (b) hypo- and hypercholesterolemic individuals do not differ markedly, if at all, in n-3 fatty acids (the fatty acid in question); and (c) one of the monkey studies demonstrated serotonergic and behavioral differences between groups of animals consuming diets that differed in cholesterol but not fatty acid composition (Kaplan et al., 1994).

Cholesterol and Serotonin

As described earlier, the cholesterol–serotonin hypothesis presumes three associations. Data bearing on the first of these, that between cholesterol and behavior, were presented in the preceding paragraphs. Two studies linking variability in TC to differences in central serotonergic activity are described here. The first of these used the serum prolactin response after acute fenfluramine infusion as an index of overall CNS serotonergic activity (Muldoon, Kaplan, Manuck, & Mann, 1992). Fenfluramine is an indirect serotonergic agonist, and the change in serum prolactin after exposure to fenfluramine is suggested to provide a measure of net pre- and post-synaptic serotonergic activity (Coccaro et al., 1989; Kwiterovich, 1986). Fasting plasma prolactin concentrations were measured 1 hr after injection of placebo and after fenfluramine (4 mg/kg), with evaluations separated by 1 week. Nine adult male monkeys were fed a standard, laboratory "chow" diet (12% calories from fat, 0.02 mg cholesterol/kilocalorie, equivalent to human consumption of 40 mg/cholesterol per day), and 10 monkeys were fed a diet relatively high in fat (41% of calories) and cholesterol (0.40 mg/kilocalorie, equivalent to human consumption of 800 mg/day). The resulting TC concentrations were 154 ($SEM = 9$) versus 420 ($SEM = 35$) mg/dl, respectively, $t(18) = 7.36$, $p < 0.001$. The groups did not differ

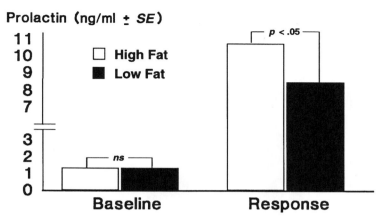

Figure 7. Serum prolactin concentrations at baseline and after fenfluramine injection, among animals that consumed diets either high or low in fat and cholesterol. From "Effects of a Low-Fat Diet on Brain Serotonergic Responsivity in Cynomolgus Monkeys," by Muldoon et al., 1992, *Biological Psychiatry, 31*, p. 741. Copyright 1992 by the Society of Biological Psychiatry. Reprinted with permission of Elsevier Science Inc.

significantly in body weight: For low-fat condition, $\bar{\chi}^2 = 4.33$; for high-fat condition, $\bar{\chi}^2 = 4.97$. All of these animals were housed in individual cages, precluding observations of social behavior. Prolactin concentrations after the injection of a placebo were identical in both groups; in contrast, the distributions of prolactin responses in the two groups given fenfluramine differed significantly ($p < .05$ by Kolmogorov–Smirnov median test), with the lowest prolactin concentrations aggregating in the low-fat-diet group (see Figure 7).

A second study involved the 17 juvenile monkeys used in Comparison 3 (Kaplan et al., 1994). As described previously, these animals consumed diets that contained 40% of calories as fat, which were either low (0.03 mg/kilocalorie) or high (0.80 mg/kilocalorie) in cholesterol (see Table 1). This investigation assessed the influence of dietary and TC on central serotonergic, noradrenergic, and dopaminergic activity by evaluation of the metabolites of these monoamines found in cerebrospinal fluid. Hence, on two occasions after the animals had consumed the experimental diet for an average of 6 months, all monkeys were sedated, and a 1–2 ml sample of cerebrospinal fluid was taken from the cisterna magna. This was used to measure concentrations of the metabolites of serotonin (5-hydroxyindoleacetic acid), norepinephrine (3-methoxy-4-hydroxyphenyl-glycol), and dopamine (homovanillic acid). Of these, cerebrospinal fluid serotonin concentrations were substantially and significantly lower in the animals consuming the low-cholesterol diet than in their high-cholesterol counterparts ($p < .001$; see Figure 8). Concentrations of the other monoaminergic metabolites, dopamine and norepinephrine, did not differ significantly between dietary conditions.

Like the behavioral studies, the two investigations linking consumption of a diet low in fat or cholesterol to reduced central serotonergic ac-

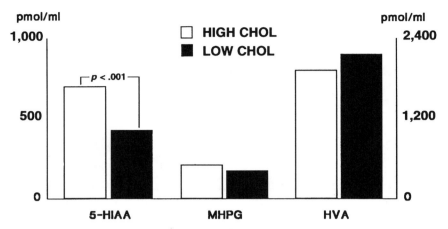

Figure 8. Cerebrospinal fluid metabolites in the low-cholesterol and high-cholesterol experimental conditions. Each bar represents a grand mean (± *SEM*) that consists of the mean of two samples per monkey. Chol = cholesterol, 5-HIAA = serotonin, MHPG = norepinephrine, HVA = dopamine. From "Demonstration of an Association Among Dietary Cholesterol, Central Serotonergic Activity, and Social Behavior in Monkeys," by Kaplan et al., 1994, *Psychosomatic Medicine, 56,* p. 482. Copyright 1994 by the American Psychosomatic Society. Reprinted with permission.

tivity are somewhat limited by the small numbers of animals involved and by absence of pre- and postexperimental measures of cholesterol and central monoaminergic activity. Nonetheless, these studies do provide initial data supporting the suggestion that dietary or plasma cholesterol influences central serotonergic activity. Note that this effect seems specific to serotonin, because there was no association between the dietary manipulations and the other monoaminergic neurotransmitters in the one study that directly assessed these neurotransmitters.

Serotonin and Behavior

The third association underlying the cholesterol–serotonin hypothesis is that between serotonin and violent or impulsive behavior. There is an extensive literature derived from studies of human beings indicating that reduced central serotonergic activity potentiates impulsive, violent, or suicidal behavior (Brown, Ebert, et al., 1982; Brown, Goodwin, et al., 1979; Kruesi et al., 1990; Roy et al., 1988, 1989; Virkkunen, DeJong, Bartko, Goodwin, & Linnoila, 1989; Virkkunen, DeJong, Bartko, & Linnoila, 1989). In this section are presented data from one study demonstrating that violent or antisocial behavior is similarly associated with low central serotonergic activity in laboratory-housed monkeys of the same species used to evaluate the first two elements of the cholesterol–serotonin hypothesis (Botchin et al., 1993).

In this investigation, we again assessed serum prolactin responses to fenfluramine challenge as an index of brain serotonin responsivity. The participants were 75 adult male cynomolgus monkeys housed for 28

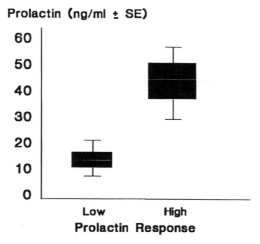

Figure 9. Bimodal distribution of serum prolactin response to fenfluramine (prolactin after response − prolactin at baseline) among 75 adult male monkeys, all consuming a diet moderately high in fat and cholesterol. From "High Versus Low Prolactin Responders to Fenfluramine Challenge: Marker of Behavioral Differences in Adult Male Cynomolgus Macaques," by Botchin et al., 1993, *Neuropsychopharmacology, 9,* p. 96. Copyright 1993 by the American College of Neuropsychopharmacology. Adapted with permission of Elsevier Science Inc.

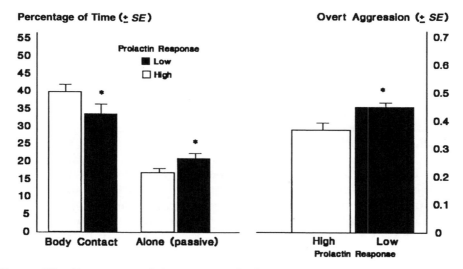

Figure 10. Percentage of time spent in body contact or alone (not within touching distance) and percentage of fights involving overt aggression among monkeys with high and low serum prolactin responses after exposure to fenfluramine. From "High Versus Low Prolactin Responders to Fenfluramine Challenge: Marker of Behavioral Differences in Adult Male Cynomolgus Macaques," by Botchin et al., 1993, *Neuropsychopharmacology, 9,* p. 97. Copyright 1993 by the American College of Neuropsychopharmacology. Adapted with permission of Elsevier Science Inc.

months in 5-member social groups. The study did not involve any experimental manipulation of diet or plasma lipids, as all animals consumed the same moderately atherogenic diet. Behavioral assessment consisted of all-occurrence sampling; in addition to the usual measures of aggression, submission, and grooming, an index of overt aggression again was calculated as the ratio of severe forms (e.g., biting, grabbing, chasing) to total aggression (including facial threats and displacements). The fenfluramine challenge was performed once during the final 6 months of the study. The prolactin response was bimodal, with the mean for high responders three times the mean for low responders ($p < .01$) and no overlap between groups (see Figure 9). As depicted in Figure 10, low responders, in comparison with their high-responder counterparts, exhibited 20% higher levels of overt aggression ($p < .05$) and spent 25% less time in passive body contact with other animals and more time alone ($p < .05$). The increased aggressivity of the low-prolactin responders was not limited to the social setting. We also observed that as individuals, low responders were twice as likely to attack an inanimate object (a slide projection of a person or a monkey, $p < .05$, (Kyes et al., 1995).

An association between aggressive or impulsive behavior and reduced serotonergic activity has been reported in other studies involving monkeys, in both free-living and captive populations (Mehlman et al., 1994; Raleigh, McGuire, Brammer, Pollack, & Yuwiler, 1991). It seems likely, therefore, that the association between low serotonergic activity and impulsivity or violence that occurs prominently in studies of human beings extends also to nonhuman primates, regardless of housing conditions.

Discussion

General Considerations

The data and literature reviewed here provide evidence of a heretofore unanticipated association among plasma cholesterol, central serotonergic activity, and antagonistic or antisocial behavior. This association has been termed the *cholesterol–serotonin hypothesis*. It underscores a growing body of data suggesting that dietary lipids influence the lipid content of the brain, with potential consequences for brain function and behavior (Baldwin, 1986; Coscina, Yehuda, Dixon, Kish, & Leprohon-Greenwood, 1986; Crane & Greenwood, 1987; Farquharson, Cockburn, Patrick, Jamieson, & Logan, 1992; Kessler, Kessler, & Yehuda, 1986; Yehuda, Leprohon-Greenwood, Dixon, & Coscina, 1986; Young, 1993). In particular, the cholesterol–serotonin hypothesis may be relevant to understanding the puzzling epidemiologic association between reduced or naturally low plasma cholesterol concentrations and a high incidence of depression, suicidality, antisocial personality disorders, or violence-related mortality (i.e., accident, suicide, and homicide; Freedman et al., 1995; Muldoon et al., 1990, 1993; Virkkunen, 1979, 1983; Virkkunen & Penttinen, 1984). Several investigators have suggested that the foregoing outcomes either represent epiphenomena or are causal in the opposite direction (i.e., alterations in mental states influence diet or metabolism and, thus, plasma cholesterol concentrations; LaRosa, 1993; Rossouw & Gotto, 1993). More recently, elevated mortality among individuals with low TC has been attributed to the possibility that the blood of such individuals is less capable of transporting lipid-soluble toxins to the liver for detoxification; this would cause ill individuals with low TC to be at greater risk than equally ill individuals with high TC (Jacobs, Muldoon, & Rästam, 1995). Such an explanation, however, does not readily encompass the behavioral and psychiatric conditions associated with low TC. Alternatively, the outcome of the studies reviewed here suggests that reduced plasma cholesterol, directly or indirectly, influences antisocial behavior in human beings as in monkeys and underlies the cited associations between reduced or low plasma cholesterol and increased psychiatric pathology or mortality due to trauma. In recognition of this possibility, one National Institutes of Health panel concluded the following: "Further exploration is needed on whether the active lowering of total cholesterol by various means has deleterious effects in some persons or situations" (Jacobs et al., 1992, p. 1057).

This further exploration is called forth, in part, by numerous unanswered questions concerning the universality and strength of the cholesterol–serotonin–behavior association, as well as the mechanism(s) underlying it. It remains unclear, for example, whether males and females are equally vulnerable to any adverse effects of reduced or low cholesterol. Most of the studies reporting such effects either involved only men or found that the effects applied disproportionately to the males within a sample of males and females (Golier et al., 1995; Lindberg et al., 1992). There were no differences between males and females in the one study of monkeys that contained both sexes (Comparison 3); however, these animals were all sexually immature, which may have reduced or precluded any sex-specific effects. Among human beings, it also is unclear if particular individuals, such as those with inherently low central serotonergic activity or underlying psychiatric illness, are predisposed to exhibit an adverse outcome in response to a reduction in TC. No studies to date have addressed this possibility.

Regarding the strength of the effects, experimental findings do not clarify the degree of cholesterol reduction or difference that is necessary to produce behavioral or other functional changes. In population surveys, for example, it is often only individuals with somewhat-to-very low cholesterol who experience an increased incidence of violent death or psychiatric morbidity. In contrast, the cholesterol-lowering trials, which were characterized by significant increases in violence-related mortality among treated individuals, involved only modest reductions in plasma cholesterol (10% to 20% Muldoon et al., 1990). This latter result suggests that a slight change in cholesterol may be sufficient to produce an adverse effect. Again, the animal studies offer little insight, as the dietary manipulations in all of them led to substantial differences in cholesterol between conditions.

Proximate Cause and Evolutionary Speculations

The question of underlying mechanism can be approached in terms of either proximate or ultimate cause. *Proximate* cause involves consideration of immediate physiologic precursors, whereas *ultimate* cause refers to adaptive value and, thus, evolutionary origins. With respect to proximate cause, the existing evidence identifies central serotonergic activity as part of the putative mechanism mediating the effects of cholesterol on behavior, presumably through effects on the cholesterol:phospholipid ratio in neuronal membranes, with consequent alterations in membrane fluidity, viscosity, and function (including receptor activity; Iso, Jacobs, Wentworth, Neaton, & Cohen, 1989; Jacobs et al., 1992). However, there has not yet been an in vivo demonstration that alterations in blood cholesterol lead directly to functionally significant changes in serotonergic activity. Nor do existing data eliminate the possibility that cholesterol or fatty acids influence not membrane characteristics, but rather the likelihood of tryptophan or other monoaminergic precursors crossing the blood—brain barrier. At the organismic level, additional mediating factors, such as alcohol abuse, may play a role in the epidemiologic associations between low or reduced cholesterol and violent death (Golomb, 1996). Additional studies are clearly necessary to illuminate further the proximate mechanisms mediating the observed association among cholesterol, serotonin, and behavior.

Although much attention has focused on proximate cause, it is possible to view the cholesterol—serotonin hypothesis in an adaptive or evolutionary context. For example, the brain's high lipid content may incidentally predispose this organ to respond to changes in dietary (and thus circulating) lipids with alterations in cellular structure (e.g., neuronal membrane fluidity and viscosity) having potential functional sequelae (Aiello & Wheeler, 1995; Foley & Lee, 1991; Leonard & Robertson, 1992; Mason et al., 1991; Young, 1993). In this context, the influence of cholesterol on behavior might be interpreted as an epiphenomenon and not itself the product of selection pressure.

Alternatively, it could be speculated that the behavioral and physiologic responses induced by a reduction in TC were shaped by natural selection because these responses provided an adaptive advantage. For example, it has been suggested that an inverse association between antagonistic, impulsive behavior and cholesterol, although disadvantageous in modern society, may represent a negative feedback mechanism providing for appropriate changes in behavior in response to the threat of dietary privation (Erickson, 1994; Kaplan et al., 1994). Specifically, during periods of caloric abundance, individuals would be physiologically prompted (through high central serotonergic activity?) to exhibit behavioral complacency. This particular effect may be enhanced by serotonin-mediated suppression of the sympathetic nervous system (i.e., attenuation of the defense response) induced by a diet containing animal fat (Uemura & Young, 1994). In contrast, scarcity, particularly in calories derived from animal sources, would reduce plasma cholesterol and (through low central serotonergic activity?) trigger impulsive, risk-taking behavior such as

Model

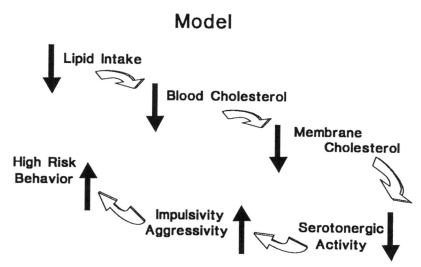

Figure 11.   Model depicting a presumed adaptive cascade after a decline in lipid intake; direction of arrows is reversed after an increase in dietary lipids.

hunting or competitive foraging. These relationships are depicted in Figure 11.

Note that nutritional deficiencies affecting the brain may be a particular threat to human beings, providing a strong basis for protective adaptations. Our species is characterized by a large brain that imposes a significant metabolic load (absorbing 20% to 25% of calories at rest) and thus requires a large caloric input (Leonard & Robertson, 1992). It has been suggested that the development of relatively large brains in human beings was based on a commensurate reduction in gut size. The change in gut size, in turn, is believed to have required a shift to a higher quality diet, including increased consumption of animal matter (Aiello & Wheeler, 1995). However, nutritional need may not have been the only factor driving a cholesterol–serotonin–behavior relationship. Recent evidence relates variability in TC to speed of mental processing, a correlate of intelligence (Benton, 1995). Specifically, individuals with higher TC concentrations have greater processing speeds. This suggests that those human populations that altered their dietary practices to include a greater reliance on animal products, and thus increased their consumption of fat and cholesterol, may have also gained a mental advantage over their competitors. Any such advantage would have acted synergistically to have accelerated the evolution of a syndrome linking TC levels to behavior.

Some ecologic support for the preceding adaptive hypothesis is provided by studies indicating that human beings primitively sought and consumed large quantities of wild game, which often contains a considerable amount of cholesterol and protein, although usually not much fat (Eaton & Konner, 1985). Notably, humans appear to respond to the cues provided by fat, rather than meat per se; traditional hunters almost universally exhibit a preference for fat species and for targeting a species at the time of year when it is likely to contain the most fat (e.g., Bunn & Ezzo, 1993;

Milton, 1991). The consumption of fat, along with cholesterol, not only maintains appropriate levels of cholesterol in cell membranes, provides a dense and efficient source of calories, and perhaps enhances the speed of mental processing, it also prevents metabolic problems associated with protein overconsumption (as occurs with a diet of lean meat, Speth, 1991).

We have speculated in the preceding paragraphs that periodic dietary shortages could have made it difficult for early humans to maintain optimal levels of critical brain nutrients, leading to the evolution of a mechanism that would ensure adaptive changes in behavior in response to a decline in a sentinel compound such as cholesterol. On the other hand, there would be no need for the evolution of a countervailing mechanism to protect against extreme elevations in cholesterol, as such elevations would no doubt have been unusual and transitory under the ecological conditions faced by early human beings. Analogously, the body has numerous adaptive defenses against a decline in blood pressure, a situation both life threatening and probably common under primitive conditions involving a high risk of violent competition and accidental injury. There is, however, no particular compensatory mechanism against sustained elevations in blood pressure.

It is perhaps not surprising that the behavioral and physiologic adaptations to a hunter–gatherer way of life could be dysfunctional in modern societies. Thus, a primitive taste for fat (developed perhaps for the reasons outlined above) leads to its frequent overconsumption in those industrialized countries where it is readily available. Such overconsumption is widely believed to underlie the high prevalence of heart disease, obesity, and adult-onset diabetes in these societies and, in turn, has led to recommendations that such populations reduce their intake of cholesterol and fat (Widdowson, 1992). Similarly, the overconsumption of salt as well as fat and other nutrients not superabundantly available under primitive conditions, combined with the stresses and strains of life in a modern industrialized society, is thought to contribute to the development of hypertension (Widdowson, 1992). Ironically, current recommendations to avoid cholesterol and fat as a means of preventing chronic disease (sometimes termed *the diseases of civilization*) may now lead some individuals to engage in impulsive and risk-taking behavior that is inappropriately expressed in modern societies not characterized by the need for competitive foraging or hunting.

Conclusion

Data from several experiments using monkeys indicate that reductions in TC may influence the tendency to engage in impulsive or violent behavior through a mechanism involving central serotonergic activity. This idea, termed the *cholesterol–serotonin hypothesis*, may be relevant to understanding the epidemiologic association between low or lowered TC levels and an increased incidence of violent death (due largely to suicides and accidents). It was speculated that the cholesterol–serotonin–behavior association represents a mechanism evolved to increase impulsive and competitive behavior in the face of nutritional threats signaled by a decline in TC. The evolution of this syndrome could have been encouraged further by the increase in mental-processing speed believed to accompany higher TC levels. Although this adaptive explanation is intriguing, an association between cholesterol and behavior is as yet unsupported by any experimental data from human beings. Moreover, although a cholesterol–behavior mechanism may be reasonable with respect to a hunting–scavenging species such as our own, the adaptiveness of such a mechanism for largely frugivorous monkeys that typically consume little cholesterol or animal fat under natural conditions remains unclear (although, cf. Aiello & Wheeler, 1995; Hamilton, 1987). Also problematic is the absence of a clear homology between the behavior of nonhuman primates and the pattern of increased suicidality that is linked prominently to low TC among human beings. Relevant experimental data from human beings, as well as a resolution of the foregoing logical inconsistencies, would strengthen substantially an adaptive interpretation for the inverse association between antisocial behavior and cholesterol observed in monkeys. Finally, any clinical practice implications of the evidence discussed await research examining this hypothesis as well as the many unanswered questions concerning interactions between serum lipids and behavior.

References

Aiello, L. C., & Wheeler, P. (1995). The expensive tissue hypothesis. *Current Anthropology, 36*, 199–221.

Altmann, J. (1974). Observational study of behavior: Sampling methods. *Behaviour, 49*, 221–261.

Anderson, I. M., Parry-Billings, M., Newsholme, E. A., Fairburn, C. G., & Cowen, P. J. (1990). Dieting reduces plasma tryptophan and alters brain 5-HT function in women. *Psychological Medicine, 20*, 785–791.

Baldwin, J. D. (1986). Behavior in infancy: Exploration and play. In G. Mitchell & J. Erwin (Eds.), *Behavior, conservation, and ecology* (Vol. 2, Part A, pp. 295–326). New York: Alan R. Liss.

Benton, D. (1995). Do low cholesterol levels slow mental processing? *Psychosomatic Medicine, 57*, 50–53.

Bernstein, I. S. (1991). An empirical comparison of focal and ad libitum scoring with commentary on instantaneous scans, all occurrence, and one-zero techniques. *Animal Behavior, 42*, 721–728.

Botchin, M. B., Kaplan, J. R., Manuck, S. B., & Mann, J. J. (1993). High versus low prolactin responders to fenfluramine challenge: Marker of behavioral differences in adult male cynomolgus macaques. *Neuropsychopharmacology, 9*, 93–99.

Brown, G. L., Ebert, M. H., Goyer, P. F., Jimerson, D. C., Klein, W. J., Bunney, W. E., & Goodwin, F. K. (1982). Aggression, suicide, and serotonin: Relationships to CSF amine metabolites. *Journal of Psychiatry, 139*, 741–746.

Brown, G. L., Goodwin, F. K., Ballenger, J. C., Goyer, P. F., & Major, L. F. (1979). Aggression in humans correlates with cerebrospinal fluid amine metabolites. *Psychiatry Research, 1*, 131–139.

Bunn, H. T., & Ezzo, J. A. (1993). Hunting and scavenging by Plio-Pleistocene hominids: Nutritional constraints, archaeological patterns, and behavioural implications. *Journal of Archaeological Science, 20*, 365–398.

Coccaro, E. F. (1989). Central serotonin and impulsive aggression. *British Journal of Psychiatry, 155,* 52–62.

Coccaro, E. F., Siever, L. J., Klar, H. M., Maurer, G., Cochrane, K., Cooper, T. B., Mohs, R. C., & Davis, K. L. (1989). Serotonergic studies in patients with affective and personality disorders: Correlates with suicidal and impulsive aggressive behavior. *Archives of General Psychiatry, 46,* 587–599.

Coscina, D. V., Yehuda, S., Dixon, L. M., Kish, S. J., & Leprohon-Greenwood, C. E. (1986). Learning is improved by a soybean oil diet in rats. *Life Sciences, 8,* 1789–1794.

Crane, S. B., & Greenwood, C. E. (1987). Dietary fat source influences neuronal mitochondrial monoamine oxidase activity and macronutrient selection in rats. *Pharmacology, Biochemistry, and Behavior, 27,* 1–6.

Eaton, S. B., & Konner, M. (1985). Paleolithic nutrition, a consideration of its nature and current implications. *New England Journal of Medicine, 312,* 283–289.

Engleberg, H. (1992). Low serum cholesterol and suicide. *The Lancet, 339,* 727–729.

Erickson, M. (1994, June). *Serum cholesterol and aggression: A conjecture.* Paper presented at the meeting of the Human Behavior and Evolution Society, Ann Arbor, Michigan.

Farquharson, J., Cockburn, F., Patrick, W. A., Jamieson, E. C., & Logan, R. W. (1992). Infant cerebral cortex phospholipid fatty-acid composition and diet. *The Lancet, 340,* 810–813.

Foley, R. A., & Lee, P. C. (1991). Ecology and energetics of encephalization in hominid evolution. *Philosophical Transactions of the Royal Society of London [B], 334,* 223–232.

Freedman, D. S., Byers, T., Barrett, D. H., Stroup, N. E., Eaker, E., & Monroe-Blum, H. (1995). Plasma lipid levels and psychologic characteristics in men. *American Journal of Epidemiology, 141,* 507–517.

Golier, J. A., Marzuk, P. M., Leon, A. C., Weiner, C., & Tardiff, K. (1995). Low serum cholesterol level and attempted suicide. *American Journal of Psychiatry, 152,* 419–423.

Golomb, M. (1996). Cholesterol and violence: Is there a serotonin connection? Manuscript submitted for publication.

Hamilton, W., III. (1987). Omnivorous primate diets and human overconsumption of meat. In M. Harris & E. R. Ross (Eds.), *Food and Evolution: Toward a theory of human food habits* (pp. 117–132). Philadelphia: Temple University Press.

Hatch, F. T., Reissell, P. K., Poon-King, T. M. W., Canellos, G. P., Lees, R. S., & Hagopian, L. M. (1966). A study of coronary heart disease in young men. *Circulation, 33,* 679–703.

Heron, D. S., Shinitzky, M., Hershkowitz, M., & Samuel, D. (1980). Lipid fluidity markedly modulates the binding of serotonin to mouse brain membranes. *Proceedings of the National Academy of Sciences, USA, 77,* 7463–7467.

Hibbein, J. R., & Salem, N., Jr. (1995). Dietary polyunsaturated fatty acids and depression: When cholesterol does not satisfy. *American Journal of Clinical Nutrition, 62,* 1–9.

Hillbrand, M., Spitz, R. T., & Foster, H. G. (1995). Serum cholesterol and aggression in hospitalized male forensic patients. *Journal of Behavioral Medicine, 18,* 33–43.

Hulley, S. B., Walsh, J., & Newman, T. B. (1992). Health policy on blood cholesterol. *Circulation, 86,* 1–4.

Iso, H., Jacobs, D. R., Wentworth, D., Neaton, J. D., & Cohen, J. D. (1989). Serum cholesterol levels and six-year mortality from stroke in 350,977 men screened for the Multiple Risk Factor Intervention Trial. *New England Journal of Medicine, 320,* 904–910.

Jacobs, D., Blackburn, H., Higgins, M., Reed, D., Iso, H., McMillan, G., Neaton, J., Nelson, J., Potter, J., Rifkind, B., Rossouw, J., Shekelle, R., & Yusuf, S. (1992). Report of the Conference on Low Blood Cholesterol: Mortality associations. *Circulation, 86,* 1046–1060.

Jacobs, D. R., Jr., Muldoon, M. F., & Rästam, L. (1995). Low blood cholesterol, nonillness mortality, and other nonatherosclerotic disease mortality: A search for causes and confounders. *American Journal of Epidemiology, 141,* 518–522.

Jenkins, C. D., Hames, C. G., Zyzanski, S. J., Rosenman, R. H., & Friedman, M. (1969). Psychological traits and serum lipids. *Psychosomatic Medicine, 31,* 115–128.

Kaplan, J. R., Fontenot, M. B., Manuck, S. B., & Muldoon, M. F. (1996). An inverse association between dietary lipids and agonistic and affiliative behavior in *Macaca fascicularis. American Journal of Primatology, 38,* 333–347.

Kaplan, J. R., Manuck, S. B., Adams, M. R., Weingand, K. W., & Clarkson, T. B. (1987). Inhibition of coronary atherosclerosis by propranolol in behaviorally predisposed monkeys fed an atherogenic diet. *Circulation, 76*, 1364–1372.

Kaplan, J. R., Manuck, S. B., Adams, M. R., Williams, J. K., Register, T. C., & Clarkson, T. B. (1993). Plaque changes and arterial enlargement in atherosclerotic monkeys after manipulation of diet and social environment. *Arteriosclerosis and Thrombosis, 13*, 254–263.

Kaplan, J. R., Manuck, S. B., & Shively, C. A. (1991). The effects of fat and cholesterol on social behavior in monkeys. *Psychosomatic Medicine, 53*, 634–642.

Kaplan, J. R., Shively, C. A., Botchin, M. B., Morgan, T. M., Howell, S. M., Manuck, S. B., Muldoon, M. F., & Mann, J. J. (1994). Demonstration of an association among dietary cholesterol, central serotonergic activity, and social behavior in monkeys. *Psychosomatic Medicine, 56*, 479–484.

Kessler, R. A., Kessler, B., & Yehuda, S. (1986). *In vivo* modulation of brain cholesterol level and learning performance by a novel plant lipid: Indications for interactions between hippocampal-cortical cholesterol and learning. *Life Sciences, 38*, 1185–1192.

Ketterer, M. W., Brymer, J., Rhoads, K., Kraft, P., & Goldberg, A. D. (1994). Lipid-lowering therapy and violent death: Is depression a culprit? *Stress Medicine, 10*, 233–237.

Kruesi, M. J., & Rapoport, J. L. (1986). Diet and human behavior: How much do they affect each other? *Annual Review of Nutrition, 6*, 113–130.

Kruesi, M. J. P., Rapoport, J. L., Hamburger, S., Hibs, E., Potter, W. Z., Lenane, M., & Brown, G. L. (1990). Cerebrospinal fluid monoamine metabolites, aggression, and impulsivity in disruptive behavior disorders of children and adolescents. *Archives of General Psychiatry, 47*, 419–426.

Kwiterovich, P. O., Jr. (1986). Biochemical, clinical, epidemiologic, genetic, and pathologic data in the pediatric age group relevant to the cholesterol hypothesis. *Pediatrics, 78*, 349–362.

Kyes, R. C., Botchin, M. B., Kaplan, J. R., Manuck, S. B., & Mann, J. J. (1995). Aggression and brain serotonergic responsivity: Response to slides in male macaques. *Physiology and Behavior, 52*, 205–208.

LaRosa, J. C. (1993). Cholesterol lowering, low cholesterol, and mortality. *American Journal of Cardiology, 72*, 776–786.

Leonard, W. R., & Robertson, M. L. (1992). Nutritional requirements and human evolution: A bioenergetics model. *American Journal of Human Biology, 195*, 179–194.

Lindberg, G., Rästam, L., Gullberg, B., & Eklund, G. A. (1992). Low serum cholesterol concentration and short term mortality from injuries in men and women. *British Medical Journal, 305*, 277–279.

Mason, R. P., Herbette, L. G., & Silverman, D. I. (1991). Can altering serum cholesterol affect neurologic function? *Journal of Molecular and Cellular Cardiology, 23*, 1339–1342.

McMurchie, E. J., & Patten, G. S. (1988). Dietary cholesterol influences cardiac β-adrenergic receptor adenylate cyclase activity in the marmoset monkey by changes in membrane cholesterol status. *Biochimica et Biophysica Acta, 942*, 324–332.

McMurchie, E. J., Patten, G. S., Charnock, J. S., & McLennan, P. L. (1987). The interaction of dietary fatty acid and cholesterol on catecholamine-stimulated adenylate cyclase activity in the rat heart. *Biochimica et Biophysica Acta, 898*, 137–153.

Mehlman, P. T., Higley, J. D., Faucher, I., Lilly, A. A., Taub, D. M., Vickers, J., Suomi, S. J., & Linnoila, M. (1994). Low CSF 5-HIAA concentrations and severe aggression and impaired impulse control in nonhuman primates. *American Journal of Psychiatry, 151*, 1485–1491.

Milton, K. (1991). Comparative aspects of diet in Amazonian forest-dwellers. *Philosophical Transactions of the Royal Society of London [B], 334*, 253–263.

Morgan, R. E., Palinkas, L. A., Barrett-Connor, E., & Wingard, D. (1993). Plasma cholesterol and depressive symptoms in older men. *The Lancet, 341*, 75–79.

Muldoon, M. F., Kaplan, J. R., Manuck, S. B., & Mann, J. J. (1992). Effects of a low-fat diet on brain serotonergic responsivity in cynomolgus monkeys. *Biological Psychiatry, 31*, 739–742.

Muldoon, M. F., & Manuck, S. B. (1992). Health through cholesterol reduction: Are there unforeseen risks? *Annals of Behavioral Medicine, 14*, 101–108.

Muldoon, M. F., Manuck, S. B., & Matthews, K. A. (1990). Lowering cholesterol concentrations and mortality: A quantitative review of primary prevention trials. *British Medical Journal, 301*, 309–314.

Muldoon, M. F., Rossouw, J., Manuck, S. B., Glueck, C. J., Kaplan, J. R., & Kaufmann, P. G. (1993). Low or lowered cholesterol and risk of death from suicide and trauma. *Metabolism, 42*(Suppl. 1), 45–56.

National Cholesterol Education Program Expert Panel on Detection, Evaluation, and Treatment of High Blood Cholesterol in Adults. (1988). Report of the National Cholesterol Education Program Expert Panel on Detection, Evaluation, and Treatment of High Blood Cholesterol in Adults. *Archives of Internal Medicine, 148*, 36–69.

National Cholesterol Education Program Expert Panel on Detection, Evaluation, and Treatment of High Blood Cholesterol in Adults. (1993). *Report of the expert panel on population strategies for blood cholesterol reduction*. Bethesda, MD: National Institutes of Health.

Neaton, J. D., Blackburn, H., Jacobs, D., Kuller, L., Lee, D.-J., Sherwin, R., Shih, J., Stamler, J., & Wentworth, D. (1992). Serum cholesterol level and mortality findings for men screened in the Multiple Risk Factor Intervention Trial. *Archives of Internal Medicine, 152*, 1490–1500.

Oliver, M. F. (1991). Might reduction of plasma cholesterol imperil cell physiology? *Journal of Molecular and Cellular Cardiology, 23*, 1335–1337.

Raleigh, M. J., McGuire, M. T., Brammer, G. L., Pollack, D. B., & Yuwiler, A. (1991). Serotonergic mechanisms promote dominance acquisition in adult male vervet monkeys. *Brain Research, 559*, 181–190.

Report of the Expert Panel on Population Strategies for Blood Cholesterol Reduction. (1991). A statement from the National Cholesterol Education Program, National Heart, Lung, and Blood Institute, National Institutes of Health. *Circulation, 83*, 2154–2232.

Rossouw, J., & Gotto, A. M., Jr. (1993). Does low cholesterol cause death? *Cardiovascular Drugs and Therapy, 7*, 789–793.

Roy, A., Adinoff, B., & Linnoila, M. (1988). Acting out hostility in normal volunteers: Negative correlation with levels of 5HIAA in cerebrospinal fluid. *Psychiatry Research, 24*, 187–194.

Roy, A., DeJong, J., & Linnoila, M. (1989). Cerebrospinal fluid, monoamine metabolites and suicidal behavior in depressed patients: A 5-year follow-up study. *Archives of General Psychiatry, 46*, 609–612.

Shepherd, J., Cobbe, S. M., Ford, I., Isles, C. G., Lorimer, A. R., Macfarlane, P. W., McKillop, J. H., & Packard, C. J., for the West of Scotland Coronary Prevention Study Group. (1995). Prevention of coronary heart disease with pravastatin in men with hypercholesterolemia. *New England Journal of Medicine, 333*, 1301–1307.

Sletten, I. W., Nilsen, J. A., Young, R. C., & Anderson, J. T. (1964). Blood lipids and behavior in mental-hospital patients. *Psychosomatic Medicine, 26*, 261–266.

Speth, J. D. (1991). Protein selection and avoidance strategies of contemporary and ancestral foragers: Unresolved issues. *Philosophical Transactions of the Royal Society of London [B], 334*, 265–270.

Uemura, K., & Young, J. B. (1994). Effects of fat feeding on epinephrine secretion in the rat. *American Journal of Physiology, 267*, R1329–R1335.

Virkkunen, M. (1979). Serum cholesterol in antisocial personality. *Neuropsychobiology, 5*, 27–30.

Virkkunen, M. (1983). Serum cholesterol levels in homicidal offenders. A low cholesterol level is connected with a habitually violent tendency under the influence of alcohol. *Neuropsychobiology, 10*, 65–69.

Virkkunen, M., DeJong, J., Bartko, J., Goodwin, F. K., & Linnoila, M. (1989). Relationship of psychobiological variables to recidivism in violent offenders and impulsive fire setters. *Archives of General Psychiatry, 46*, 600–603.

Virkkunen, M., DeJong, J., Bartko, J., & Linnoila, M. (1989). Psychobiological concomitants of history of suicide attempts among violent offenders and impulsive fire setters. *Archives of General Psychiatry, 46*, 604–606.

Virkkunen, M., & Penttinen, H. (1984). Serum cholesterol in aggressive conduct disorder: A preliminary study. *Biological Psychiatry, 19,* 435–439.

Widdowson, E. M. (1992). Contemporary human diets and their relation to health and growth: Overview and conclusions. *Philosophical Transactions of the Royal Society of London [B], 334,* 289–295.

Young, S. N. (1993). Cholesterol, heart disease, and the brain: An opportunity in research and a disaster in public health education? *Journal of Psychiatry and Neuroscience, 18,* 1–3.

10

Plasma Lipoproteins and Apolipoproteins in Individuals Convicted of Violent Crimes

Frank M. Corrigan, Ronald F. Gray, E. Roy Skinner, Amanda Strathdee, and David F. Horrobin

This chapter reports the findings of a study on cholesterol levels in a sample of violent offenders. The results of this study are then compared with those of related studies, and finally, hypotheses regarding the link between violence and apolipoproteins and fatty acids are offered. First, however, we discuss the hypotheses concerning the mechanisms of the relationship between cholesterol and violence.

Relationships Between Cholesterol and Violence

The early primary prevention trials in cardiovascular disease (CVD) demonstrated that the lowering of serum cholesterol concentrations in middle-aged participants by various means led to an excess of violent deaths, including those from suicide (Horrobin, 1989; McLoughlin & Clarke, 1989; Muldoon, Manuck, & Mathews, 1990). Although there are a number of theories as to why this was so (Ernste, 1994), the most likely one would still appear to be that of a direct causal relationship. Nonetheless, it seems important to remain open to other possible explanations and not to get entrenched in a position without very strong supportive evidence (Marmott, 1994). There is an obvious and pressing need for large, well-designed trials to look specifically at the psychiatric correlates of lowering cholesterol levels and, in particular, at suicidality, impulsivity, and aggression. It is likely to be a pronounced change in cholesterol concentration rather than a characteristically low cholesterol concentration that is associated with changes in impulsivity and aggression.

The increased mortality from violent causes resulting from lowering of plasma cholesterol (described in detail in chapter 9) might have more heuristic validity if some adaptive behavior were associated with an acute fall in plasma cholesterol in humans at one stage or another of the evolution of the human race. It is conceivable that in societies dependent on hunting for food, an increase in aggressive risk taking, at times of low availability of fatty foods, would be advantageous to the person as well as to the social group of which he or she was a part. The high fat content of the typical Western diet even may have contributed biochemically to the development of civilization, with its careful regulation of violence, if it predisposes to increasing contentment and reduced impulsive aggression (Hughes, 1994).

In 1979, Virkkunen found low serum cholesterol concentrations in participants with antisocial personality disorders. Following on from this, he showed that participants with aggressive conduct disorder and attention deficit disorder had lower serum cholesterol concentrations than nonaggressive participants with attention deficit disorder and that habitual violence under the influence of alcohol also was associated with lower serum cholesterol levels (Virkkunen, 1983; Virkkunen & Penttinen, 1984). This relationship between cholesterol and aggression was replicated by some (Hillbrand, Spitz, & Foster, 1995) but not by others (Stewart & Stewart, 1981). An interesting hypothesis was put forward by Engelberg (1992) to explain the mechanism of low serum cholesterol being associated with suicide. Engelberg proposed that reducing serum cholesterol may reduce cholesterol levels in the brain, thus altering the cell membrane lipid microviscosity and decreasing the exposure of serotonin receptors on the membrane surface. This would lead to a poor uptake of serotonin from the blood and a resulting decrease in serotonin entry into brain cells, with a consequent disinhibition of aggressive impulses or an increase in such impulses.

The Apolipoprotein Hypothesis

Human serum lipoproteins, which carry cholesterol in the blood, are composed of apolipoproteins, triacylglycerol, phospholipids, and cholesterol. High density lipoprotein (HDL) contains about 50% apolipoproteins and 20% cholesterol and cholesteryl ester, whereas low density lipoprotein (LDL) consists of about 20% apolipoproteins and 46% cholesterol and cholesteryl ester (Gurr & James, 1980). As discussed below, our hypothetical position states that apolipoprotein subtypes (i.e., apoA-IV and apoE), as constituents of HDL cholesterol, may vary in specific subpopulations due to genetic and environmental factors.

Lipoproteins and Cholesterol Transport

The plasma lipoproteins, with the enzymes and factors that act on them, form a complex system for the transport of cholesterol and other lipids and the maintenance of their proper distribution in the tissues of the body (Nilsson-Ehle, Garfinkel, & Schotz, 1980). Whereas the chylomicrons and very low density lipoproteins (VLDLs), released by the intestine and liver, respectively, are concerned primarily with the transport of triglycerides, the task of maintaining cholesterol homeostasis is performed by LDL and

HDL. Low density lipoprotein is the main vehicle of cholesterol transport in the circulation and is responsible for cholesterol uptake by the peripheral tissues; HDL serves a major role in the removal of cholesterol from these tissues and integrates the activities of the other lipoprotein classes by mediating the exchange of cholesterol and other lipids between them, as well as with cell membranes. High density lipoprotein consists of a mixture of small lipoprotein particles, which differ in size and lipid, and apolipoprotein composition and in their metabolic role (Skinner, 1994). Therefore, we studied, in violent offenders, the apolipoproteins associated with HDL (Gray et al., 1993), because this lipoprotein class is most directly concerned with cholesterol transport.

Apolipoproteins and Cholesterol Transport

High density lipoprotein, thus, plays a vital role in *reverse cholesterol transport* (i.e., removing excess cholesterol from peripheral tissues and transporting it to the liver for excretion). The metabolic function of HDL, as with other lipoproteins, is directed by the properties of its constituent apolipoproteins. These serve to maintain the structural integrity of the lipoprotein particle; to act as cofactors for the action of lipolytic or transferring enzymes; and to provide ligands for the specific receptor-mediated uptake by tissues of lipoprotein particles containing them.

Among the 14 or so known apolipoproteins, apoA-IV and apoE play a special role in cholesterol transport and metabolism. Because it facilitates cellular cholesterol efflux, apoA-IV, which is present in chylomicrons and HDL, as well as in a free form in plasma, is implicated in reverse cholesterol transport (Stein, Halperin, & Stein, 1986; Steinmetz et al., 1990). It is also reported to activate lecithin:cholesterol acyltransferase (Steinmetz & Utermann, 1985), which catalyzes the esterification of free cholesterol, an essential step in the mobilization of cholesterol in the plasma.

A polymorphic protein, apoE is associated with plasma chylomicrons, VLDL, and a subfraction of HDL. ApoE mRNA, is present in many tissues, but the largest amounts are in the liver and brain (Boyles, Pitas, Wilson, Mahley, & Taylor, 1985). It has a wide diversity of functions, some of which have only recently been recognized (Weisgraber, 1994). It provides the ligand for the receptor that takes up chylomicron remnants for the liver. Animals fed a high-cholesterol diet produce a novel species of HDL with a high content of apoE and cholesterol (Mahley, 1982), and it is not surprising that a subfraction of HDL rich in apoE has been shown to be significantly reduced in patients with CVD (Johnansson, Carlson, Landou, & Hamsten, 1991; Wilson, Patel, Russell, & Skinner, 1993). Of special interest in the present study is the observation that damage to neurons triggers an increased rate of synthesis of apoE in the surrounding glial cells (Ignatius et al., 1986). It has been proposed that the cholesterol released by the degenerating neurons forms a complex with apoE to form an HDL-like particle, which preserves a local supply of cholesterol for use in membrane formation during subsequent nerve cell regeneration (Poirier, 1994). Furthermore, apoE is increased in several neurodegenerative diseases, and in Alzheimer's disease it is bound to the extracellular amyloid senile plaques, to the intracellular neurofibrillary tangles, and at sites of cerebral congophilic angiopathy. The apoE4 phenotype has been reported to be associated with increased incidence and earlier age of onset of Alzheimer's disease (Poirier et al., 1993; Strittmatter et al., 1993). It is therefore abundantly clear that apoE is intimately associated with cholesterol homeostasis and is implicated to a great extent in normal brain function.

These two apolipoproteins, apoA-IV and apoE, are therefore important candidates for examination in violent offenders, in whom the management of cholesterol is reported to be impaired.

The Argyll and Bute Study of Apolipoproteins in Violent Offenders

Method

After gaining permission from the Scottish prison service and the ethics committee of the Argyll and Bute Hospital, Lochgilphead, Argyll, Scotland, we approached men serving prison sentences for offenses involving violence and asked them to participate in the study. We obtained informed consent from 15 male offenders, who were given a semistructured psychiatric interview to exclude major mental or physical disorder. We obtained details of the men's current and previous convictions and took a blood sample from each man. We did not apply any rating scales for measuring impulsivity and aggression at the time of the blood sampling, but we did ensure that the prisoners from whom blood was obtained were in prison for violent offenses and had committed violent offenses other than those leading to the relevant conviction. Given the difficulties of rating aggression (Bech & Mak, 1995), we considered that this approach gave us a population for whom violence was not a once-in-a-lifetime response to an extremely provoking event, but a recurring problem behavior. The control group consisted of 25 men, mainly members of staff at the Argyll and Bute Hospital, who did not have criminal convictions. We submitted the blood samples to low-speed centrifugation for 15 min, after which the plasma was then separated and stored at −20°C. By means of sequential ultracentrifugation at increasing solvent density (Skinner, 1992), VLDL, LDL, and HDL were separated from the plasma.

We measured plasma and lipoprotein cholesterol concentrations by enzymic assays. As previously described (Skinner, 1992), HDL subfractions were separated by polyacrylamide gradient gel electrophoresis. We obtained apolipoproteins from HDL by delipidization with ethanol:ether mixtures and quantitated the apolipoproteins by scanning the gels after sodium dodecyl sulphate electrophoresis. Because methods for the determination of the absolute concentration of apolipoproteins were not available, their concentrations were expressed in terms of relative peak areas.

Table 1. Lipoprotein Cholesterol, HDL Subfractions, and Apolipoproteins for Violent Offenders and Controls

Measure	Offenders		Controls		
	M	SD	M	SD	p
Total cholesterol	179.91	35.60	192.47	38.70	ns
HDL-C	38.09	11.29	38.16	8.98	ns
LDL-C	79.23	20.15	72.99	20.91	ns
VLDL-C	17.03	9.22	25.33	17.33	ns
HDL2b	11.78	9.47	12.53	5.30	ns
HDL2a	19.73	5.94	22.19	4.92	ns
HDL3a	39.61	7.20	24.80	4.25	ns
HDL3b	23.81	5.55	4.30	5.68	ns
HDL3c	5.06	2.75	4.30	2.87	ns
apoA-IV	3.62	1.43	0.85	0.39	<.000001
apoE	7.70	2.01	5.19	1.38	<.0002
apoA-I	39.25	8.18	44.48	4.34	<.006
apoA-III/apoD	2.57	0.88	2.62	1.23	ns
apoA-II	9.52	2.44	10.35	2.04	ns
apoC-I, apoC-II, apoC-III	36.14	5.72	34.57	3.69	ns
n	15		25		

Note: HDL-C = high density lipoprotein cholesterol concentrations, LDL-C = low density lipoprotein cholesterol concentrations, VLDL-C = very low density lipoprotein cholesterol concentrations. These were measured in mg/100 mL^{-1}. HDL subfractions are percentages of HDL. apo = apolipoprotein. These measures are percentages of total apolipoproteins on HDL. p values were obtained by Mann–Whitney U tests. ns = nonsignificant.

The two groups (offenders and controls) differed little in age (M for offenders = 28.7 years, SD = 4.5; M for controls = 28.7 years, SD = 5.1); height (M for offenders = 1.74 m, SD = 0.06; M for controls = 1.75 m, SD = 0.07); weight (M for offenders = 70.8 kg, SD = 8.4; M for controls = 75.3 kg, SD = 10.6); and smoking history. There were differences in alcohol consumption between the two groups in that all the offenders had been abstinent for the duration of their prison stay, whereas most of the control participants consumed alcohol in moderation. It was not possible to match the two groups for diet, but the magnitude of the differences in the HDL apolipoproteins make it unlikely that diet was responsible for them. There were no correlations between the length of time already spent in prison (M = 29.5 months, SD = 19.3, range = 9–78 months) and the lipid variables.

Results

There were no significant differences in total plasma cholesterol concentrations; in HDL cholesterol (HDL-C), LDL-C, or VLDL-C concentrations; or in the HDL subfractions (Table 1). The most significant differences were in the apolipoproteins apoA-IV and apoE, which were both present in much higher concentrations in the offenders than in the control participants. ApoA-I was slightly lower in the violent offenders. We subsequently checked the apoE phenotypes and found no evidence of a trend toward a particular phenotypic expression in the violent offenders.

Very significant differences were observed in the fatty acids in the blood of these offenders in whom there were raised apoE and apoA-IV concentrations (Corrigan et al., 1994). In the HDL of the offenders, there was higher oleic acid (18:1n9; M for offenders = 15.78, SD = 1.27; M for controls = 14.10, SD = 1.33; $p < .0001$) and lower linoleic acid (18:2n6; M for offenders = 20.78, SD = 4.79; M for controls = 24.48, SD = 3.27; $p < .005$); arachidonic acid (20:4n6; M for offenders = 7.25, SD = 1.44; M for controls = 9.90, SD = 2.13; $p < .0001$); adrenic acid (22:4n6; M for offenders = 0.23, SD = 0.15; M for controls = 0.38, SD = 0.12; $p < .0005$); and docosahexaenoic acid (DHA; 22:6n3; M for offenders = 2.01, SD = 0.54; M for controls = 3.00, SD = 1.00; $p < .001$). It is therefore possible that altered phospholipid fatty acids could alter the binding characteristics of the HDL particles in such a way that the apolipoproteins would be dissociated from the HDL at different rates in blood from offenders and from controls. We thus looked at the correlations of the HDL apolipoproteins with the HDL fatty acids although the groups were small. For the controls, there were no correlations of the proportion of DHA (22:6n3) in the HDL with the apolipoprotein constitution of the HDL (see Table 2), although there were significant correlations for the offenders of the DHA content with the apolipoproteins apoE, apoA-I, apoA-II, and apoC.

Discussion

Evidence has been provided to suggest the existence of a relationship between plasma cholesterol concentrations and mortality from CVD (Isles, Mole, Gillis, Hawthorne, & Lever, 1989). Epidemiological studies have suggested that lowering plasma cholesterol levels in the population by just 10% might be associated with a 25% reduction in CVD (Law, Wald, & Thompson, 1994). However, there may be costs of doing this, especially if the relationship between CVD and cholesterol is correlational rather than etiological. In addition, the issue of increases in non-illness-related mortality (e.g., violence and suicide) associated with cholesterol lowering warrants further consideration of the putative link between violent behavior and serum lipid levels. Because apolipoprotein distribution provides a major determinant of cholesterol metabolism, it would be of considerable interest to establish whether this distribution was different in individuals with violent tendencies. The present study demonstrated a strong association between the levels of apoE and apoA-IV in HDL makeup and violence.

Some apolipoproteins are known to be dissociated from HDL during the preparation of the latter in the ultracentrifuge. Although identical ultracentrifugation procedures were used in the preparation of HDL from the two participant groups, the dissociation of the apolipoproteins from the HDL may have been abnormal in the offenders. Of interest is that the dissociation of apoA-IV from the HDL is dependent to some degree on the

Table 2. Correlations for HDL Fatty Acids and Apolipoproteins in Violent Offenders and Controls

Offenders	18:0	18:1n9	18:3n6	18:3n3	20:4n6	20:5n3	22:5n3	22:6n3
apoE				.62		.56		.62
apoA-I		.53	.57		-.71	-.61		-.89
apoA-III/apoD							-.57	
apoA-II	-.57	-.53	.66		.58	.66		.56
apoC-I, apoC-II, apoC-III								.58

Controls	18:0	18:2n6	18:3n6	20:2n6	20:3n6	22:4n6
apoA-IV						
apoA-I		.57	.43	.45	-.54	
apoA-II		-.4			.51	
apoC-I, apoC-II, apoC-III	.47			-.42		-.58

Note: Significant (*p* < .05) Spearman rank correlation coefficients for high density lipoprotein (HDL) fatty acids and HDL apolipoproteins in violent offenders (*n* = 14) and in controls (*n* = 25).

concentrations of VLDL, LDL, and cholesteryl ester transfer protein (Liang, Rye, & Barter, 1994). It is of particular interest that the observed alterations in apoE and apoA-IV were not accompanied by changes in the distribution of the different HDL subfractions, because many previous studies have established that these apolipoproteins are normally associated with specific HDL subspecies. These studies, however, have been largely concerned with coronary patients and normal control participants, in which large variations occur in the large HL2b fraction, which contains a large proportion of the total HDL apoE (Wilson et al., 1993). The results of the present study might therefore suggest that a different type of apoE-containing HDL particle may be present in the violent offenders, as has been suggested in the case of Alzheimer patients with a history of neuronal damage (Poirier, 1994). Such particles may have escaped detection on the gradient gel electrophoresis system used in this study, because of a large difference in particle size.

Although screening for ischemic heart disease does not usually involve measurement of apolipoproteins (Wald et al., 1994), it would still be important to monitor the apolipoproteins during cholesterol reduction, to understand the behavioral effects. Because apolipoprotein A-IV is involved in cholesterol removal from peripheral cells (Steinmetz et al., 1990), lowering cholesterol concentrations could result in a compensatory increase in ApoA-IV, or the cholesterol lowering effect might itself be achieved by a reduction in apoA-IV. In transgenic mice, overexpression of apoE was associated with marked reduction in plasma cholesterol and triglyceride concentrations, but not with a reduction in total HDL, although alteration in the subfraction of HDL that contained apoE was not measured (Shimano et al., 1992). There was a striking reduction in the plasma level of apoB, and the transgenic mice did not develop hypercholesterolemia when they were fed a high-cholesterol diet. A tendency for low cholesterol might result in an increase in apoA-IV, to take cholesterol from peripheral cells into circulation, whereas an increase in apoE might occur to provide a means of preserving available cholesterol for cell membrane function. Again this could be clarified by studies of apoA-IV and apoE during cholesterol lowering, whether by diet or by drugs.

Apolipoproteins and Fatty Acids

Weinberg and Jordan (1990) studied the binding of apoA-IV to phospholipid, by means of egg phosphatidylcholine vesicles. They reported that apoA-IV does not penetrate deeply into the phospholipid fatty acyl chain region but is held between the charged phospholipid head groups. The differences in HDL fatty acids could change the binding of the apolipoproteins to HDL so that the apolipoprotein dissociation from HDL would be different in the two groups (offenders and controls). However, there were no prominent correlations in Table 2 that would have suggested that apoA-IV was less firmly held in the HDL from offenders because of the different fatty acid constitution. For apoE, there were correlations with the omega-

3 fatty acids in the offender group but not in the control group. Although it remains a possibility that apolipoprotein dissociation from the HDL particles is different in offenders and although it is possible that this may relate to the different fatty acid composition of the HDL in offenders, the fatty acid differences may relate to nutritional and environmental factors in very early life or to minor differences in the enzymes regulating fatty acid metabolism and membrane composition, for example, as may happen also in schizophrenia (Horrobin, Glen, & Vaddadi, 1994) and dyslexia (Horrobin, Glen, & Hudson, 1995).

Although we found no significant relationships when we looked at the apoE phenotypes, we did not study apoA-IV polymorphism, which has been reported to be important in insulin metabolism (Kamboh, Hamman, Iyengar, Aston, & Ferrell, 1991). It is not inconceivable, therefore, that altered apolipoprotein concentrations may mediate the differences in insulin metabolism, which was reported in some studies of violent offenders (Virkunnen et al., 1994).

Conclusion

It has been hypothesized that violent offenders, and perhaps other individuals with impulse-control disorders, have a tendency, biologically determined, to have plasma cholesterol levels that are too low to maintain their normal membrane function. In the present study, however, the group of violent offenders investigated showed no tendency toward a reduced plasma cholesterol concentration. This result was not due to compensatory changes in the levels of the different lipoprotein classes, because we demonstrated that there was no difference in VLDL, LDL, or HDL. It is possible that these individuals may have reduced membrane cholesterol levels because of a defect in the mechanism by which their membranes acquire cholesterol from the circulating lipoproteins, probably from the HDL (Eisenberg, 1984). The increased concentrations of apoE and apoA-IV in the HDL fraction might be part of a homeostatic mechanism that is designed to increase cholesterol concentrations toward a level suited to better overall functioning. If this were so, it would be important to study total blood apoA-IV concentrations, because we might have detected a difference in the binding of apoA-IV to HDL, this association being weak and subject to disruption by ultracentrifugation (Lagrost, Gambert, Boquillon, & Lallemant, 1989). However, the increased apoE concentrations could not so readily be explained in the same way, in view of the study of the transgenic mice, in which the apoE expression was increased and the plasma cholesterol was reduced (Shimano et al., 1992). Possibly, additional apoE is present to combine with and preserve the available supply of cholesterol. We hope that groups that are now studying psychological changes in patients undergoing cholesterol reduction will also look at the changes in the total blood apolipoproteins and in the HDL apolipoproteins, because this may be of great significance, not only for the occurrence of ischemic heart disease in certain populations but also for the variable occurrence of violent death.

References

Bech, P., & Mak, M. (1995). Measures of impulsivity and aggression. In E. Hollander & D. Stein (Eds.), *Impulsivity and aggression.* Chichester, England: Wiley.

Boyles, J. K., Pitas, R. E., Wilson, E., Mahley, R. W., & Taylor, J. M. (1985). Apolipoprotein E associated with astrocytic glia of the central nervous system and with nonmyelinating glia of the peripheral nervous system. *Journal of Clinical Investigation, 76,* 1501–1513.

Corrigan, F. M., Gray, R., Strathdee, A., Skinner, R., Van Rhijn, A. G., & Horrobin, D. F. (1994). Fatty acid analysis of blood from violent offenders. *Journal of Forensic Psychiatry, 5,* 83–92.

Eisenberg, S. (1984). High density lipoprotein metabolism. *Journal of Lipid Research, 25,* 1017–1058.

Engelberg, H. (1992). Low serum cholesterol and suicide. *The Lancet, 339,* 727–729.

Ernste, E. (1994). Cholesterol and violence: More questions than answers. *British Journal of Hospital Medicine, 51,* 329–333.

Gray, R. F., Corrigan, F. M., Strathdee, A., Skinner, E. R., Van Rhijn, A. G., & Horrobin, D. F. (1993). Cholesterol metabolism and violence: A study of individuals convicted of violent crimes. *NeuroReport, 4,* 754–756.

Gurr, M. I., & James, A. T. (1980). *Lipid biochemistry: An introduction* (3rd ed.). New York: Chapman & Hall.

Hillbrand, M., Spitz, R. T., & Foster, H. G. (1995). Serum cholesterol and aggression in hospitalized male forensic patients. *Journal of Behavioral Medicine, 18,* 33–43.

Horrobin, D. F. (1989). Lipid-lowering drugs and violence. *British Journal of Psychiatry, 154,* 882–883.

Horrobin, D. F., Glen A. I. M., & Hudson, C. J. (1995). Possible relevance of phospholipid abnormality and genetic interactions in psychiatric disorders: The relationship between dyslexia and schizophrenia. *Medical Hypotheses, 45,* 605–613.

Horrobin, D. F., Glen, A. I. M., & Vaddadi K. (1994). The membrane hypothesis of schizophrenia. *Schizophrenia Research, 13,* 195–207.

Hughes, M. (1994). Diets, violence and civilisation. *British Medical Journal, 309,* 1228.

Ignatius, M. J., Gebicke-Harter, P. J., Skene, J. H. P., Schilling, J. W., Weisgraber, K. H., Mahley, R. W., & Shooter, E. M. (1986). Expression of apolipoprotein E during nerve degeneration and regeneration. *Proceedings of the National Academy of Science, 83,* 1125–1129.

Isles, C. G., Mole, D. J., Gillis, C. R., Hawthorne, V. M., & Lever, A. F. (1989). Plasma cholesterol, coronary heart disease, and cancer in the Renfrew and Paisley survey. *British Medical Journal, 298,* 920–924.

Johansson, J., Carlson, L. A., Landou, C., & Hamsten, A. (1991). High density lipoproteins and coronary atherosclerosis: A strong inverse relation with the largest particles is confined to normotriglyceridemic patients. *Arteriosclerosis and Thrombosis, 11,* 174–182.

Kamboh, M. I., Hamman, R. F., Iyengar, S., Aston, C. E., & Ferrell, R. E. (1991). Apolipoprotein A-IV polymorphism, and its role in determining variation in lipoprotein-lipid, glucose and insulin levels in normal and non-insulin-dependent diabetic individuals. *Atherosclerosis, 91,* 25–34.

Lagrost, L., Gambert, P., Boquillon, M., & Lallemant, C. (1989). Evidence for high density lipoproteins as the major apolipoprotein A-IV-containing fraction in normal human serum. *Journal of Lipid Research, 30,* 1525–1534.

Law, M. R., Wald, N. J., & Thompson, S. G. (1994). By how much and how quickly does reduction in serum cholesterol concentration lower risk of ischaemic heart disease? *British Medical Journal, 308,* 367–373.

Liang, H.-Q., Rye, K.-A., & Barter, P. J. (1994). Dissociation of lipid-free apolipoprotein A-I from high density lipoproteins. *Journal of Lipid Research, 35,* 1187–1199.

Mahley, R. W. (1982). Atherogenic hyperlipoproteinaemia: The cellular and molecular biology of plasma lipoproteins altered by dietary fat and cholesterol. *Medical Clinics of North America, 66,* 375–402.

Marmott, M. (1994). The cholesterol papers. *British Medical Journal, 308,* 351–352.

McLoughlin, I., & Clarke, P. (1989). Lipid-lowering drugs. *British Journal of Psychiatry, 154,* 275–276.

Muldoon, M. F., Manuck, S. B., & Matthews, K. A. (1990). Lowering cholesterol concentrations and mortality: A quantitative review of primary prevention trials. *British Medical Journal, 301,* 309–314.

Nilsson-Ehle, P., Garfinkel, A. S., & Schotz, M. C. (1980). Lipolytic enzymes and plasma lipoprotein metabolism. *Annual Review of Biochemistry, 49,* 667–693.

Poirier, J. (1994). Apolipoprotein E in animal models of CNS injury and in Alzheimer's disease. *Trends in Neurological Science, 17,* 525–530.

Poirier, J., Davignon, J., Bouthillier, D., Kogan, S., Bertrand, P., & Gauthier, S. (1993). Apolipoprotein E polymorphism and Alzheimer's disease. *The Lancet, 342,* 697–699.

Shimano, H., Yamada, N., Katsuki, M., Shimada, M., Gotoda, T., Harada, K., Murase, T., Fukazawa, C., Takaku, F., & Yazaki, Y. (1992). Overexpression of apolipoprotein E in transgenic mice: Marked reduction in plasma lipoproteins except high density lipoprotein and resistance against diet-induced hypercholesterolemia. *Proceedings of the National Academy of Science, 89,* 1750–1754.

Skinner, E. R. (1992). The separation and analysis of high-density lipoprotein (HDL) and low-density lipoprotein (LDL) subfractions. In C. A. Converse & E. R. Skinner (Eds.), *Lipoprotein analysis: A practical approach* (pp. 85–118). London: Oxford University Press.

Skinner, E. R. (1994). High-density lipoprotein subclasses. *Current Opinion in Lipidology, 5,* 241–247.

Stein, O., Halperin, G., & Stein, Y. (1986). Cholesteryl ester efflux from extracellular and cellular elements of the arterial wall: Model systems in culture with cholesteryl linoleyl ether. *Arteriosclerosis and Thrombosis, 6,* 70–78.

Steinmetz, A., Barbaras, R., Ghalim, N., Clavey, V., Fruchart, J.-C., & Ailhaud, G. (1990). Human apolipoprotein A-IV binds to apolipoprotein A-I/A-II receptor sites and promotes cholesterol efflux from adipose cells. *Journal of Biological Chemistry, 265,* 7859–7863.

Steinmetz, A., & Utermann, G. (1985). Activation of lecithin: Cholesterol acyltransferase by human apolipoprotein A-IV. *Journal of Biological Chemistry, 260,* 2258–2264.

Stewart, A. M., & Stewart, S. G. (1981). Serum cholesterol in antisocial personality: A failure to replicate earlier findings. *Neuropsychobiology, 7,* 9–11.

Strittmatter, W. J., Saunders, A. M., Schmechel, D., Pericak-Vance, M., Enghild, J., Salvesen, G. S., & Roses, A. D. (1993). Apolipoprotein E: High-avidity binding to β-amyloid and increased frequency of type 4 allele in late-onset familial Alzheimer disease. *Proceedings of the National Academy of Science, 90,* 1977–1981.

Virkkunen, M. (1979). Serum cholesterol in antisocial personality. *Neuropsychobiology, 5,* 27–30.

Virkkunen, M. (1983). Serum cholesterol levels in homicidal offenders. *Neuropsychobiology, 10,* 65–69.

Virkkunen, M., & Penttinen, H. (1984). Serum cholesterol in aggressive conduct disorder: A preliminary study. *Biological Psychiatry, 19,* 435–439.

Virkkunen, M., Rawlings, R., Tokola, R., Poland, R. E., Guidotti, A., Neneroff, C., Bissette, G., Kalogeras, K., Karonen, S.-L., & Linnoila, M. (1994). CSF biochemistries, glucose metabolism, and diurnal activity rhythms in alcoholic, violent offenders, fire setters and healthy volunteers. *Archives of General Psychiatry, 51,* 20–27.

Wald, N. J., Law, M., Watt, H. C., Wu, T., Bailey, A., Johnson, A. M., Craig, W. Y., Ledue, T. B., & Haddow, J. E. (1994). Apolipoproteins and ischaemic heart disease: Implications for screening. *The Lancet, 343,* 75–79.

Weinberg, R. B., & Jordan, M. K. (1990). Effects of phospholipid on the structure of human apolipoprotein A-IV. *Journal of Biological Chemistry, 265,* 8081–8086.

Weisgraber, K. H. (1994). Apolipoprotein E: Structure−function relationships. *Advances in Protein Chemistry, 45*, 249−302.

Wilson, H. M., Patel, J. C., Russell, D., & Skinner, E. R. (1993). Alterations in the concentration of an apolipoprotein E−containing subfraction of plasma high density lipoprotein in coronary heart disease. *Clinica Chimica Acta, 220*, 175−187.

11

Schizophrenia and Membrane Lipids

David F. Horrobin

The lipid content of the brain is very high. Lipids make up a substantial proportion of all neuronal membranes and form the matrix within which membrane-associated proteins, such as receptors and ion channels, are embedded. Lipids are required for the normal structure of synaptic vesicles. Lipid messengers, such as free fatty acids, diacylglycerols, prostaglandins, leukotrienes, and hydroxy fatty acids, are absolutely required for normal neuronal function.

In spite of these obvious fundamental roles, lipids have been ignored, to a substantial degree, by those seeking a biochemical or a genetic basis for psychiatric illness. Instead, the emphasis primarily has been on neurotransmitter function. It has not been widely appreciated, for example, that the lipid environment may profoundly modulate neurotransmitter action and the function of neuronal proteins.

Many examples of this could be provided, but just one will be given, to illustrate the importance of this phenomenon. Witt and Nielsen (1994) studied the impact of changing the lipid environment on the amount of diazepam bound by an isolated diazepam receptor (Figure 1). Incubating the receptor with saturated fatty acids of a wide variety of chain lengths has no impact on diazepam binding. But the insertion of just a single *cis* double bond into the carbon chain of 16-, 18-, or 20-carbon fatty acids approximately doubled diazepam binding, as did adding two carbon atoms to a 14-carbon monounsaturated fatty acid. These are small changes, compared with what can happen in neuronal membranes that are exceptionally rich in highly unsaturated essential fatty acids (EFAs), such as arachidonic acid (AA), with 20 carbons and 4 double bonds, or docosahexaenoic acid (DHA), with 22 carbons and 6 double bonds. Equally, the lipid environment of the neuron can be modified in major ways by changing the proportions of the major phospholipids, cholesterol, and cholesteryl esters that each neuron contains. Because protein folding, and, hence, the tertiary and quaternary structures of neuronal proteins—such as receptors, ion channels, and protein kinase—depend substantially on electrical and fluidity parameters and because these parameters are to a large degree determined by the lipid environment, it is clear that the precise functional structure of the proteins will be influenced by the details of neuronal lipid composition. Lipids, as in the example provided by the work of Witt and Nielsen, may therefore have major effects on neuronal

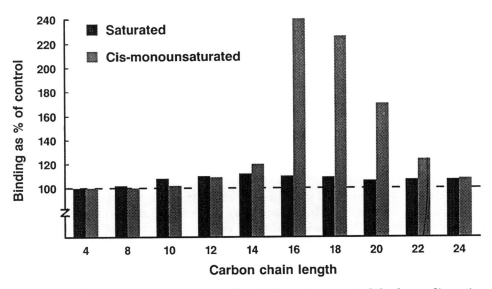

Figure 1. The impact of changes in the lipid environment of the benzodiazepine receptor on the binding of diazepam. Apparently small changes, such as the insertion of a single double bond or the addition of two carbon atoms, can produce large changes in binding, presumably because of changes in receptor protein configuration. (Redrawn from data in Witt & Nielsen, 1994.)

behavior through modulating the function of neuronal proteins. The lipids also may have much more direct effects on neuronal function, in that at least four of the main regulating systems of neurons, protein kinases, intracellular calcium, cyclic nucleotides, and the inositol cycle, are controlled or influenced by free fatty acids, diacylglycerols, and eicosanoids, such as prostaglandins, leukotrienes, and hydroxyacids.

It is therefore not implausible to suggest that a lipid abnormality might be one of the bases of the neuronal disturbance found in schizophrenia (Horrobin, Glen, & Vaddadi, 1994). Indeed, a lipid abnormality might provide a parsimonious explanation for the fact that as schizophrenic patients are investigated more thoroughly, it is clear that not just the dopamine system, but all neurotransmitter systems are functioning abnormally. It is of course possible to construct Ptolemaic epicycles to explain this, in which an abnormality in dopaminergic neurons leads, with ever-expanding ripples, to secondary abnormalities in all other neurotransmitter systems. Alternatively, if one postulates a membrane abnormality in a lipid system, then, as an inevitable consequence, all neurotransmitter systems would be defective to a greater or lesser degree. In this case, all the neurotransmitter, neurodevelopmental, and neuroanatomical abnormalities would follow logically from a single underlying abnormality.

This chapter summarizes the evidence leading to the concept that the single defect may lie in the regulation by phospholipase A_2 of the long-chain polyunsaturated fatty acid composition of neuronal and other cell membranes.

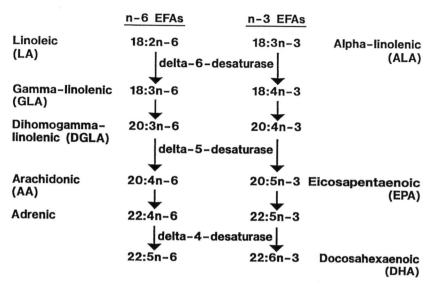

Figure 2.   An outline of the metabolism of the essential fatty acids.

Background

Neurochemistry

The background neurochemistry that indicates that such a proposition is not fundamentally implausible has recently been reviewed (Horrobin et al., 1994). In addition to the general concepts, which were outlined in our introduction, a number of specific items are worth mention here.

The most important fatty acids in the brain are AA and DHA, which constitute as much as 15% of the brain by weight. Arachidonic acid derives from dietary linoleic acid, and DHA derives from dietary alpha-linolenic acid, by the sequence of reactions shown in Figure 2. There are alternating *desaturations*, which insert double bonds into the carbon chain, and *elongations*, which add two carbon atoms. On the whole, the desaturations are slow, rate limiting, and regulated by many hormonal factors, whereas the elongations are rapid (Brenner, 1982; Horrobin, 1990c, 1992a). Arachidonic acid and DHA may be provided directly from the diet, also. Impor-

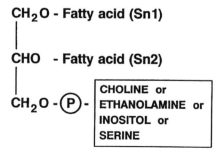

Figure 3.   The structure of phospholipids.

tant dietary sources of AA are breast milk, meats, eggs, and seafood, whereas sources of DHA are similar, except for eggs. Arachidonic acid and DHA, either formed by endogenous metabolism or provided in the food, readily cross the blood–brain barrier and are incorporated into phospholipids, primarily into the Sn2 position (Figure 3).

Red cell membranes from schizophrenics may show important abnormalities in DHA and AA composition (Glen et al., 1994; Peet, Laugharne, Horrobin, & Reynolds, 1994). Phospholipid composition shows a biphasic distribution, with about two thirds of individuals in the normal range and about one third showing much lower levels of AA and DHA. The group that exhibits low AA and DHA levels appears to encompass many individuals who clinically have features of the negative, or deficit, syndrome.

A simple biochemical test may be able to identify this group of individuals. It was noted some years ago that a proportion of individuals with schizophrenia fail to show facial flushing when given oral doses of niacin over 100 mg (Horrobin, 1980a). Such flushing occurs in almost all normal individuals and is due to release of vasodilator prostaglandin (PG) E_1 formed from dihomogammalinolenic acid (DGLA), and, particularly, of prostaglandin D_2, formed from AA (Morrow, Awad, Oates, & Roberts, 1992). A lack of flushing may indicate a lack of DGLA and AA to act as substrates. Although one group failed to confirm the observation, they may have used doses of niacin that were too low (Fiedler, Wolkin, & Rotrosen, 1986). Three other groups of investigators (Hudson, Lin, Cogan, & Warsh, 1995; Rybakowski & Weterle, 1991; Ward, Sutherland, Glen, & Glen, 1996) all obtained results in agreement with the original observation. As with the membrane fatty acid distribution, the abnormal group seemed to have many individuals who manifested the negative syndrome of schizophrenia.

The NMDA (N-methyl-D-aspartate) receptor is receiving increasing attention as a possible contributor to the biology of schizophrenia and other psychiatric disorders (Ulas & Cotman, 1993). It is therefore relevant that AA is a major second messenger in the receptor system and that changes in AA metabolism will have important influences on the functioning of this system.

Another relevant observation is the interaction between prostaglandin E_2, derived from AA, and prostaglandin E_1 with the dopaminergic system. Dopamine and the PGEs have opposite actions on the regulation of cyclic AMP (adenosine monophosphate) levels, dopamine lowering them and the PGEs raising them (Myers, Blosser, & Shain, 1978). There is also a behavioral antagonism, with prostaglandin E_1 opposing the effects of dopaminergic compounds in animals (Brus, Herman, Szkilnik, & Cichon, 1983; Oka, Manku, & Horrobin, 1981; Schwartz, Uretsky, & Bianchine, 1972). Furthermore, in cats, it has been shown that deficits of n-3 and n-6 EFAs during development have important effects on dopamine function, greatly attenuating the re-uptake of dopamine by presynaptic sites (Davidson, Kustiens, Patton, & Cantrill, 1988). D_2 receptors function in part by stimulating the release of AA (Berry-Kravis, Freedman, & Dawson, 1984; Di Marzo & Piomelli, 1992). This release of AA is mediated by cytoplasmic phospholipase A_2 and may be regulated by prostaglandin E_1 (Horrobin,

1980b). Thus, it would be at least plausible to construct a hypothesis that suggested that the abnormalities of the dopamine system observed in schizophrenia might be secondary to preexisting abnormalities of the EFA–prostaglandin system.

Similarly, the dopaminergic abnormalities of dyskinesias may be secondary to lipid changes. In a prospective study of dyskinesias in a random sample of 60-year-old men in Göteberg, Sweden, 37 individuals with orofacial dyskinesias were identified, most of whom had never been exposed to neuroleptic therapy (Nilsson & Horrobin, 1995). The plasma phospholipids of these individuals as compared with controls, showed significant deficits of DGLA, AA, and, especially, DHA (Nilsson and Horrobin, 1995).

Thus, the neurochemical observations are in keeping with the idea that fatty acid–phospholipid metabolism is a candidate worthy of investigation by those seeking to identify a biological basis for schizophrenia.

Clinical Observations

Most biological and clinical research in schizophrenia understandably concentrates on the purely psychiatric aspects of the disease. Obviously, the psychiatric symptomatology must be ultimately explicable in terms of neurochemistry, but the links are likely to be complex and tortuous. It is unlikely that clinical psychiatric symptoms will provide any clues, except in so far as they may possibly suggest particular areas of brain involvement. But there are other types of clinical observation, which are simpler and which may point to particular biochemical possibilities. Some of these observations are outlined below. They have been discussed in a series of papers (Horrobin, 1977; Horrobin, 1979; Horrobin, 1985; Horrobin, 1986; Horrobin, 1990b; Horrobin, 1992b; Horrobin et al., 1978; Horrobin et al., 1994; Horrobin & Manku, 1989; Kaiya, Horrobin, Manku, & Morse-Fisher, 1991).

1. Schizophrenic patients are relatively free of certain inflammatory disorders, notably rheumatoid arthritis. This is a robust and consistent finding, first noted in 1932 and confirmed many times since (Horrobin, 1977; Vinogradov, Gottesman, Moises, & Nichol, 1991). However, close relatives of schizophrenics may show the reverse phenomenon, a great increase in inflammatory disorders and in other diseases such as diabetes (Holden, 1995; Holden & Mooney, 1995).

2. Some schizophrenics are highly resistant to pain. This also is a robust and repeated observation (Davis, Buchsbaum, van Kammen, & Bunney, 1979; Horrobin et al., 1978).

3. Some schizophrenics show a brief but dramatic remission of psychotic symptoms during febrile episodes. Discovery of the abatement of psychosis during fever-inducing malaria won Wagner-Jauregg a Nobel Prize in 1926 (Horrobin et al., 1978; Lipper & Werman, 1977).

4. There is a modest but consistent increase in schizophrenia in populations exposed to viral infections, especially the influenza virus in pregnancy (Murray, O'Callaghan, Castle, & Lewis, 1992).
5. Starvation during pregnancy, low infant birth weight, and low infant head circumference are associated with an increased risk of schizophrenia (McNeil, Cantor-Graae, Nordstrom, & Rosenlund, 1993; Rifkin, Jones, & Murray, 1993; Susser & Lin, 1992).
6. Males are at greater risk of early development of schizophrenia than are females. This is counterbalanced by an increased female risk in later life (Iacono & Beiser, 1992; Murray et al., 1992; Wahl & Hunter, 1992).
7. Whereas the incidence of schizophrenia was similar in all countries in the World Health Organization study, the severity of the disease differed considerably from country to country (World Health Organization, 1979). Intensive work has failed to provide plausible explanations on the basis of health care system, economic environment, or social structure.
8. A plethora of studies demonstrated that stress of any sort may elevate the risk of a schizophrenic breakdown (Warner, 1994).

These observations are all robust, and all must be explained by any hypothesis of schizophrenia. Most of them cannot easily be incorporated into either neurotransmitter or psychodynamic explanations of schizophrenia.

Schizophrenia: A Lipid Hypothesis

Three sets of observations point rather directly to the idea that schizophrenia may be related to excessive activity of one of the PLA_2 group of enzymes. These enzymes selectively remove fatty acids, especially unsaturated fatty acids, from the Sn2 position of phospholipids. They are usually said to be rather specific for AA, but that may be because AA is the most widely studied of the EFAs. There is recent evidence that a phospholipase A_2 found in brain cells is equally effective in removing both AA and DHA from phospholipids (Garcia & Kim, 1995). The three observations are as follows:

1. In some schizophrenics, red cell membranes are depleted of AA and DHA (Glen et al., 1994). This is exactly what would be expected if there were increased phospholipase A_2 activity.
2. In the cortex of schizophrenics, there is evidence obtained from using P^{31} magnetic resonance imaging that there is an increased rate of breakdown of phospholipids (Hinsberger et al., 1995; Pettegrew, Keshavan, & Minchew, 1993; Pettegrew, Keshavan, & Panchalingam, 1991).
3. In the blood of schizophrenics, there is evidence of increased cir-

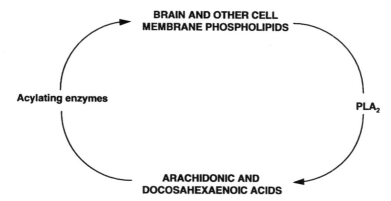

Figure 4. The balance between the incorporation into membranes of arachidonic acid and docosahexaenoic acid and their removal. Schizophrenia is due to excessive activity of a PLA_2 (phospholipase A_2) which removes arachidonic and docosahexaenoic acids from membrane phospholipids.

culating concentrations of an enzyme with phospholipase A_2 activity (Gattaz, Hubner, & Nevalainen, 1990).

As has been pointed out (Horrobin et al., 1994), different degrees of increased phospholipase A_2 activity, possibly related to heterozygotes and homozygotes, would be expected to lead to abnormalities both of fatty acid flux into and out of cell membrane phospholipids and of fatty acid concentrations in those phospholipids. The membrane phospholipids are not static but are constantly remodeled by complex enzyme systems that incorporate fatty acids into phospholipids (the acylating enzymes) and other systems that remove fatty acids from phospholipids (the phospholipases). This balance is shown in a greatly simplified form in Figure 4. A modest overactivity of a phospholipase A_2 is likely to be relatively easily compensated by a physiological increase in the activity of the acylating enzyme systems. There will thus be an increased flux of fatty acids, such as AA and DHA, into and out of the membrane, but no changes in the fatty acid composition of the membrane. Such an increased flux may make the neuronal membranes less stable and also hyperresponsive to stimuli that involve the release of AA or other EFA-related second messengers.

Higher levels of excess phospholipase A_2 activity may not be capable of compensation in this way. Thus, one would reach a state of actual depletion of membrane phospholipid AA and DHA with all the additional consequences that would follow such a change in membrane composition and membrane structure. The functions of all membrane-associated proteins would change, and in particular, AA- and DHA-dependent second-messenger systems would cease to function normally.

This second level of change would be exacerbated by any factors that reduced the supply of AA and DHA and would be alleviated by factors that increased such supplies. It is on this basis that many of the features of schizophrenia outlined in the Background, Clinical Observations, section may be explained (Horrobin et al., 1994).

1. Resistance to inflammatory disorders. Arachidonic acid is of vital importance in mounting an inflammatory response and, if AA is depleted, then inflammation will be diminished. On the other hand, a mild phospholipase A_2 defect, which resulted in increased AA flux but with maintenance of AA concentrations, might lead to increased inflammation and explain the increased risk of inflammatory and immune disorders in relatives of schizophrenics.

2. Arachidonic acid–derived metabolites are involved in producing pain, and a reduction in AA availability might diminish pain responses.

3. Elevation of temperature is associated with increased conversion of AA to its metabolites. If these metabolites are important in modulating schizophrenic symptoms, then the relief that may occur during fever might be interpreted biochemically as making the best of the available AA.

4. Viral infections block the conversion of linoleic and alpha-linolenic acids to their AA and DHA metabolites (Horrobin, 1990a), and so would be expected to increase risk of deficits of AA and DHA.

5. During starvation in pregnancy, EFA deficiency may develop rapidly. Fetal growth is closely tied to the availability of AA (Koletzko, 1992).

6. Females have lower EFA requirements than do males (Huang, Horrobin, Watanabe, Bartlett, & Simmons, 1990; Pudelkiewicz, Seufert, & Holman, 1968). A deficit of AA and DHA might therefore be expected to be more readily expressed in males, whereas, because estrogen seems important in this gender difference, females would lose some of their protection in later life.

7. Christensen and Christensen (1988) drew attention to the possibility of explaining the World Health Organization findings on incidence and severity of schizophrenia on the basis of diet. They pointed out that a poor outcome of schizophrenia is positively correlated with consumption of foods rich in saturated fat, whereas a good outcome is positively correlated with consumption of fish and other foods rich in the EFAs required for the brain. The ratio of the one to the other produces a very highly significant correlation with clinical outcome (Horrobin, 1992b). Thus, relatively high intakes of EFAs appear protective, whereas relatively high intakes of saturated fats, which compete with EFAs for incorporation into membranes, have an adverse influence. This finding is in keeping with the relapse studies of Yao et al. (Yao, van Kammen, & Gurklis, 1994; Yao, van Kammen, & Welker, 1994), which showed that AA levels tend to be low in red cell membranes in some schizophrenics and that low AA levels are predictive of early relapse after withdrawal of neuroleptic therapy. There have been no published reports of attempts to treat schizophrenia with AA or DHA, but several studies of the use of relatively low doses of the AA precursors, gamma-linolenic acid (GLA) and DGLA, reported modest beneficial effects (Bourgignon, 1984; Soulairac, Lambinet, &

Heuman, 1990; Vaddadi, in press; Vaddadi, Courtney, Gilleard, Manku, & Horrobin, 1988; Vaddadi, Gilleard, Mindham, & Butler, 1986). Of most interest is a study in which at the end of a period of GLA treatment, Vaddadi (1992) added a series of mineral and vitamin cofactors known to be important in EFA metabolism and in EFA incorporation into membranes. Essential fatty acid levels in red cell membranes increased sharply without any increase in EFA intake, and there was a simultaneous sudden improvement in psychotic symptoms.

8. Hormones released in stress, both catecholamines and glucocorticoids, strongly inhibit the first desaturase reaction that converts linoleic and alpha-linolenic acids to their respective metabolites (Brenner, 1982; Horrobin, 1990c, 1992a). Administration of GLA, which bypasses the blocked step in the n-6 EFA pathway, reduces blood pressure elevation and lowers catecholamine levels during stress (Kreysel & Nissen, 1992; Mills, Huang, Narce, & Poisson, 1994). Thus, stress would be expected to diminish the availability of AA and DHA.

Apparently an abnormality of phospholipase A_2 provides plausible explanations for a range of clinical observations that must be accounted for, but which are usually ignored, when devising clinical or biochemical hypotheses to explain schizophrenia.

A Genetic Abnormality in Phospholipase A_2 Regulation

All of these observations led a research group from the Clarke Institute of Psychiatry in Toronto, Ontario, Canada, and from Scotia Pharmaceuticals, Guildford, England, to seek a genetic abnormality in one of the phospholipase A_2 enzymes in schizophrenic individuals. Initially, we chose to look at a cytoplasmic phospholipase A_2, which had been identified by another research group from the Hospital for Sick Children in Toronto (Tay et al., 1995). This cytoplasmic phospholipase A_2 was of particular interest because the Tay et al. group had found a region with considerable polymorphism both in rats and in humans. Like all genes that control proteins, a structural component of the gene determines the amino acid region of the protein, and a promoter region determines how many copies of the protein will be made. Gene promoter regions often contain what are known as *simple sequence reports*. One of the simple sequence reports in the cytoplasmic phospholipase A_2 gene was a string of adenines (polyA). Of particular interest was the finding that in an apparently normal population, there were 10 different alleles for this polyA sequence, each with a different number of adenines. Because variations in the promoter region may lead to variations in the number of enzyme copies made, it seemed possible that this area of the gene might be worth investigating.

Hudson, Kennedy, et al., (in press) therefore, obtained blood samples from 50 schizophrenics, identified on the basis of criteria from the *Diag-

nostic and Statistical Manual of Mental Disorders (American Psychiatric Association, 1987) and analyzed the allele frequencies in the polyA region of the cytoplasmic phospholipase A_2 gene. Their distribution turned out to be very different from the distribution in the normal population. In the normal population, 92% of the alleles were in the A1–A6 group, and only 8% in the A7–A10 region. In a group of schizophrenics who failed to flush with niacin, 100% of the alleles were in the A7–A10 group (Hudson, Kennedy, & Horrobin, 1995).

It seems possible that the expression of the cytoplasmic phospholipase A_2 gene is regulated in part by the polyA sequence and that the more alleles there are in the sequence, the more copies of the enzyme will be made. It also seems possible that the amount of enzyme produced in the presence of alleles A1–A6 is normal and that variation within this range can be dealt with by the body's normal regulating mechanisms, whereas the presence of alleles A7–A10 leads to excess synthesis of phospholipase A_2, which is beyond the ability of normal regulation to cope. Individuals who are homozygous for the A7–A10 region will be more likely to have a clear abnormality than those who are heterozygous.

Whether the cytoplasmic phospholipase A_2 gene alone is adequate to explain schizophrenia is of course unknown at present. Its importance may be amplified or attenuated by the simultaneous presence or absence of other genes, either for neurotransmitter function or for fatty acid metabolism. One possible interaction is with the gene for dyslexia, which may lead to mildly impaired incorporation of AA and DHA into cell membranes (Stordy, 1995). Obviously, a genetic abnormality that led to increased removal of AA and DHA would have more serious consequences in the presence of another genetic abnormality that led to reduced incorporation of the same fatty acids (Horrobin, Glen, & Hudson, 1995).

If each allele in the promoter cytoplasmic phospholipase A_2 region does lead to a different rate of synthesis of copies of the enzyme, there are clearly 10^2, or 100, possible combinations of the two polyA region alleles in each cell. If the dyslexia gene interacts with the cytoplasmic phospholipase A_2 gene, then, assuming that the dyslexia gene has only two alleles, normal and abnormal, there will be 300 possible biochemical syndromes leading to abnormalities of membrane AA and DHA metabolism. Each cytoplasmic phospholipase A_2 genotype may be present in individuals who are homozygous normal, heterozygous, or homozygous abnormal for the dyslexia gene. If there are more alleles of the dyslexia gene, the numbers of possible genotypes will increase further. The possible interactions between dyslexia and schizophrenia are discussed in some detail elsewhere (Horrobin et al., 1995).

If each biochemical variant leads to a slightly different clinical syndrome, then there opens up the possibility of biochemical explanations for many of the wide variety of disorders in the schizophrenia spectrum. One interesting possibility is that homozygotes for the A7–A10 region may have a high risk of deficit-syndrome schizophrenia, and even of borderline mental handicap, because new observations by Glen, Glen, Skinner, and McDonnell (1995a) confirmed a previously reported relationship between schizophrenia and mental handicap (Heston & Denney, 1968). Another possibility is that heterozygotes may have a milder spectrum of disorders, which could include the positive syndrome of schizophrenia, bipolar manic–depression, borderline personality, and psychopathy, because all of these occur with increased frequency in families identified by the presence of a schizophrenic proband (Glen et al., 1995a; Heston & Denney, 1968; Rosenthal et al., 1968).

Of even greater interest is the possibility that abnormalities in the cytoplasmic phospholipase A_2 gene could extend well beyond psychiatric illness, into what is normally regarded as physical illness. Whereas narrow-definition schizophrenics have a reduced risk of inflammatory disorders, relatives of schizophrenics have an increased risk of inflammatory disorders and of diabetes (Holden, 1995). Bipolar disorder and multiple sclerosis also seem to be associated (Horrobin, 1981; Horrobin & Nilsson, 1995). Dyslexics and relatives of schizophrenics seem to have a higher risk of asthma, allergic disorders, and attention deficit disorder (hyperactivity). The delineation of autism, Asperger's syndrome, and fragile x syndrome from the other psychiatric disorders mentioned here is not always as clear as might be thought, and they, too, could be components of this spectrum.

There is, therefore, the possibility, which can be tested rapidly over the next 3 years, that a whole spectrum of psychiatric and physical disorders may be linked by abnormalities in phospholipases. If this is so, then we have suggested that the old terms, particularly for the psychiatric disorders, will no longer be appropriate (Horrobin et al., 1995). We have proposed the term *phospholipase spectrum disorder*, which might be written as PSD, followed by a more defining term in brackets, to specify exactly which disorder is present. The next few years will determine whether this or a similar concept is appropriate.

Interactions Between Genes and Environment and the Prevention of Schizophrenia

One of the most important statistics in the field of schizophrenia is that around 40%–50% of identical-twin pairs are concordant for the disease, whereas for other siblings, including dizygotic twins, if one individual is affected, the risk for the other individual is only 10%–15%. There is obviously a strong genetic component to schizophrenia. Equally, however, the concordance rate in identical twins falls far short of 100%, indicating that environmental factors profoundly influence the expression of the schizophrenia gene. The risk of schizophrenia in the descendants of affected and nonaffected identical twins is the same, so that the presence of the normal phenotype does not reduce the likelihood of passing on the disease.

This strong influence of environmental factors is one reason why the nature of the inheritance of schizophrenia has been so difficult to elucidate. It is something that is shared with most of the psychiatric and somatic diseases mentioned in the previous section. Bipolar disorders, mental handicap, rheumatoid arthritis, diabetes, multiple sclerosis, asthma, and others all share this tantalizing confusion between genetic and environmental effects.

The clinical evidence therefore suggests that the biochemical problem that should be sought is one in which there is the possibility of a clear interaction between genetic and environmental factors. Membrane lipid composition is one such point of interaction (Horrobin, 1995). The enzymes that are involved in modeling and remodeling membranes, such as the acylating systems and the phospholipases, are clearly genetically determined. But these enzymes, although they show preferences for particular fatty acids, will act on other fatty acids, and they have no control over the composition of the pool of fatty acids that may be available. The composition of that pool is to some degree determined by genetic factors, such as the enzyme sequences illustrated in Figure 2, but is also heavily influenced by environmental factors, such as the foods that are available and frequently eaten, the occurrence of viral infections, and the presence of stress-induced changes in hormone levels (Figure 4; Horrobin, 1990a, 1990c, 1992b, 1995). Thus, final membrane composition will unequivocally be determined by both genetic and environmental factors and provides a clear battleground on which these factors can interact.

In the case of schizophrenia, the 40%–50% concordance role in identical twins indicates that environmental factors must be capable of suppressing the phenotype expression of the psychiatric disorder and, therefore, probably of the underlying biochemical disorder. The work of the Christensens (e.g., Christensen & Christensen, 1988) strongly suggests that the lipid composition of the diet is one of the most important environmental factors.

If the supply of AA and DHA for membranes can be increased, then the impact of enhanced cytoplasmic phospholipase A_2 activity may be diminished or blocked altogether. If AA and DHA are combined with GLA or DGLA, fatty acids that through the prostaglandin E_1–cyclic AMP route are known to be able to inhibit phospholipase A_2 (Horrobin, 1980b), then it may be possible to regulate the abnormality effectively by the physiological manipulation of biochemical pathways, as opposed to the use of drugs that block dopamine or other receptors or inhibit cytoplasmic phospholipase A_2. In this context, it is of interest that clozapine has a structure that may make it able to bind to prostaglandin E receptors and to inhibit phospholipase A_2 (Horrobin et al., 1978). If the physiological and biochemical issues are addressed, then the drugs, if they are required, may be effective at much lower doses than usual, and consequently, with fewer side effects.

Perhaps the most exciting potential implication of this work is that schizophrenia and related disorders could be completely prevented. Children from families that had a schizophrenic member in the past three generations, or who are showing unusual behavior, could be tested for the presence of abnormal cytoplasmic phospholipase A_2 alleles. If these alleles were present, the children could be treated by an appropriate mix of fatty acids, to suppress both the biochemical and the psychiatric expression of the gene. Simultaneously, family, social, and educational measures might be instituted to assist in increasing the efficacy of the biochemical approach. At the moment, this is, of course, fantasy. But it is not an entirely irrational fantasy and does raise the small possibility of actually being able to eliminate schizophrenia in the great majority of those at risk.

Conclusion

Investigation of the membrane lipid hypothesis of schizophrenia has led to the identification of a candidate gene for the disease. The gene appears to be capable of environmental manipulation. Its identification raises the possibility that schizophrenia might become preventable. This could be achieved by identifying the genetic abnormality at an early age by screening children from families who have had a schizophrenic member in the past two generations. Individuals with the abnormality could then be given higher amounts of the specific fatty acids, such as arachidonic acid and docosahexaenoic acid, which are present in reduced amounts in cell membranes from schizophrenics. Alternatively, or in addition, other lipids, such as gamma-linolenic acid or eicosapentaenoic acid, which inhibit phospholipase A_2. There is a reasonable possibility that such procedures could moderate the effects of the gene, although only clinical testing will prove whether or not this hypothesis is valid.

References

American Psychiatric Association. (1987). Diagnostic and statistical manual of mental disorders (3rd ed., rev.). Washington, DC: Author.

Bates, C., Horrobin, D. F., & Ells, K. (1991). Fatty acids in plasma phospholipids and cholesterol esters from identical twins concordant and discordant for schizophrenia. Schizophrenia Research, 6, 1–7.

Berry-Kravis, E., Freedman, S. B., & Dawson, G. (1984). Specific receptor-mediated inhibition of cyclic AMP synthesis by dopamine in a neuroblastoma X brain hybrid cell line NCB-20. Journal of Neurochemistry, 43, 413–420.

Bourgignon, A. (1984). Trial of evening primrose oil in the treatment of schizophrenia. L'Encephale, 10, 241–250.

Brenner, R. R. (1982). Nutritional and hormonal factors influencing desaturation of essential fatty acids. Progress in Lipid Research, 20, 41–48.

Brus, R., Herman, Z. S., Szkilnik, R., & Cichon, R. (1983). Effect of prostaglandins on chloropromazine induced catalepsy in mice. Biomedica Biochimica Acta, 42, 1211–1244.

Christensen, O., & Christensen, E. (1988). Fat consumption and schizophrenia. Acta Psychiatrica Scandinavica, 78, 587–591.

Davidson, B., Kustiens, N. P., Patton, J., & Cantrill, R. C. (1988). Essential fatty acids modulate apomorphine activity at receptors in cat caudate slices. European Journal of Pharmacology, 149, 317–322.

Davis, G. C., Buchsbaum, M. S., van Kammen, D. P., & Bunney, W. E. (1979). Analgesia to pain stimuli in schizophrenics and its reversal by naltrexone. Psychiatry Research, 1, 61–69.

Di Marzo, V., & Piomelli, D. (1992). Participation of prostaglandin E_2 in dopamine D_2 receptor-dependent potentiation of arachidonic response. Journal of Neurochemistry, 59, 379–382.

Fiedler, P., Wolkin, A., & Rotrosen, J. (1986). Niacin-induced flush as a measure of prostaglandin activity in alcoholics and schizophrenics. Biological Psychiatry, 21, 1347–1350.

Garcia, M. C., & Kim, H. Y. (1995, June). *Release of arachidonate and docosahexaenoate from rat C6 glioma cells*. Poster presented at the meeting of the 2nd International ISSFAL Congress, Bethesda, MD.

Gattaz, W. F., Hubner, C. v. K., & Nevalainen, T. J. (1990). Increased serum phospholipase A_2 activity in schizophrenia: A replication study. *Biological Psychiatry, 28*, 495–501.

Glen, A. I. M., Glen, E. M. T., Horrobin, D. F., Vaddadi, K. S., Spellman, M., Morse-Fisher, N., Ells, K., & Shinner, F. S. (1994). A red cell abnormality in a subgroup of schizophrenic patients: Evidence for two diseases. *Schizophrenia Research, 12*, 53–61.

Glen, A. I. M., Glen, E., Skinner, F., & McDonnell, L. (1995). *Psychiatric illness in the families of schizophrenics in Northern Scotland*. Manuscript in preparation.

Heston, L. L., & Denney, D. (1968). Interactions between early life experience and biological factors in schizophrenia. In D. Rosenthal & S. S. Kety (Eds.), *The transmission of schizophrenia* (pp. 363–376). Oxford, England: Pergamon Press.

Hinsberger, A., Williamson, P. C., Carr, T., Stanley, J., Drost, D., Densmore, M., MacFabe, G., & Montemurro, D. (1995). MRI volumetric measures and ^{31}P MRS in schizophrenia. *Schizophrenia Research, 15*, 83–84.

Holden, R. J. (1995). The estrogen connection: The etiological relationship between diabetes, cancer, rheumatoid arthritis and psychiatric disorders. *Medical Hypotheses, 45*, 169–189.

Holden, R. J., & Mooney, P. A. (1995). Schizophrenia is a diabetic brain state: An elucidation of impaired neurometabolism. *Medical Hypotheses, 43*, 420–435.

Horrobin, D. F. (1977). Schizophrenia as a prostaglandin deficiency disease. *The Lancet, 1*, 936–937.

Horrobin, D. F. (1979). Schizophrenia: Reconciliation of the dopamine, prostaglandin and opioid concepts and the role of the pineal. *The Lancet, i*, 529–531.

Horrobin, D. F. (1980a). Niacin flushing, prostaglandin E and evening primrose oil: A possible objective test for monitoring therapy in schizophrenia. *Journal of Orthomolecular Psychiatry, 9*, 33–34.

Horrobin, D. F. (1980b). The regulation of prostaglandin biosynthesis: Negative feedback mechanisms and the selective control of the formation of 1 and 2 series prostaglandins: Relevance to inflammation and immunity. *Medical Hypotheses, 6*, 687–709.

Horrobin, D. F. (1985). Schizophrenia. In M. M. Cohen (Ed.), *Biological protection with prostaglandins* (Vol. 1, pp. 254–262). Boca Raton, FL: CRC Press.

Horrobin, D. F. (1986). Essential fatty acids and prostaglandins in schizophrenia and alcoholism. In C. Shagass (Ed.), *Biological psychiatry* (pp. 1163–1165), Amsterdam: Elsevier.

Horrobin, D. F. (1990a). Essential fatty acids, immunity and viral infections. *Journal of Nutritional Medicine, 1*, 145–151.

Horrobin, D. F. (1990b). Essential fatty acids, prostaglandins and schizophrenia. In C. N. Stefanis (Ed.), *Psychiatry: A world perspective* (Vol. 2, pp. 140–144). Amsterdam: Elsevier.

Horrobin, D. F. (1990c). Gamma-linolenic acid. *Review of Contemporary Pharmacotherapy, 1*, 1–41.

Horrobin, D. F. (1992a). Nutritional and medical importance of gamma-linolenic acid. *Progress in Lipid Research, 31*, 163–192.

Horrobin, D. F. (1992b). The relationship between schizophrenia and essential fatty acids and eicosanoid production. *Prostaglandins Leukotrienes and Essential Fatty Acids, 46*, 71–77.

Horrobin, D. F. (1995). DNA-protein and membrane-lipid: Competing paradigms in biomedical research. *Medical Hypotheses, 44*, 229–232.

Horrobin, D. F., Ally, A. I., Karmali, R. A., Karmazyn, M., Manku, M. S., & Morgan, R. O. (1978). Prostaglandins and schizophrenia: Further discussion of the evidence. *Psychological Medicine, 8*, 43–48.

Horrobin, D. F., Glen, A. I. M., & Vaddadi, K. (1994). The membrane hypothesis of schizophrenia. *Schizophrenia Research, 13*, 195–207.

Horrobin, D. F., Glen, A. I. M., & Hudson, C. J. (1995). Possible relevance of phospholipid abnormalities and genetic interactions in psychiatric disorders: The relationship between dyslexia and schizophrenia. *Medical Hypotheses*, *45*, 605–613.

Horrobin, D. F., & Lieb, J. (1981). A biochemical basis for the actions of lithium on behaviour and on immunity: Relapsing and remitting disorders of inflammation and immunity such as multiple sclerosis or recurrent herpes as manic-depression of the immune system. *Medical Hypotheses*, *7*, 891–905.

Horrobin, D. F., & Manku, M. S. (1989). Possible role of prostaglandin E_1 in the affective disorders and in alcoholism. *British Medical Journal*, *280*, 1363–1366.

Horrobin, D. F., & Nilsson, A. (1995). *Association between multiple sclerosis and manic-depression*. Manuscript in preparation.

Huang, Y.-S., Horrobin, D. F., Watanabe, Y., Bartlett, M. E., & Simmons, V. A. (1990). Effects of dietary linoleic acid on growth and liver phospholipid fatty acid composition in intact and gonadectomized rats. *Biochemical Archives*, *6*, 47–54.

Hudson, C. J., Kennedy, J., & Horrobin, D. F. (1995). *Alleles in the promoter region of phospholipase A_2 in schizophrenics who do and do not flush in response to niacin*. Manuscript in preparation.

Hudson, C. J., Kennedy, J., Gotowiec, A., Lin, E. P., King, N., Gojtan, K., Macciardi, F., Skorecki, K., Meltzer, H. Y., Warsh, J. J., & Horrobin, D. F. (in press). Genetic variant near cytosolic phospholipase A_2 associated with schizophrenia. *Schizophrenia Research*.

Hudson, C. J., Lin, A., Cogan, S., & Warsh, J. J. (1995). Clinical detection of altered prostaglandin function in a schizophrenia sub-type. *Schizophrenia Research*, *15*, 60.

Iacono, W. G., & Beiser, M. (1992). Where are the women in the first-episode studies of schizophrenia? *Schizophrenia Bulletin*, *18*, 471–480.

Kaiya, H., Horrobin, D. F., Manku, M. S., & Morse-Fisher, N. (1991). Essential and other fatty individuals from Japan. *Biological Psychiatry*, *30*, 357–362.

Koletzko, B. (1992). Fats for brains. *European Journal of Clinical Nutrition*, *46*(Suppl. 1), 551–562.

Kreysel, H. W., & Nissen, H. P. (1992, June). *Effect of N-6 polyunsaturated fatty acid supplementation on the level of catecholamines and lipid peroxides in atopic eczema*. Poster presented at the meeting of the 18th World Congress of Dermatology, New York.

Lipper, S., & Werman, D. S. (1977). Schizophrenia and intercurrent physical illness: A critical review of the literature. *Comprehensive Psychiatry*, *18*, 11–22.

McNeil, T. F., Cantor-Graae, E., Nordstrom, L. G., & Rosenlund, T. (1993). Head circumference in "preschizophrenic" and control neonates. *British Journal of Psychiatry*, *162*, 517–523.

Mills, D. E., Huang, Y.-S., Narce, M., & Poisson, J.-P. (1994). Psychological stress, catecholamines and essential fatty acid metabolism in rats. *Proceedings of the Society for Experimental Biology and Medicine*, *205*, 1–6.

Morrow, J. D., Awad, J. A., Oates, J. A., & Roberts, L. J. (1992). Identification of skin as a major site of prostaglandin D_2 release following oral administration of niacin in humans. *Journal of Investigative Dermatology*, *98*, 812–815.

Murray, R. M., O'Callaghan, E., Castle, D. J., & Lewis, S. W. (1992). A neurodevelopmental approach to the classification of schizophrenia. *Schizophrenia Bulletin*, *18*, 319–332.

Myers, P. R., Blosser, J., & Shain, W. (1978). Neurotransmitter modulation of prostaglandin E_1-stimulated increases in cyclic AMP: II. Characterisation of a cultured neuronal cell line treated with dibutyryl cyclic AMP. *Biochemical Pharmacology*, *27*, 1173–1177.

Nilsson, A., & Horrobin, D. F. (1995). Abnormal involuntary movements (AIMS) and red cell lipids. *Schizophrenia Research*, *15*, 208–209.

Oka, M., Manku, M. S., & Horrobin, D. F. (1981). Interactions between dopamine and prostaglandins on vascular reactivity of noradrenaline: Dopamine inhibits the action of PGE_1. *Prostaglandins and Medicine*, *7*, 267–280.

Peet, M., Laugharne, J. D., Horrobin, D. F., & Reynolds, G. P. (1994). Arachidonic acid: A common link in the biology of schizophrenia. *Archives of General Psychiatry*, *51*, 665–666.

Pettegrew, J. W., Keshavan, M. S., & Minchew, N. J. (1993). 31P nuclear magnetic resonance spectroscopy: Neurodevelopment and schizophrenia. *Schizophrenia Bulletin*, *19*, 35–53.

Pettegrew, J. W., Keshavan, M. S., & Panchalingam, K. (1991). A pilot study of the dorsal prefrontal cortex using in vivo phosphorus 31 nuclear magnet resonance spectroscopy. *Archives of General Psychiatry, 48,* 563–568.

Pudelkewicz, C., Seufert, J., & Holman, R. T. (1968). Requirements of the female rat for linoleic and linolenic acids. *Journal of Nutrition, 64,* 138–148.

Rifkin, L., Jones, P., & Murray, R. M. (1993). Low birth weight and poor premorbid childhood function predict cognitive impairment in schizophrenia. *Schizophrenia Research, 9,* 138–139.

Rosenthal, D., Wender, P. H., Kety, S. S., Schulsinger, F., Welner, J., & Østergaard, L. (1968). Schizophrenics offspring reared in adoptive homes. In D. Rosenthal & S. S. Kety (Eds.), *The transmission of schizophrenia* (pp. 377–391). Oxford, England: Pergamon Press.

Rybakowski, J., & Weterle, R. (1991). Niacin test in schizophrenia. *Biological Psychiatry, 29,* 834–836.

Schwartz, R. D., Uretsky, N. J., & Bianchine, J. R. (1972). Prostaglandin inhibition of apomorphine-induced circling in mice. *Pharmacological Biochemical Behaviour, 17,* 1233.

Soulairac, A., Lambinet, H., & Heuman, J. C. (1990). Schizophrenia and PGs: Therapeutic effects of PG precursors in the form of evening primrose oil. *Annals of Medical Psychology (Paris), 8,* 883–890.

Stordy, J. (1995). Benefit of docasahexaenoic acid supplements to dark adaptation in schizophrenia. *The Lancet, 346,* 385.

Susser, E., & Lin, S. P. (1992). Schizophrenia after prenatal exposure to the Dutch hunger winter of 1944–1945. *Archives of General Psychiatry, 49,* 983–988.

Tay, A., Simon, J. S., Squire, J., Hamel, K., Jacob, H. J., & Skorecki, K. (1995). Cytosolic phospholipase A_2 gene in human and rat: Chromosomal localization and polymorphic markers. *Genomics, 26,* 138–141.

Ulas, J., & Cotman, C. W. (1993). Excitatory amino acid receptors in schizophrenia. *Schizophrenia Bulletin, 19,* 105–117.

Vaddadi, K. S. (in press). Use of gamma-linolenic acid and other essential fatty acids in the treatment of schizophrenia. *Prostaglandins Leukotrienes and Essential Fatty Acids.*

Vaddadi, K. S., Courtney, P., Gilleard, C. J., Manku, M. S., & Horrobin, D. F. (1988). A double-blind trial of essential fatty acid supplementation in patients with tardive dyskinesia. *Psychiatry Research, 27,* 313–323.

Vaddadi, K. S., Gilleard, C. J., Mindham, R. H. S., & Butler, R. A. (1986). A controlled trial of prostaglandin E_1 precursor in chronic neuroleptic resistant schizophrenic patients. *Psychopharmacology, 88,* 362–367.

Vinogradov, S., Gottesman, I. I., Moises, H. W., & Nicol, S. (1991). Negative association between schizophrenia and rheumatoid arthritis. *Schizophrenia Bulletin, 17,* 669–678.

Wahl, O. F., & Hunter, J. (1992). Are gender effects being neglected in schizophrenia research? *Schizophrenia Bulletin, 18,* 313–317.

Ward, P., Sutherland, J., Glen, E., & Glen, A. I. M. (1996). *Niacin skin flush in schizophrenia.* Manuscript submitted for publication.

Warner, R. (1994). Recovery from schizophrenia (2nd ed.). New York: Routledge.

Witt, M. R., & Nielsen, M. (1994). Characterization of the influence of unsaturated free fatty acids on brain GABA/benzodiazepine receptor binding in vitro. *Journal of Neurochemistry, 62,* 1432–1439.

World Health Organization. (1979). *Schizophrenia: An international follow-up study.* New York: Wiley.

Yao, J. K., van Kammen, D. P., & Gurklis, J. (1994). Red blood cell membrane dynamics in schizophrenia: III. Correlation of fatty acid abnormalities with clinical measures. *Schizophrenia Research, 13,* 227–232.

Yao, J. K., van Kammen, D. P., & Welker, J. A. (1994). Red blood cell membrane dynamics in schizophrenia: II. Fatty acid composition. *Schizophrenia Research, 13,* 217–226.

Part IV

Diet, Lipids, and Cognitive Processes

12

Brain Lipids and Diet

Maria Teresa Tacconi, Federico Calzi, and Mario Salmona

The term *lipids* includes several classes of compounds with different roles in cells in general and nerve cells in particular. Cholesterol, phospholipids (PLs), cerebrosides, gangliosides, and sulfatides are the lipids found most in the brain (see Appendix A and Figure 1). Lipids account for over half the dry weight of the brain. This depends on the extensive surface area, formed by a complex system of biological membranes, with a number of specialized functions.

Along with being structurally important for building the bilayers of the various brain cell membranes, PLs play an important role as secondary messengers and signal mediators (Hawthorne & Pickard, 1977; Kikkawa, Kishimoto, & Nishizuka, 1989; Shukla & Halenda, 1991). Cholesterol has a stabilizing effect on cell membranes (Shinitzky, 1984; Spector & Yorek, 1985). Also, findings related to the formation of neurosteroids acting on specific receptors in the brain suggest that cholesterol may be involved in the regulation of brain function (Hu, Bourreau, Jung-Testas, Robel, & Baulieu, 1987). Fatty acids (FAs) are normally present as esters in PLs, and their composition strongly influences membrane fluidity (Shinitzky, 1984; Spector & Yorek, 1985). Some of them, when released after stimulation, act as secondary messengers or may be precursors of eicosanoids (Clandinin, Suh, & Hargreaves, 1992; Galli et al., 1977). The brain FA profile is unique in that it contains large amounts of essential FAs (EFAs), which become polyunsaturated FAs (PUFAs). This profile is maintained in all species, and the availability of these FAs is a limiting factor in brain development. The specific role of other lipids, such as cerebrosides and sulfatides, is less clearly established, but their abundance in nerve axons suggests their importance in nerve impulse conduction (Hannun & Bell, 1989).

In addition, lipids appear to have some role as a fuel source in glial cells, although not in neurons, which do not use FA oxidation for energy production (Newsholme, Calder, & Yaqoob, 1993). In glial cells, almost 50% of palmitate can be used for carbon dioxide production, whereas the rest is incorporated into amino acids, especially glutamine and glutamate. This must not be underestimated, considering that nonneuronal cells outnumber neurons.

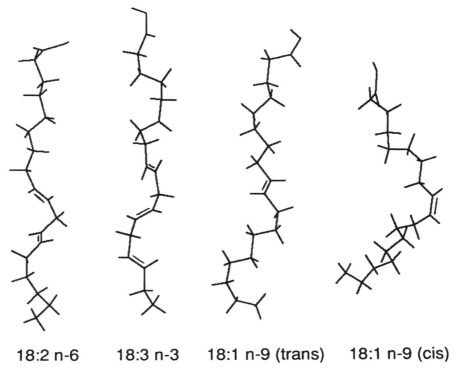

18:2 n-6   18:3 n-3   18:1 n-9 (trans)   18:1 n-9 (cis)

Figure 1. Spatial configuration of some fatty acids, depending on the number of double bonds (from left to right: linoleic acid, alpha-linolenic acid, trans oleic acid, cis oleic acid). Note the difference between cis and trans oleic acid.

Changes in lipid content and composition in the brain have been observed in relation to alteration of brain function, such as the activity of neurotransmitters and cognitive impairment (Bourre et al., 1992; Cimino et al., 1984; Clandinin et al., 1992). Lipids are only partially synthetized in the brain; most of them derive from the circulatory system, with other preformed elements that serve to construct 10^{10} neurons and 10^{11} other cells.

Nutritional factors influence many biochemical parameters in the central nervous system, including lipids. The vulnerability of the developing brain to nutritional stress is well documented; adult brain lipids seem less susceptible to diet-induced changes. During development, lipid accretion in the brain from the diet serves for building cell body and axon membranes. In this case, FA composition is important for brain development, especially in premature infants during the first month of life, when their desaturase system (see Figure 2) is not yet completely developed. This enzymatic pathway, in fact, is of crucial importance in the elongation and desaturation of EFA to form long-chain PUFA of the n-6 and n-3 family, components of which brain membranes are particularly rich. Later in life, peroxidative processes, diet composition, its calorie content, and other fac-

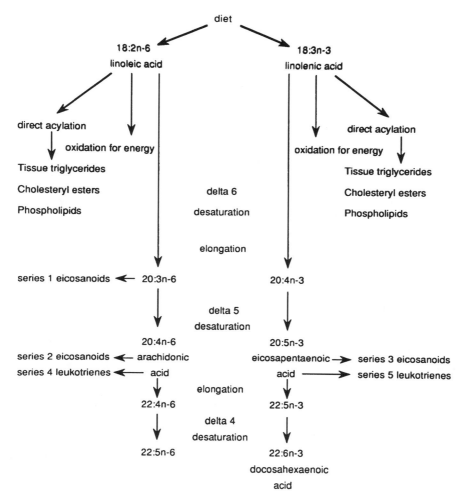

Figure 2. Main metabolic pathway of elongation and desaturation of essential fatty acids.

tors not all completely known influence lipid content and composition of most tissues, including the brain.

In this chapter, we review the role of nutrition in brain lipid composition during early development, in adulthood, and in senescence. The effect on the brain of macronutrients, total calories, and micronutrients is examined, with the effect of dietary manipulations. For obvious reasons, the data derive mostly from animal experiments and often only can be extrapolated to the human brain.

Before discussing the role of nutrients in brain lipids, it is necessary to define, if possible, the normal levels and normal composition of lipids in the brain. It is particularly difficult to produce an exhaustive list of lipid levels and composition, because of the complexity of the definition itself (see Appendix A). In fact, a vast number of compounds fall under the definition of lipids, which are variably distributed in different parts of

Table 1. Lipid Composition in the Human Frontal Lobe Cortex

Component	Cortex	White matter
Protein	75.0	94.0
Phospholipids	59.7	36.6
Cholesterol	35.7	41.1
Gangliosides	4.5	0.4
Cerebrosides	—	16.9
Sulfatides	—	4.9

Note: All entries are precentages of total lipids except protein, which is in milligrams per
gram. $N = 21$ men age 20–39 years. From "Membrane Lipids of the Adult Human Brain:
Lipid Composition of the Frontal and Temporal Lobe in Subjects of Age 20 to 100 Years,"
by L. Svennerholm et al., 1994, *Journal of Neurochemistry, 63*, p. 1806. Copyright 1994
by Raven Press, Ltd. Adapted with permission.

the brain (i.e., grey and white matter) and in different cell types (neurons
and glia). In addition, within each cell, each organelle and cell membrane
has a lipid-specific distribution. Another source of variability is the age at
which brain lipids are measured.

Presented here are data about the lipid composition of the adult human brain. Even if not complete, this gives a general view of the parameters that need to be looked at when speaking of dietary modifications of
brain lipids. Rat brain data are given for comparison, because many of the
studies on the effect of nutrition on brain lipids have been done in this
species.

A first distinction regards the different composition of the grey matter

Table 2. Lipid Composition in the Adult Rat Brain

Lipid	Mole % of total lipid phosphorus ± SD
Phosphatidylethanolamine	39.2 ± 1
Plasmalogen	22.1
Diacyl	17.1
Phosphatidylcholine	33.5 ± 0.4
Phosphatidylserine	14.8 ± 0.3
Sphingomyelin	5.5 ± 0.2
Phosphatidylinositol	3.5 ± 0.2
Phosphatidic acid	2.4 ± 0.1
Cardiolipin	1.0 ± 0.05
Lysophosphatidylethanolamine	0.36 ± 0.02
Unknown phospholipids at origin	0.42 ± 0.06
Total phospholipid recovery	102 ± 1.5
Cholesterol[a]	24.4 ± 0.7
Cerebrosides[a]	64.5 ± 0.6

Note: From "Effects of Storage Conditions on Rat Brain Ethanolamine Glycerophospholipids, Cerebrosides, and Cholesterol," by E. A. Mascatelli and J. A. Duff, 1978, *Lipids, 13,*
p. 204. Copyright 1978 by AOCS Press. Adapted with permission.
[a]For comparison with phospholipid composition, these values are expressed as molar ratios,
where total lipid phosphorus was 100.

Table 3. Lipid Composition of Human Neurons, Glia, and Myelin

Component	% of total lipids			
	Neurons	Astrocytes	Oligodendrocytes	Myelin
Cholesterol	11	14	31	28
Galactolipids	2	2	—	—
Cerebrosides	—	—	11	25
Sphingomyelin	3	4	6	8
Phosphatidylcholine	40	36	14	11
Phosphatidylethanolamine	18	20	17	17
Phosphatidylglycerol	5	4	1	1
Phosphatidylserine	4	5	10	7

Note: Data are from Mead (1975).

(cortex) and the white matter. Table 1 (Svennerholm, Boström, Jungbjer, & Olsson, 1994) shows data from the frontal lobe of healthy adult men, and Table 2 (Moscatelli & Duff, 1978) lists the composition and content of the various lipid components in the adult rat brain. White matter contains more cerebrosides and sulfatides as a percentage of total lipids; grey matter is enriched with gangliosides. Cholesterol:PL ratio is also different in the two. Differences between sexes in cholesterol and PL content have not been found either in white or grey matter (Svennerholm, Boström, Helander, & Jungbjer, 1991). Instead, lipid composition differs within various cells in the nervous system (see Table 3; Mead, 1975). Astrocytes and neurons display a pattern of cholesterol and PL different from that of oligodendrocytes. If we consider individual membranes within the cell, we would find, for example, that mitochondria have a different pattern of distribution of PL from microsomes or synaptic membranes, being the richest in cardiolipin. Fatty acids introduce a further factor of variability, because each PL or glycolipid part of each membrane has its own FA composition (see Table 4; Soderberg, Edlund, Kristensson, & Dallner, 1991; and

Table 4. Main Fatty Acid (FA) Composition of Phosphatidylethanolamine (PE) and Phosphatidylcholine (PC) in the Adult Human Brain

FA	Frontal grey matter		Frontal white matter	
	PC	PE	PC	PE
14:0	2.9	—	2.3	—
16:0	52.4	10.3	33.8	6.4
18:0	12.8	36.2	17.0	10.1
18:1	23.8	10.7	40.0	44.4
20:1	0.4	1.2	1.0	7.5
20:4	0.4	8.2	0.8	18.3
22:4	0.4	8.2	0.8	18.3
22:6	1.5	21.5	Trace	3.7

Note: From "Fatty Acid Composition of Brain Phospholipids in Aging and in Alzheimer's Disease," by M. Soderberg et al., 1991, *Lipids, 26*, pp. 421–425. Copyright 1991 by AOCS Press. Adapted with permission.

Table 5. Fatty Acid Composition of Various Subcellular Fractions of Rat Brain Phosphatidylcholine

Fatty acid carbon no.	Mitochondria (% ± SD)	Synaptosomes (% ± SD)	Myelin (% ± SD)
14:0	0.2 ± 0.04	0.4 ± 0.3	0.3 ± 0.1
16:0	43.1 ± 1.8	51.5 ± 0.7	40.7 ± 1.7
16:1	<0.1	1.7 ± 0.2	0.7 ± 0.3
18:0	10.3 ± 0.4	10.3 ± 0.4	14.6 ± 0.6
18:1	25.4 ± 1.1	24.2 ± 0.4	31.3 ± 1.4
18:2n-6	0.9 ± 0.2	0.4 ± 0.04	0.8 ± 0.01
20:1	0.8 ± 0.3	0.7 ± 0.08	1.6 ± 0.3
20:2	0.5 ± 0.06	0.1 ± 0.05	0.6 ± 0.1
20:3n-6	0.6 ± 0.01	0.1 ± 0.05	0.2 ± 0.01
20:4n-6	9.0 ± 0.3	5.4 ± 0.5	3.6 ± 0.1
22:0 + 20:5n-6	0.2 ± 0.4	0.6 ± 0.4	0.8 ± 0.2
22:4n-6	1.2 ± 0.5	0.5 ± 0.06	0.3 ± 0.3
22:5n-3	<0.1	0.8 ± 0.07	0.8 ± 0.2
22:6n-3	6.5 ± 0.7	3.4 ± 0.2	1.9 ± 0.3
Others	0.5 ± 0.5	0.2 ± 0.4	0.8 ± 1.6

Note: From "Effect of Hypothyroidism Induced in Adult Rats on Brain Membrane Fluidity and Lipid Content and Composition," by M. T. Tacconi et al., 1991, *Research Communications in Chemical Pathology and Pharmacology, 71,* pp. 85–103. Copyright 1991 by PJD Publications Ltd. Adapted with permission.

Table 6. Fatty Acid Composition of Various Subcellular Fractions of Rat Brain Phosphatidylethanolamine

Fatty acid carbon no.	Mitochondria	Synaptosomes	Myelin
14:0	0.5 ± 0.1	0.1 ± 0.03	0.5 ± 0.01
16:0	7.2 ± 0.4	8.2 ± 0.06	4.8 ± 0.8
16:1	0.5 ± 0.5	0.5 ± 0.2	0.5 ± 0.1
18:0	22.5 ± 2.2	25.7 ± 1.2	18.3 ± 0.8
18:1	10.8 ± 1.3	8.4 ± 0.4	32.3 ± 2.1
8:2n-6	1.1 ± 0.4	0.2 ± 0.02	0.6 ± 0.02
18:3n-3	<0.1	<0.1	<0.1
20:1	1.3 ± 0.8	0.2 ± 0.03	4.6 ± 0.7
20:3n-6	0.7 ± 0.3	0.2 ± 0.05	0.7 ± 0.1
20:4n-6	14.3 ± 0.8	16.3 ± 0.1	12.9 ± 0.5
22:0 + 20:5n-6	1.2 ± 0.3	0.1 ± 0.04	0.2 ± 0.02
22:4n-6	4.2 ± 1.0	6.6 ± 0.1	6.4 ± 0.4
22:5n-3	2.0 ± 1.1	1.6 ± 0.1	1.9 ± 0.4
22:6n-3	29.2 ± 3.2	30.9 ± 1.2	13.1 ± 2.0
Others	1.6 ± 1.8	0.7 ± 0.5	1.2 ± 1.8

Note: From "Effect of Hypothyroidism Induced in Adult Rats on Brain Membrane Fluidity and Lipid Content and Composition," by M. T. Tacconi et al., 1991, *Research Communications in Chemical Pathology and Pharmacology, 71,* pp. 85–103. Copyright 1991 by PJD Publications Ltd. Adapted with permission.

Tables 5 and 6; Tacconi, Cizza, Fumagalli, Sarzi Sartori, & Salmona, 1991).

Effect of Nutrients During Early Development

At term, the human infant's brain weighs about 350 g, which is approximately 10% of total body weight. The infant's brain reaches about 750 g after 1 year. Sixty percent of the infant's total energy intake during the 1st year is used by the brain to construct neuronal membranes and deposit myelin. This energy intake comes mostly from dietary fat.

The period immediately before and immediately after birth is critical for brain growth, because the number of neurons and the myelination processes are being established, even if brain growth velocity differs among species. For example, the guinea pig's brain matures completely before birth; however, rat myelination is not complete before the 17th day of age. In pigs and humans, the rate of brain growth is fastest around birth (Davis & Dobbing, 1974).

It is easy to imagine that brain lipid deposition plays a major part in this process. The mother's nutrition during pregnancy and lactation is therefore very important, although there are many other factors of variability in the biochemical and behavioral changes due to dietary habits, the duration and severity of any deficit in the main nutrients, the brain region studied, and the age and prior nutritional status (Nowak & Munro, 1977).

Macronutrients

Protein malnutrition and undernutrition. On feeding the dam a low-protein diet during pregnancy, a reduction in cholesterol, PL, and galactolipids was observed in the rat pups at 2 weeks of age, and an increase in FA of the n-9 family in phosphatidylcholine was observed (de Tomas, Mercuri, & Serres, 1991). Undernutrition during development has adversely affected the growth of the brain, especially the production of myelin, in experimental animals. Suckling rats with restricted food intake have low brain weight and content of DNA, RNA, protein, and lipids. Phospholipids and cholesterol are reduced to 75%–80% of those of normal littermates (Perry, Gamallo, & Bernard, 1986). Glycolipids, proteolipids, and plasmalogen, lipid classes considered associated with the myelin membrane, show greater deficits in undernourished animals (Egwim, Cho, & Kummerow, 1986). The chemical composition of myelin (as percentage of total lipids), prepared from the frontal brain of undernourished rats (achieved by increasing the litter size), did not differ from that of normally fed littermates, in spite of the reduction in weight (Fishman, Madyastha, & Prensky, 1971). In the brain of normally fed rats, undernourished during the suckling period by restricting their feeding time, the ganglioside content was reduced in certain areas (e.g., the cerebellum), and major changes in the pattern of gangliosides and in neuroaminidase activity were found in others (e.g., the hypothalamus; Bhargava, Rao, Vajreshwari, & Shankar, 1984).

In rats, maternal dietary restriction, known to reduce milk production, consistently causes growth retardation of the offspring. Yeh (1988) showed that such dietary restriction caused similar decreases in the amounts of individual PL and cholesterol in brain myelin of offspring. Consequently, the molar ratios of these lipids did not change, suggesting that undernutrition of this type does not selectively affect the accumulation of any particular lipid in myelin. However, FA composition of cerebrosides in 19-day-old undernourished pups was consistently altered, with increased amounts of 16:0, 18:0, 18:1, and 18:2 and reduced amounts of 22:0 and 24:0, suggesting an impairment in elongation. Ten days of nutritional rehabilitation failed to restore the FA imbalances. In humans, protein malnutrition has an effect on EFA metabolism: promoting impairment of the elongation–desaturation processes in erythrocyte membranes (Marin, De Tomas, Mercuri, Fernandez, & de Serres, 1991).

These data suggest that a general reduction of food intake impairs brain growth and lipid deposition, affecting the composition of myelin glycolipids in particular. With lipid content and composition, nutrition deficiencies appear to be associated with alterations of brain biochemistry and behavior, particularly enzymes of the glutamate metabolism (glucose dehydrogenase and glyceroaldehyde dehydrogenase) and carbohydrate metabolism (isocitrate dehydrogenase, succinic dehydrogenase, and malic enzyme; Rajalakshmi, 1975).

Essential fatty acid deficiency. Important structural components of the brain are long-chain PUFAs located on cell membrane PLs. The major brain PUFAs are docosahexaenoic acid (22:6n-3), arachidonic acid (20:4n-6), and adrenic acid (22:4n-6). Two EFAs, linoleic acid (18:2n-6) and alphalinolenic acid (18:3n-3), are their precursors and must be supplied with the diet. Each year, some 1.4 million babies are born with or develop severe neurodevelopmental disorders that can sometimes be overcome with appropriate nutritional intervention. In other cases, severe handicaps develop—such as poor cognitive ability, mental retardation, poor vision or hearing, cerebral palsy, retinopathy, and autism—which all correlate with low body weight.

Since the late 1960s, an enormous amount of data has been produced that show that both neural integrity and function can be permanently disturbed by dietary deficit in n-3 and n-6 PUFA (Bourre et al., 1993; Neuringer, Connor, Lin, Barstad, & Luck, 1986; Uauy, Birch, Birch, & Peirano, 1992). Table 7 shows the changes in FA composition with time in the human fetal cerebrum (Rao & Rao, 1973). Polyunsaturated FA content increases with the maturity of the brain, and the ratio of the linoleic acid–linolenic acid series rises, compared with earlier in gestation. This is probably due to increased accretion of PUFA from the mother and due to the fetus's increasing capacity to elongate and desaturate FA (see Figure 2). This enzymatic activity, however, is not fully active until 4–6 months

Table 7. Main Fatty Acid Composition of Total Phospholipids in the Developing Fetal Cerebrum

Fatty acid carbon no.	Gestational age					
	11–13	20–22	24–26	30–32	33–35	Term
14	2.9	3.3	3.9	3.5	3.1	1.4
16	36.7	30.9	35.6	35.1	37.1	24.1
16:1	5.2	5.3	7.4	5.2	5.1	4.3
18	23.7	22.5	20.9	21.7	24.7	26.7
18:1	26.1	19.6	21.3	23.0	18.4	20.3
18:2	0.2	1.1	0.2	0.4	0.1	1.4
18:3	0.1	0.2	0.2	0.8	0.6	1.1
20:4w6	3.4	7.9	6.3	6.1	6.2	7.3
22:5w3	0.2	2.7	1.9	1.2	1.8	2.8
22:6w3	0.1	2.2	1.0	1.2	1.8	2.8
Others	—	1.6	—	0.7	1.3	2.5

Note: Gestational age is given in weeks. All entries are percentages of total methyl esters. From "Fatty Acid Composition of Phospholipids in Different Regions of Developing Human Fetal Brain," by P. S. Rao and K. S. Rao, 1973, *Lipids, 8,* pp. 374–377. Copyright 1973 by AOCS Press. Reprinted with permission.

after birth, and inappropriate availability may affect neuronal FA content and brain development.

Investigations on the biochemical effects of essential FA deficiency in experimental animals have clarified the pattern and metabolism of PUFA in many tissue lipids, including the brain. The major modification consisted of a decrease of PUFA of the linoleate and linolenate families and an increase of trienes, especially 20:3, derived from oleic acid (n-9 family; Sun, Go, & Sun, 1974). Feeding an EFA-deficient diet to rats during pregnancy and lactation results in a major reduction in brain weight and brain lipid and PL content and in considerable changes in PUFA (Galli, White, & Paoletti, 1971).

Many studies in which oils containing different types of FA were fed to animals during development have shown that dietary manipulations modify the FA composition of the brain (Alling & Karlsson, 1973; Bell & Slotkin, 1985; Foote, Hrboticky, MacKinnon, & Innis, 1990) and alter the synthetic pathways of FA (Hargreaves & Clandinin, 1990; Menon & Dhopeshwarkar, 1982).

The question of n-3 supplementation of formulas. Whether alpha linolenate is essential has been debated for many years, because no signs of n-3 deficiency could be detected in laboratory animals fed n-3-deficient diets (Tinoco et al., 1978). In 1982, Holman, Johnson, and Hatch described, for the first time, visual disturbances in a patient under parenteral nutrition that regressed after 18:3n-3 administration. This question has been widely addressed recently, because in brain synapses and in retina particularly high levels of FA, derived from linolenic elongation and desaturation, were found (Makrides, Neumann, Byard, Simmer, & Gibson, 1994; Martinez, 1992), and the use of formulas poor in n-3 FA results in im-

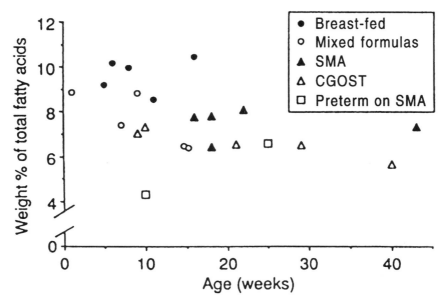

Figure 3. Cerebral cortex phospholipid docosahexaenoic acid in relation to infants' diet and age. Participants were previously well infants who died suddenly in the home. SMA-children fed formulas with a linoleic:linolenic acid ratio of 10:1, CGOST-children fed formulas with a linoleic:linolenic acid ratio of 40:1. From "Infant Cerebral Cortex Phospholipid Fatty-Acid Composition and Diet," by J. Farquharson et al., 1992, *The Lancet*, *340*, pp. 810–813. Copyright 1992 by The Lancet. Reprinted with permission.

pairment in brain development in animals (Sanders, Mistry, & Naismith, 1984) and in a reduction in visual acuity and brain cognitive disorders in human (especially preterm) babies (Lanting, Fidler, Huisman, Touwen, & Boersma, 1994; Uauy et al., 1992; Uauy-Dagach, Mena, & Hoffman, 1994).

In various animals, the accretion of n-3 FA in brain lipids is reduced by an n-3-deficient diet, although later in age the brain becomes more resistant to this deficit (Anderson & Connor, 1994). With a diet very low in linolenic acid, FA composition changes in many tissues (Arbuckle & Innis, 1992; Hoy, Holmer, Kaur, Byrjalsen, & Kirstein, 1983; Sanders et al., 1984).

Clinical evidence has been presented of n-3 deficiency caused by poor supply of 18:3n-3. Martinez and Ballabriga (1987) reported that a relative deficit in n-3 long-chain PUFA could be produced by supplying a great excess of 18:2n-6 (n-6:n-3 ratio of 66:1, in comparison with a ratio of 5:1–10:1 in mothers' milk). Brain and retinal docosahexaenoic acid and docosahexaenoic:arachidonic ratios were reduced, suggesting that the n-6:n-3 ratio may be important to ensure a balance between FA of the two families. Farquharson, Cockburn, Patrick, Jamieson, and Logan (1992) showed that the proportion of brain docosahexaenoic acid in brain PL was larger in breast-fed infants than in PL of infants receiving a diet with high n-6:n-3 ratio (40:1; CGOST group in Figure 3). In infants fed a diet in which the ratio was within the recommended range (10:1; SMA group in

Figure 3), the docosahexaenoic acid content was greater than in the CGOST group but lower than in breast-fed infants. Similar data were obtained by Makrides et al. (1994): The brain and retinas of infants fed formulas with an n-6:n-3 ratio similar to that of mother's milk contained less docosahexaenoic acid, and this seemed to correlate with impairment in visual acuity, suggesting that mother's milk may be an important source of docosahexaenoic acid.

This problem has been debated in relationship to dietary requirements of neonates receiving formulas, in particular for the increasing numbers of babies born preterm, whose desaturase activity is too limited to guarantee an adequate supply of long-chain PUFA. Mother's milk contains not only the precursors of n-3 and n-6 families but also small amounts of long-chain PUFA, which could probably compensate for the reduced desaturase activity in preterm babies.

Recent studies have shown that PUFA supplementation to formulas is beneficial for brain and retina development (Decsi & Koletzko, 1994; Hoffman, Birch, Birch, & Uauy, 1993; Innis, Nelson, Rioux, & King, 1994), and formulas are being produced with a ratio of n-6:n-3 no higher than 10:1.

In conclusion, during the period of fastest brain growth, an adequate supply of EFA is needed for balanced brain growth. An EFA deficiency in early age cannot be corrected easily, affecting mostly myelination, a process that continues for years after birth in humans.

Dietary cholesterol and brain development. Humans are capable of endogenous cholesterol synthesis. During intrauterine growth, the fetus receives no cholesterol of dietary origin but synthesizes its own using glucose and FA. At birth, most of the plasma cholesterol is in high density lipoprotein. In the first weeks of life, the concentration of plasma total and low density lipoprotein-cholesterol rises steeply until it reaches levels that are then maintained throughout the first 2 decades of life (Kwiterovich, 1986). Reiser and Sidelman (1972) proposed that newborns exposed to high levels of cholesterol are more able to cope with dietary cholesterol when adults. Reiser and Sidelman then suggested that the presence of cholesterol in human milk (10–15 mg/dL; whereas it is present only in trace amounts in formulas) might explain these findings.

Studies in monkeys (Mott, Jackson, DeLallo, Lewis, & McMahan, 1995) and humans (Hamosh, 1988) have investigated the possible role of dietary cholesterol during development. Fall et al. (1992) concluded that the age of weaning and possibly the type of milk may permanently influence serum low density lipoprotein-cholesterol concentration and death rates from ischemic heart disease. However, it is still not clear whether this effect is really due to the higher concentration of cholesterol in human milk or to other milk components, such as FA composition, immunoglobulins, and especially hormones, that may affect cholesterol metabolism during development and its homeostasis later in life.

Dietary cholesterol has no effect on the cholesterol synthesis in the brain (Zhang, Wong, Hachey, Pond, & Klein, 1994), but it inhibits its synthesis in the whole body. Deuterated cholesterol fed to rat pups did not accumulate in their brains, suggesting that during development, the cholesterol content of the diet does not affect brain levels (Edmond, Korsak, Morrow, Torok-Both, & Catlin, 1991).

Micronutrients

Adequate intake of vitamins and micronutrients is of fundamental importance for tissue function. Deficiencies can occur not only in developing countries but also in the industrialized ones, where a wide variety of food is available. The categories most affected are people with illnesses that cause malnourishment, pregnant women, alcoholics, and persons who choose bizarre diets.

In many cases, micronutrient deficiencies can induce nervous system disorders; brain lipids are often involved, though sometimes only secondarily to other metabolic derangements.

This chapter does not attempt an exhaustive report of the role of micronutrients in brain function but focuses on those conditions in which alterations of brain lipid content and composition have been shown and related to alterations of brain functions or behavior.

Vitamins. Vitamins are defined as compounds that cannot be synthesized by the body; they are present in small amounts in foods and are cofactors for enzymatic reactions vital for the cells, including the brain cells. They are classified in two major groups: water soluble and lipid soluble (see Appendix B).

The importance of all vitamins during development is obvious, particularly for the brain, which grows very rapidly during the first period of life. Some of them are involved more directly in lipid synthesis, and their deficiency can affect the brain lipid content, composition, and myelination. Here, we briefly review the vitamins whose deficiency affects brain lipids.

Vitamin B_1 (thiamine) is transformed in the body to thiamine pyrophosphate, which regulates decarboxylase and transketolase reactions. A relationship has been found between lipid content and transketolases (Dakshinamurti, 1977). In thiamine-deficient rat pups, deposition of cerebrosides, PL, and cholesterol was impaired (Trostler, Guggenheim, Havivi, & Sklan, 1977).

Vitamin B_3 (nicotinic acid, niacin, or nictinamide) is an essential part of NAD and NADP, which are required in glycolysis and cell respiration. Its deficiency impairs cerebroside content and myelination in rat pups (Nakashima & Suzue, 1982).

Vitamin B_6 (pyridoxine and derivatives) catalyzes more than 50 enzymes; most of them are related to amino acid synthesis, but two are not. One of the two is involved in the synthesis of sphingosine; the other is involved in the synthesis of glycogen phosphorylase. Vitamin B_6–deficient rat pups have significantly lower levels of myelin lipids and PUFA in the cerebellum (Thomas & Kirksey, 1976). Infants are more sensitive to vita-

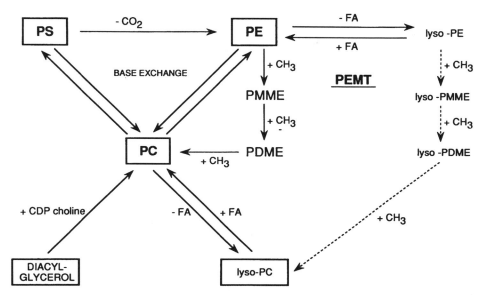

Figure 4. Role of the methylation pathway in phosphatidylcholine synthesis. CDP-choline = cytidyl-diphosphocholine; FA = fatty acids; PC = phosphatidylcholine; PDME = phosphatidyl N-dimethylethanolamine; PE = phosphatidylethanolamine; PEMT = phosphatidylethanolamine methyltransferase; PMME = phosphatidyl N-methylethanolamine; PS = phosphatidylserine.

min B_6 deficiency than are adults. Most nursing mothers, despite a good intake of vitamin B_6, produce milk that does not provide the full recommended dietary allowance for infants (Heiskanen, Salmenpera, Perheentupa, & Siimes, 1994). Chronic deficiency may lead to mental retardation.

Folates and vitamin B_{12} (cyanocobalamine) participate in the methyl group metabolism (Ordonez, 1977), by regulating methylmalonyl coenzyme A mutase and methionine synthase; the latter reaction produces phosphatidylcholine through phosphatidylethanolamine transmethylation (see Figure 4) and methylation of important constituent proteins of myelin. Vitamin B_{12} deficiency induces demyelination in the spinal cord and axonal degeneration. Cerebral white matter is often affected. The damage is believed to be due to impaired synthesis of phosphatidylcholine and myelin basic protein (Metz, 1992). It is the only vitamin found only in meat and in food of animal origin (e.g., milk). Deficiency has been widely reported.

Folic acid and derivatives are active carriers of one carbon group in important biological transfers, including transmethylation (production of serine from glycine and methionine from homocysteine). Folate deficiency can induce severe impairment of the brain function. Folate-deficient mothers can have infants with malformation of the central nervous system, including microcephaly and dilation of the cerebral ventricles (Growdon, 1979). Folate deficiency is endemic among malnourished individuals, especially those with severe chronic gastrointestinal disorders.

Table 8. Effect of Aging on Membrane Microviscosity and Cholesterol:
Phospholipid and Sphingomyelin:Phosphatidylcholine Molar Ratios in the Rat
Brain Cortex

Age (months)	Microviscosity (poise ± SEM)	CHOL/PL (molar ratio ± SEM)	SPH/PC (molar ratio ± SEM)
4	2.17 ± 0.08	0.77 ± 0.03	0.157 ± 0.02
32	2.33 ± 0.04*	0.97 ± 0.02*	0.215 ± 0.01*

Note: Rat age is in months. SPH = sphingomyelin, PC = phosphatidylcholine, CHOL =
cholesterol, PL = phospholipid. Reprinted by permission of the publisher from "Aging and
Food Restriction: Effect on Lipids of Cerebral Cortex," by M. T. Tacconi et al., 1991, *Neurobiology of Aging, 12*, pp. 55–59. Copyright 1991 by Elsevier Science Inc.
*$p < .01$.

Trace elements. Brain function depends on the organic metal constituents of the central nervous system. In addition to sodium and potassium, whose role in the brain electrical activity, fluid balance, and synaptic communication is well known (Smith, 1990), other ions have received attention because of their roles in the brain metabolism or their toxicity. Eight divalent and trivalent metals are essential to the brain function and must be supplied in adequate amounts in the diet to sustain normal cerebral concentrations. They are calcium, magnesium, iron, copper, zinc, manganese, cobalt, and molybdenum (Smith, 1990). Selenium has now been added to the list, in view of its antioxidant activity (Levander & Burk, 1992).

Zinc (Odutuga, 1982) and copper (Cunnane, McAdoo, & Prohaska, 1986) deficiencies are particularly damaging in regard to the maturation of the brain and can worsen impaired lipid deposition due to EFA deficiency.

Effect of Nutrients During Adulthood and Senescence

The adult nervous tissue system is very resistant to undernutrition, starvation, and EFA deficiency, although alterations in lipid patterns can be observed in response to dietary manipulations. One explanation lies in the homeostatic mechanisms that work to maintain a balance in the membrane lipid composition and in the ratios of membrane stability determinants (cholesterol:PL and n-6:n-3; Gibson, McMurchie, Charnok, & Kneebone, 1984). However, with age, brain lipid composition tends to change, to buffer membranes from the effects of dietary lipid changes. Cholesterol:PL and sphingomyelin:phosphatidylcholine ratios and membrane microviscosity increase with age in the rat brain (see Table 8; Tacconi, Lligona, Salmona, Pitsikas, & Algeri, 1991). In humans, a decrease in cholesterol and PL content in the frontal and temporal lobes was observed especially in white matter, starting as early as 20 years of age (see Figure 5; Svennerholm et al., 1994). Gangliosides tend to rise, up to 50 years of age, and then also decline.

The causes of these changes are not really known. There may be some

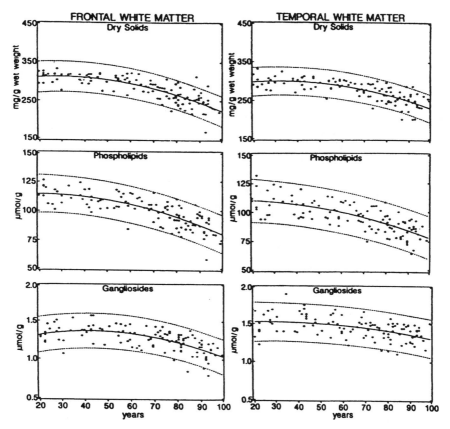

Figure 5.   Concentration of dry solids, phospholipids, and gangliosides in frontal and temporal grey matter of humans age 20–100 years. From "Membrane Lipids of Adult Human Brain: Lipid Composition of Frontal and Temporal Lobe in Subjects of Age 20 to 100 Years," by L. Svennerholm et al., 1994, *Journal of Neurochemistry, 63*, p. 1807. Copyright 1994 by Raven Press, Ltd. Reprinted with permission.

inefficiency in maintaining homeostasis (FA use seems impaired with age; Gatti et al., 1986) and impairment of lipid-metabolizing enzyme activities (e.g., desaturase activity, important among other things in modulating prostaglandin synthesis, declines with age; Dillon, 1987). These defects may depend on extensive oxidative damage to DNA, protein, and lipids — produced by oxidant by-products of normal energy metabolism or by the oxidative burst that protects against bacterial and viral infections (Noda, McGeer, & McGeer, 1982; Shigenaga, Hagen, & Ames, 1994).

Do such age-related changes in lipid content and enzyme activities have a real pathological effect on brain functions? A relationship has been found between the ratio of brain weight to body weight and longevity (Torello, Yates, Hart, & Leon, 1986). Lipid composition, in particular cholesterol:PL and sphingomyelin:phosphatidylcholine ratios, and the FA saturation index are determinants of membrane fluidity, which in turn affects the function of enzymes and neuromediators located on the plasma membrane (Bourre et al., 1992; Cimino et al., 1984; Clandinin et al., 1992). This regulation affects brain function.

Can dietary components or changes in dietary habits affect the induction or prevention of age-related damage? Severe caloric restriction, protein and lipid malnutrition, and vitamin and oligomineral deficiency can negatively influence brain weight and metabolic turnover of lipids, protein, and nucleic acids, especially during senescence and in some pathological states related to the aging process. On the other hand, calorie restriction has been shown to increase longevity in animals (Masoro, 1992) and in humans (K. G. Kinsella, 1992; Leis, 1991).

Dietary habits in developed countries with the tendency to substitute fats of animal origin (mostly saturated) for complex carbohydrates have been related to an increase in cardiovascular and cerebrovascular diseases, hypertension, and tumors. However, little is known in regard to the brain. Traditionally, it was thought that manipulation of dietary lipids in adult age had little or no effect on brain lipid content (Turley, Andersen, & Dietschy, 1981; Gibson et al., 1984). However, recent reports suggest that this may not be true: Exogenous lipids can affect brain membranes, and this modification may influence directly signal transduction components (Dyer & Greenwood, 1991; Kelly et al., 1995; Meydani, Meydani, Shapiro, Macauley, & Blumberg, 1991). Some relation between dietary lipid content and behavior was demonstrated. Modification of dietary n-6: n-3 balance affects behavior and sensitivity to drugs (Nakashima et al., 1993), memory function, pain threshold, and thermoregulation (Yehuda & Carasso, 1993). Although it is not possible to offer a definitive explanation of the effect of certain FA on brain function, it seems reasonable to postulate that the beneficial effects may be directly related to their action on the brain membrane fluidity and composition. Changes in eating habits, in particular, in lipid composition of the diet, have been recommended, to prevent neurodegenerative disorders, in which free radical formation, deficiency of PUFA, or degeneration of membrane phospholipids have been implicated. We next discuss the experimental evidence in favor of these recommendations.

Macronutrients

Protein and brain lipids. Severe protein malnutrition is rare in developed countries but may occur in certain pathological conditions, such as anorexia, or among the elderly when their dietary habits are altered by economic or social factors. Very often, protein malnutrition is associated in these cases with vitamin deficiency.

If severe protein deficiency is induced in rats very early in life, only a delay in the development of neural membranes is observed, but there is always an irreversible reduction of the formation of myelin (Karlsson & Svennerholm, 1978). Myelin immaturity may be partly responsible for the lower mental performance of children severely malnourished in early life (Pollitt & Thomson, 1977).

A relation has been observed between protein intake and lipid per-oxidation, one of the factors in the onset of neurodegenerative damages related to aging. If a protein-deficient diet is associated with an excess of lipids, peroxidative damage of tissues is accelerated (Sambuichi, Lai, Kido, Shizuka, & Kishi, 1992). On the other hand, in rats fed increasing amounts of protein, a parallel increase in peroxidation and lipofuscin pig-ment accumulation was found in many tissues, including brain tissue (De, Chipalkatti, & Aiyar, 1983). This suggests that protein intake may influ-ence lipid peroxidation.

Many studies have been conducted on the role of dietary amino acids and other essential compounds on brain function. The influence of tryp-tophan, serotonin, and other amino acids on neurotransmitter production has been demonstrated (Fernstrom, 1994). Less information is available on the effect of amino acids on brain lipids. Methionine, important as a methyl donor, can affect methylation of phosphatidylethanolamine to phosphatidylcholine, influencing the production of different molecular spe-cies of the latter (Hargreaves & Clandinin, 1987).

Dietary fats. As we said before, the mature brain is less sensitive to dietary changes. Essential fatty acid deficiency can be induced in the ma-ture rat, but it is less severe than when it is started very early in life, and it is completely reversible when animals are switched to an EFA-rich diet (Sun, Winniczek, Go, & Sheng, 1975).

Nutritionally adequate diets differing in fat composition influence the content and the FA composition of polar lipids in rat brain membranes; a saturated or unsaturated FA-rich diet can affect not only lipid composition and metabolism but also the relative content of n-6 and n-3 FA. The use of dietary fat variably enriched in n-6 and n-3 PUFA considerably changes synaptosomal and microsomal membrane composition. Cholesterol and phosphatidylcholine levels can be altered by diet; the highest levels of phosphatidylcholine are found in rats fed a diet rich in n-3 FA (Clandinin et al., 1992). Microsomal cholesterol and sphingomyelin were increased by feeding sunflower oil rich in n-6 FA. Fatty acid composition was altered in response to different dietary levels of n-6 and n-3 and monounsaturated FA, but the unsaturated index remained constant (Clandinin et al., 1992).

Lipid-metabolism enzymes are also affected by diet. Animals that re-ceived a diet rich in n-6 FA had a higher n-6:n-3 ratio in synaptosomal phosphatidylethanolamine, but the rate of phosphatidylethanolamine methyltransferase was high, also, suggesting that this enzymatic pathway displays substrate selectivity for individual molecular species of PE con-taining long-chain PUFA (Hargreaves & Clandinin, 1989).

These changes indicate that brain lipid turnover, especially that of polar lipids, is very rapid, and recycling is greatly altered by 22:6n-3 de-ficiency (Gazzah et al., 1995), suggesting that dietary fat may be a signif-icant modulator in vivo of physical chemical properties of brain synapto-somes and microsomal membranes.

Alphalinolenic acid deficiency alters membrane composition and flu-idity, reduces some enzymatic activities, reduces the efficiency of the blood—brain barrier, and makes animals sensitive to neurotoxin damage. These changes interact with neurotransmitter metabolism, which is often lipid dependent; for example, changes in brain membrane composition alter the thermotropic behavior of acetylcholinesterase activity (Foot, Cruz, & Clandinin, 1983). A high-fat diet influences serotonin synthesis in the brainstem (Kimbrough & Weekley, 1984). In animals, linolenate deficiency lowers the visual acuity threshold (Connor, Neuringer, Barstad, & Lin, 1984), and reduces learning ability (Greenwood & Winocur, 1990). The dietary balance of n-6 to n-3 in the rat brain affects learning ability and memory (Umezawa et al., 1995; Yehuda & Carasso, 1993).

Is polyunsaturated fatty acid supplementation advisable? There has been great debate about the finding that long-chain PUFA, contained mostly in fish oil, (20:5n-3, 22:5n-3, and 22:6n-3) appears to be beneficial toward prevention of cardiovascular diseases (J. E. Kinsella, Lokesh, & Stone, 1990). In rats, the decrease with age of brain arachidonic acid, docosahexaenoic acid, phosphatidylethanolamine, and phosphatidylcholine seemed to be reduced by fish oil in the diet (Gerbi et al., 1994; Suzuki, Hayakawa, & Wada, 1989). In humans, n-3 FA seemed to protect from depressive symptoms in alcoholism, multiple sclerosis, and postpartum depression (Hibbeln & Salem, 1995). These data have led to recommendations to use fish oil, which is rich in docosahexaenoic acid and eicosapentaenoic acid, to prevent cardiovascular diseases and age-related deterioration of brain function (J. E. Kinsella et al., 1990).

However, a note of caution is advisable, because a certain number of risks can be envisaged with supplementation of a large amount of fish oil (Bourre et al., 1988). Yellow fat disease, seen in certain animals (e.g., horses, pigs, cats, and rabbits), is considered an expression of excess PUFA intake (Danse & Verschuren, 1978, 1979). The disease is primarily a generalized disorder of fat deposition (i.e., extensive steatosis, inflammation and fibrosis of adipose tissue, and accumulation of lipofuscin pigment, suggesting the induction of lipid peroxidation). Indeed, long-term supplementation of humans with high levels of fish oil increased plasma lipid peroxide (Meydani, Natiello, et al., 1991b) and induced extensive modification of the structure and function of red blood cell membranes (Bartoli, Palozza, Luberto, Franceschelli, & Piccioni, 1995). No data are available on the brain. Further studies are needed before recommendations can be made about the general use of n-3 long-chain PUFA, and it should still be considered the equivalent of a drug therapy. Vitamin E as antioxidant is always recommended in association with PUFA (Subramanian & Mead, 1986).

Trans fatty acids in foods. Trans FAs are geometric isomers of the cis acids abundant in nature. They are not produced by body tissues but can be formed by chemical rearrangement during commercial hydrogenation of fats. The main source of trans FA is margarine, particularly American margarines (Michels & Sacks, 1995).

Recently, the content of trans FA in food has given rise to concern, because it can be easily metabolized in the body to trans unsaturated FA, possibly interfering with the normal desaturation and chain-elongation processes (Dickson, 1995). Accumulation of trans FA in various tissues was observed after addition to the diet, but the effect on the brain is negligible in young (Pettersen & Opstvedt, 1992) and mature animals (J. E. Kinsella, Bruckner, Mai, & Shimp, 1981). However, because it cannot substitute for cis PUFA, it is believed that it may enhance signs of deficiency, for example, in the case of n-3 deficiency (Grandgirard et al., 1994).

Effect of modulation of plasma cholesterol on brain lipids. Cholesterol and PL are the principal components of biological membranes, and the cholesterol:PL ratio is the main determinant of membrane fluidity. Each membrane has its own cholesterol:PL ratio and a specific membrane-fluidity value, which is held constant by homeostatic mechanisms. In conditions in which the balance is impaired (e.g., aging and hypothyroidism), the activity of membrane-related enzymes may be altered.

In the rat brain, an atherogenic diet increased membrane cholesterol and lowered PL; at the same time, $Ca^{2+}ATP_{ase}$ activity was greatly decreased (Oner, Bekpinar, & Oz, 1991). Toffano, Leon, Benvegnu, and Cerrito (1977) showed that an atherogenic diet lowered the brain content of catecholamines and cyclic AMP, causing dopamine degradation and a modification of the glycolytic pathway. Recently, an accumulation of immuno-labeled β-amyloid, which is related in some way to Alzheimer dementia, was found in rabbits fed a diet rich in cholesterol (Sparks et al., 1994).

The conclusion is therefore that an atherogenic diet or elevated plasma cholesterol levels are harmful not only to heart and blood vessels but also to brain function, and a reduction of plasma cholesterol is always advisable.

Engelberg (1992), using meta-analysis on a number of primary prevention trials, observed a high incidence of violent death (suicide) among participants with low levels of plasma cholesterol, and previous studies reviewed by him suggested a link between low cholesterol in plasma and aggressive behavior. He suggested that low membrane cholesterol in brain cells might affect serotonin uptake from the blood and reduce its concentration in the brain. (A relationship between serotonin levels and aggressive behavior has been shown.)

This suggestion is still debated (Hawton, Cowen, Owens, Bond, & Elliott, 1993; see, also, other chapters in this book). One observation that may be pertinent in this context is by Davey Smith and Pekkanen (1992): It seems that hypocholesterolemic drugs, but not diet, increase mortality from noncardiovascular causes, thus suggesting that other factors (method, extent, and speed of the process) may be critical.

Micronutrients

Vitamins. Malnutrition and disorders involving nutrient malabsorption can induce deficiency of vitamins among adults. The categories mainly affected are pregnant and lactating women, elderly people (especially in low-income groups), and alcoholics.

Nicotinic acid deficiency is seen only in alcoholics and in people who choose bizarre diets; it produces neuronal degeneration. Pantothenic acid functions in acyl group transfer, including synthesis and oxidation of FA and synthesis of sterol and acetylcholine. Deficiency is rare because it is widely found in foods. Vitamin B_{12}, folate, and vitamin E deficiencies may be involved in neurological damage and brain dysfunction.

S-adenosylmethionine is the methyl donor to numerous methyl acceptors, such as nucleic acids, proteins, PLs, and neurotransmitter amines. Its synthesis depends on vitamin B_{12} and folates. Extensive reviews have been published recently (Bottiglieri, 1992; Metz, 1992). In monkeys treated with nitrous oxide (N_2O), which rapidly inactivates cobalamine, thus inactivating methionine synthase, demyelination is observed, indistinguishable from human subacute degeneration. A reduction in lipid content and changes in their FA composition, in addition to a marked reduction in myelin basic protein, were observed in rats and mice treated with cycloleucine, which impairs methionine adenosyl transferase. Untreated vitamin B_{12} deficiency was the cause of neuropathies, such as demyelination of the posterolateral columns of the spinal cord, probably due to impairment of methionine synthase, which reduces methylation reactions and induces demyelination.

Impairment of the methylation cycle can also be induced by folate deficiency. Folates regulate the enzyme methionine synthase, the precursor of S-adenosylmethionine. Both folates and vitamin B_{12} deficiency can cause similar neurological and psychiatric disturbances, including depression, dementia, and a demyelinating neuropathy. Involvement of reduced availability of the methyl group is suggested in depression (in which there may be folate deficiency), in dementia and cognitive impairment (as a consequence of vitamin B_{12} and folate deficiency), in multiple sclerosis (vitamin B_{12} transport is impaired in some cases), and in certain AIDS-induced neurological complications, especially in children (low levels of folates were found in many children with AIDS and neurological complications, Bottiglieri, 1992).

Vitamin E is an antioxidant, protecting unsaturated lipids from autooxidation. Being lipid soluble, it resides in the membrane where PL and PUFA are also found. Another established function of vitamin E is related to its antioxidant action against heavy metals, toxic compounds, and drugs (Bieri, 1992). Vitamin E deficiency is observed in individuals with certain intestinal disorders and in children with cystic fibrosis and biliary atresia. The utility of vitamin E supplementation in association with PUFA supplementation in preventing or reducing lipid peroxidative damage related to aging has been widely proposed, partly because an interaction was found between vitamin E deficiency and 18:3n-3 (Subramanian & Mead, 1986). In brains of animals supplemented with vitamin E in various conditions—cerebral ischemia (Yamamoto et al., 1983); dysmyelination (Bourre, Clement, & Chaudiere, 1987); and senescence (Monji, Morimoto,

Okuyama, Yamashita, & Tashiro, 1994)—protection from lipoperoxidation was observed.

Trace elements. The risk of essential trace element deficiency is higher in elderly people than in adults, but in general, a lack of information exists about mineral intake and metabolism in very old people (Wood, Suter, & Russell, 1995). The brain needs most metals only in trace amounts, with the exception of calcium and magnesium, required for synaptic transmission. The direct effects of trace element deficiency on brain lipids in adults and the elderly are not described.

Selenium supplementation, particularly in association with vitamin E, protects against oxidative damage in many tissues, including the brain (Clausen, Jensen, & Nielsen, 1988; Levander & Burk, 1992). Other metals—such as lead, aluminum and mercury—can influence the brain because of their toxicity. Their abnormal deposition has been demonstrated in a number of neurodegenerative disorders: Alzheimer's disease, Huntington's chorea, Parkinson's disease, and ALS–Parkinson–dementia complex of Guam. It is not known whether these compounds have any effect on brain lipid content or composition.

Effect of Calorie Restriction

Studies of animals have shown a beneficial effect of food restriction on age-related physiological deterioration, resulting in an increase of longevity. Long periods of dietary restriction antagonize learning deficits and reduce the loss of neurotransmitters observed in aged animals. The mechanism of this protective effect has not been clarified, although the antiaging effect appears to be due to restriction of energy intake rather than to that of specific nutrients (Masoro, 1992; Masoro, Shimokawa, & Yu, 1991). It was suggested that food restriction reduces glycemia and glycation, by keeping plasma insulin levels low, and lowers the generation of reactive oxygen species by enhancing the mechanisms that protect the cells from their damaging action (Lang, Wu, Chen, & Mills, 1989; Masoro, 1992).

Brain lipids are most susceptible to oxidative damage; their content and composition are involved in the homeostasis of membrane fluidity, a process that is important in membrane function and neurotransmitter activity. Age-related changes in membrane biochemical and biophysical parameters may be related to the loss of neurotransmitter functions or binding capacity. Restricted diets fed to rats counteracted the age-related increase in cholesterol:PL and sphingomyelin:phosphatidylcholine ratios of cortex membranes, affecting the reduction in membrane fluidity observed with age (Laganiere & Yu, 1993; Tacconi, Lligona, et al., 1991). In addition, the cognitive deficiency present in normally fed, aged rats was counteracted by dietary restriction (Pitsikas, Carli, Fidecka, & Algeri, 1990). For humans, no data are available on the effect of dietary restriction on brain lipids, or on brain functions, but the importance of a low-fat–

high-fiber diet in reducing the incidence of cardiovascular diseases and cancer has been suggested (La Vecchia, 1992; Leis, 1991).

Conclusion

The data presented here do not offer an exhaustive review of the enormous amount of studies on the interactions between brain lipids and nutrients. They are, however, enough to show that brain lipid content and composition are greatly influenced by various nutrients. Dietary FA composition plays a major role, but protein, vitamins, and trace elements, especially if intake is inadequate, are also influential.

If a deficiency of one or more of these dietary components occurs early during development, when the brain is growing very rapidly, neurological, behavioral, and cognitive function can be directly impaired. During adulthood, especially during senescence, lipid content and composition vary also, although to a lesser extent, but it is more difficult to establish direct correlation with impairment of brain function.

References

Alling, C., & Karlsson, I. (1973). Changes in lipid concentrations and fatty acid compositions in rat cerebrum during maturation. *Journal of Neurochemistry, 21*, 1051–1057.

Anderson, G. J., & Connor, W. E. (1994). Accretion of n-3 fatty acids in the brain and retina of chicks fed a low-linolenic acid diet supplemented with docosahexaenoic acid. *American Journal of Clinical Nutrition, 59*, 1338–1346.

Arbuckle, L. D., & Innis, S. M. (1992). Docosahexaenoic acid in developing brain and retina of piglets fed high or low alpha-linolenate formula with and without fish oil. *Lipids, 27*, 89–93.

Bartoli, G. M., Palozza, P., Luberto, C., Franceschelli, P., & Piccioni, E. (1995). Dietary fish oil inhibits human erythrocyte MG,NAK-ATPase. *Biochemical and Biophysical Research Communications, 213*, 881–887.

Bell, J. M., & Slotkin, T. A. (1985). Perinatal dietary supplementation with a commercial soy lecithin preparation: Effects on behavior and brain biochemistry in the developing rat. *Developmental Psychobiology, 18*, 383–394.

Bhargava, P., Rao, P. S., Vajreshwari, A., & Shankar, R. (1984). Total gangliosides, ganglioside species and the activity of neuraminidase in different brain regions and spinal cord of normal and undernourished rats. *Lipids, 19*, 179–186.

Bieri, J. G. (1992). Vitamin E. In M. L. Brown (Ed.), *Present knowledge in nutrition* (6th ed., pp. 117–121). Washington, DC: International Life Science Institute–Nutrition Foundation.

Bottiglieri, T. (1992). Methylation and neuropsychiatry. *Baylor University Medical Center Proceedings, 5*, 13–25.

Bourre, J. M., Bonneil, M., Dumont, O., Piciotti, M., Nalbone, G., & Lafont, H. (1988). High dietary fish oil alters the brain polyunsaturated fatty acid composition. *Biochimica and Biophysica Acta, 960*, 458–461.

Bourre, J. M., Bonneil, M., Chaudiere, J., Clement, M., Dumont, O., Durand, G., Lafont, H., Nalbone, G., Pascal, G., & Piciotti, M. (1992). Structural and functional importance of dietary polyunsaturated fatty acids in the nervous system. *Advances in Experimental Medical Biology, 318*, 211–229.

Bourre, J. M., Bonneil, M., Clement, M., Dumont, O., Durand, G., Lafont, H., Nalbone, G., & Piciotti, M. (1993). Function of dietary polyunsaturated fatty acids in the nervous system. *Prostaglandins, Leukotrienes and Essential Fatty Acids, 48*, 5–15.

Bourre, J. M., Clement, M., & Chaudiere, J. (1987). Alteration of the alpha-tocoferol content in the brain and peripheral nervous tissue of dysmyelinating mutants. *Neurochemical Pathology, 7*, 91–97.

Cimino, M., Vantini, G., Algeri, S., Curatola, G., Pezzoli, C., & Stramentinoli, G. (1984). Age-related modification of dopaminergic and beta-adrenergic receptor system: Restoration to normal activity by modifying membrane fluidity with S-adenosylmethionine. *Life Science, 34*, 2029–2039.

Clandinin, M. T., Suh, M., & Hargreaves, K. (1992). Impact of dietary fatty acid balance on membrane structure and function of neuronal tissues. *Advances in Experimental Medical Biology, 318*, 197–210.

Clausen, J., Jensen, G. E., & Nielsen, S. A. (1988). Selenium in chronic neurologic diseases: Multiple sclerosis and Batten's disease. *Biological Trace Element Research, 15*, 179–203.

Connor, W. E., Neuringer, M., Barstad, L., & Lin, D. S. (1984). Dietary deprivation of linolenic acid in rhesus monkeys: Effects on plasma and tissue fatty acid composition and on visual function. *Transactions of the Association of American Physicians, 97*, 1–9.

Cunnane, S. C., McAdoo, K. R., & Prohaska, J. R. (1986). Lipid and fatty acid composition of organs from copper-deficient mice. *Journal of Nutrition, 116*, 1248–1256.

Dakshinamurti, K. (1977). B vitamins and nervous system function. In R. J. Wurtman & J. J. Wurtman (Eds.), *Nutrition and the brain*, (Vol. 1, pp. 251–340). New York: Raven Press.

Danse, L. H., & Vershuren, P. M. (1978). Fish oil–induced yellow fat disease in rats: Lipolysis in affected adipose tissue. *Veterinary Pathology, 15*, 544–548.

Danse, L. H., & Vershuren, P. M. (1979). Fish oil–induced yellow fat disease in rats: Functional studies of the reticuloendothelial system. *Veterinary Pathology, 6*, 593–603.

Davey Smith, G., & Pekkanen, J. (1992). Should there be a moratorium on the use of cholesterol lowering drugs? *British Medical Journal, 304*, 431–434.

Davis, J. A., & Dobbing, J. (Eds.). (1974). *Scientific foundation of paediatrics*. London: Heineman.

De, A. K., Chipalkatti, S., & Aiyar, A. S. (1983). Some biochemical parameters of ageing in relation to dietary protein. *Mechanism of Ageing Development, 21*, 37–48.

Decsi, T., & Koletzko, B. (1994). Polyunsaturated fatty acids in infant nutrition. *Acta Pediatrica, 83*(Suppl. 395), 31–37.

De Tomas, M. E., Mercuri, O., & Serres, C. (1991). Metabolic transformation of intracranially injected [1-14C] linoleic and [1-14C] alfa linolenic acids in malnourished developing rats. *Lipids, 26*, 891–894.

Dickson, J. H. (Ed). (1995). Trans fatty acids and coronary heart disease risk. *American Journal of Clinical Nutrition, 62*, 655S–707S.

Dillon, J. C. (1987). Essential fatty acid metabolism in the elderly: Effects of dietary manipulation. In M. Horisberger & U. Bracco (Eds.), *Lipids in modern nutrition* (pp. 93–106). Vevey, Switzerland: Nestlé Nutrition.

Dyer, J. R., & Greenwood, C. E. (1991). Dietary essential fatty acids change the fatty acid profile of rat neural mitochondria over time. *Journal of Nutrition, 121*, 1548–1553.

Edmond, J., Korsak, R. A., Morrow, J. W., Torok-Both, G., & Catlin, D. H. (1991). Dietary cholesterol and the origin of cholesterol in the brain of developing rats. *Journal of Nutrition, 121*, 1323–1330.

Egwim, P. O., Cho, B. H., & Kummerow, F. A. (1986). Effects of postnatal protein undernutrition on myelination in rat brain. *Comparative Biochemistry and Physiology (A: Comparative Physiology), 83*, 67–70.

Engelberg, H. (1992). Low serum cholesterol and suicide. *The Lancet, 339*, 727–729.

Fall, C. H. D., Barker, D. J. P., Osmond, C., Winter, P. D., Clarck, P. M. S., & Hales, C. N. (1992). Relation of infant feeding to adult serum cholesterol concentration and death from ischemic heart disease. *British Medical Journal, 304*, 801–805.

Farquharson, J., Cockburn, F., Patrick, A. W., Jamieson, E. C., & Logan, R. W. (1992). Infant cerebral cortex phospholipid fatty-acid composition and diet. *The Lancet, 340*, 810–813.

Fernstrom, J. D. (1994). Dietary amino acids and brain function. *Journal of the American Dietary Association, 94*, 71–77.

Fishman, M. A., Madyastha, P., & Prensky, A. L. (1971). The effect of undernutrition on the development of myelin in the rate central nervous system. *Lipids, 6,* 458–465.

Foot, M., Cruz, T. F., & Clandinin, M. T. (1983). Effect of dietary lipid on synaptosomal acetylcholinesterase activity. *Biochemical Journal, 211,* 507–509.

Foote, K. D., Hrboticky, N., MacKinnon, M. J., & Innis, S. M. (1990). Brain synaptosomal, liver, plasma, and red blood cell lipids in piglets fed exclusively on a vegetable-oil-containing formula with and without fish-oil supplements. *American Journal of Clinical Nutrition, 51,* 1001–1006.

Galli, C., Galli, G., Spagnuolo, C., Bosisio, E., Tosi, L., Folco, G. C., & Longiave, D. (1977). Dietary essential fatty acids, brain polyunsaturated fatty acids, and prostaglandin biosynthesis. In N. G. Bazan, R. R. Brenner, & N. M. Giusto (Eds.), *Function and biosynthesis of lipids* (pp. 561–574). New York: Plenum.

Galli, C., White, H. B., & Paoletti, R. (1971). Lipid alterations and their reversion in the central nervous system of growing rats deficient in essential fatty acids. *Lipids, 6,* 378–387.

Gatti, C., Noremberg, K., Brunetti, M., Teolato, S., Calderini, G., & Gaiti, A. (1986). Turnover of palmitic and arachidonic acids in the phospholipids from different brain areas of adult and aged rats. *Neurochemical Research, 11,* 241–252.

Gazzah, N., Gharib, A., Croset, M., Bobillier, P., Lagarde, M., & Sarda, N. (1995). Decrease of brain phospholipid synthesis in free-moving n-3 fatty acid deficient rats. *Journal of Neurochemistry, 64,* 908–918.

Gerbi, A., Zerouga, M., Debray, M., Durand, G., Chanez, C., & Bourre, J. M. (1994). Effect of fish oil diet on fatty acid composition of phospholipids of brain membranes and on kinetic properties of Na^+, $K(+) - ATP_{ase}$ isoenzymes of weaned and adult rats. *Journal of Neurochemistry, 62,* 1560–1569.

Gibson, R. A., McMurchie, E. J., Charnok, J. S., & Kneebone, G. M. (1984). Homeostatic control of membrane fatty acid composition in the rat after dietary lipid treatment. *Lipids, 19,* 942–951.

Grandgirard, A., Bourre, J. M., Julliard, F., Homayoun, P., Dumont, O., Piciotti, M., & Sebedio, J. L. (1994). Incorporation of trans long-chain n-3 polyunsaturated fatty acids in rat brain structures and retina. *Lipids, 29,* 251–258.

Greenwood, C. E., & Winocur, G. (1990). Learning and memory impairment in rats fed a high saturated fat diet. *Behavior and Neural Biology, 53,* 74–87.

Growdon, J. H. (1979). Neurotransmitter precursors in the diet: Their use in the treatment of brain diseases. In R. J. Wurtman & J. J. Wurtman (Eds.), *Nutrition and the brain* (Vol. 3, pp. 117–181). New York: Raven Press.

Hamosh, M. (1988). Does infant nutrition affect adiposity and cholesterol levels in the adult? *Journal of Pediatric Gastroenterology and Nutrition, 7,* 10–16.

Hannun, Y. A., & Bell, R. M. (1989). Functions of sphingolipids and sphingolipid breakdown products in cellular regulation. *Science, 243,* 500–507.

Hargreaves, K. M., & Clandinin, M. T. (1987). Phosphatidylethanolamine methyltransferase: Evidence for influence of diet fat on selectivity of substrate for methylation in rat brain synaptic plasma membranes. *Biochimica Biophysica Acta, 918,* 97–105.

Hargreaves, K. M., & Clandinin, M. T. (1989). Co-ordinate control of CDP-choline and phosphatidylethanolamine methyltransferase pathways for phosphatidylcholine biosynthesis occurs in response to change in diet fat. *Biochimica Biophysica Acta, 1001,* 262–267.

Hargreaves, K., & Clandinin, M. T. (1990). Dietary lipids in relation to postnatal development of the brain. *Upsala Journal of Medical Science, 48*(Suppl.), 79–95.

Hawthorne, J. N., & Pickard, M. R. (1977). Metabolism of phosphatidic acid and phosphatidylinositol in relation to transmitter release from synaptosomes. In N. G. Bazan, R. R. Brenner, & N. M. Giusto (Eds.), *Functions and biosynthesis of lipids* (pp. 419–428). New York: Plenum.

Hawton, K., Cowen, P., Owens, D., Bond, A., & Elliott, M. (1993). Low serum cholesterol and suicide. *British Journal of Psychiatry, 162,* 818–825.

Heiskanen, K., Salmenpera, L., Perheentupa, J., & Siimes, M. A. (1994). Infant vitamin B-6 status changes with age and with formula feeding. *American Journal of Clinical Nutrition, 60,* 907–910.

Hibbeln, J. R., & Salem, N., Jr. (1995). Dietary polyunsaturated fatty acids and depression: When cholesterol does not satisfy. *American Journal of Clinical Nutrition, 62*, 1–9.

Hoffman, D. R., Birch, E. E., Birch, D. G., & Uauy, R. D. (1993). Effects of supplementation with ω-3 long-chain polyunsaturated fatty acids on retinal and cortical development in premature infants. *American Journal of Clinical Nutrition, 57*, 807S–812S.

Holman, R. T., Johnson, S. B., & Hatch, T. F. (1982). A case of human linolenic acid deficiency involving neurological abnormalities. *American Journal of Clinical Nutrition, 35*, 617–623.

Hoy, C. E., Holmer, G., Kaur, N., Byrjalsen, I., & Kirstein, D. (1983). Acyl group distributions in tissue lipids of rats fed evening primrose oil (γ-linolenic plus linoleic acid) or soybean oil (α-linolenic plus linoleic acid). *Lipids, 18*, 760–771.

Hu, Z. Y., Bourreau, E., Jung-Testas, I., Robel, P., & Baulieu, E. E. (1987). Neurosteroids: Oligodendrocyte mitochondria convert cholesterol to pregnenolone. *Proceedings of the National Academy of Sciences, USA, 84*, 8215–8219.

Innis, S. M., Nelson, C. M., Rioux, M. F., & King, D. J. (1994). Development of visual acuity in relation to plasma and erythrocyte omega-6 and omega-3 fatty acids in healthy term gestation infants. *American Journal of Clinical Nutrition, 60*, 347–352.

Karlsson, I., & Svennerholm, L. (1978). Biochemical development of rat forebrains in severe protein and essential fatty acid deficiencies. *Journal of Neurochemistry, 31*, 657–662.

Kelly, J. F., Joseph, J. A., Denisova, N. A., Erat, S., Preston Mason, R., & Roth, G. S. (1995). Dissociation of striatal GTPase and dopamine release responses to muscarinic cholinergic agonists in F344 rats: Influence of age and dietary manipulation. *Journal of Neurochemistry, 64*, 2755–2764.

Kikkawa, U., Kishimoto, A., & Nishizuka, Y. (1989). The protein kinase C family: Heterogeneity and its implications. *Annual Review of Biochemistry, 58*, 31–44.

Kimbrough, T. D., & Weekley, L. B. (1984). The effect of high-fat diet on brainstem and duodenal secretion (5HT) metabolism in Sprague-Dawley and Osborne Mendel rats. *International Journal of Obesity, 8*, 305–310.

Kinsella, J. E., Bruckner, G., Mai, J., & Shimp, J. (1981). Metabolism of trans fatty acids with emphasis on the effects of trans, trans-octadecadienoate on lipid composition, essential fatty acid and prostaglandins: An overview. *American Journal of Clinical Nutrition, 34*, 2307–2318.

Kinsella, J. E., Lokesh, B., & Stone, R. A. (1990). Dietary n-3 polyunsaturated fatty acids and amelioration of cardiovascular diseases: Possible mechanisms. *American Journal of Clinical Nutrition, 52*, 1–28.

Kinsella, K. G. (1992). Changes in life expectancy 1900–1990. *American Journal of Clinical Nutrition, 55*, 1196S–1202S.

Kwiterovich, P. O., Jr. (1986). Biochemical, clinical, epidemiologic, genetic, and pathologic data in the pediatric age group relevant to the cholesterol hypothesis. *Pediatrics, 78*, 349–362.

Laganiere, S., & Yu, B. P. (1993). Modulation of membrane phospholipid fatty acid composition by age and food restriction. *Gerontology, 39*, 7–18.

Lang, C. A., Wu, W. K., Chen, T., & Mills, B. J. (1989). Blood glutathione: A biochemical index of life span enhancement in the diet restricted Lobund–Wistar rat. *Progress in Clinical and Biological Research, 287*, 241–246.

Lanting, C. I., Fidler, V., Huisman, M., Touwen, B. C. L., & Boersma, E. R. (1994). Neurological differences between 9-year-old children fed breast-milk or formula milk as babies. *The Lancet, 344*, 1319–1322.

La Vecchia, C. (1992). Cancers associated with high-fat diets. *Journal of the National Cancer Institute Monographs, 12*, 79–85.

Leis, H. P., Jr. (1991). The relationship of diet to cancer, cardiovascular disease and longevity. *International Surgery, 76*, 1–5.

Levander, O. A., & Burk, R. F. (1992). Selenium. In M. L. Brown (Ed.), *Present knowledge in nutrition* (6th ed., pp. 268–273). Washington, DC: International Life Science Institute–Nutrition Foundation.

Makrides, M., Neumann, M. A., Byard, R. W., Simmer, K., & Gibson, R. A. (1994). Fatty acid composition of brain, retina, and erythrocytes in breast- and formula-fed infants. *American Journal of Clinical Nutrition, 60*, 189–194.

Marin, M. C., De Tomas, M. E., Mercuri, O., Fernandez, A., & de Serres, C. T. (1991). Interrelationship between protein-energy malnutrition and essential fatty acid deficiency in nursing infants. *American Journal of Clinical Nutrition, 53,* 466–468.

Martinez, M. (1992). Tissue levels of polyunsaturated fatty acids during early human development. *Journal of Pediatrics, 120,* S129–S138.

Martinez, M., & Ballabriga, A. (1987). Effects of parenteral nutrition with high doses of linoleate on the developing human liver and brain. *Lipids, 22,* 133–138.

Masoro, E. J. (1992). Retardation of aging processes by food restriction: An experimental tool. *American Journal of Clinical Nutrition, 55,* 1250S–1252S.

Masoro, E. J., Shimokawa, I., & Yu, B. P. (1991). Retardation of aging processes in rats by food restriction. In W. Pierpaoli & M. Fabris (Eds.), *Annals of the New York Academy of Sciences: Vol. 621.* (pp. 337–352). New York: New York Academy of Sciences.

Mead, J. F. (1975). Lipid composition and brain function. In W. W. Hawkins (Ed.), *The essential fatty acids* (pp. 73–85). Winnipeg, Manitoba: The Nutrition Society of Canada.

Menon, N. K., & Dhopeshwarkar, G. A. (1982). Essential fatty acid deficiency and brain development. *Progress in Lipid Research, 21,* 309–326.

Metz, J. (1992). Cobalamine deficiency and the pathogenesis of nervous system disease. *Annual Reviews of Nutrition, 12,* 59–79.

Meydani, M., Meydani, S. N., Shapiro, A. C., Macauley, J. B., & Blumberg, J. B. (1991). Influence of dietary fat, vitamin E, ethoxyquin and indomethacin on the synthesis of prostaglandin E2 in brain regions of mice. *Journal of Nutrition, 121,* 438–444.

Meydani, M., Natiello, F., Goldin, B., Free, N., Woods, M., Schaefer, E., Blumberg, J. B., & Gorbach, S. L. (1991). Effect of long-term fish oil supplementation on vitamin E status and lipid peroxidation in women. *Journal of Nutrition, 121,* 484–491.

Michels, K., & Sacks, F. (1995). Trans fatty acids in European margarines. *New England Journal of Medicine, 332,* 541–542.

Monji, A., Morimoto, N., Okuyama, I., Yamashita, N., & Tashiro, N. (1994). Effect of dietary vitamin E on lipofuscin accumulation with age in the rat brain. *Brain Research, 634,* 62–68.

Moscatelli, E. A., & Duff, J. A. (1978). Effects of storage conditions on rat brain ethanolamine glycerophospholipids, cerebrosides, and cholesterol. *Lipids, 13,* 294–296.

Mott, G. E., Jackson, E. M., DeLallo, L., Lewis, D. S., & McMahan, C. A. (1995). Differences in cholesterol metabolism in juvenile baboons are programmed by breast- versus formula-feeding. *Journal of Lipid Research, 36,* 299–307.

Nakashima, Y., & Suzue, R. (1982). Effect of nicotinic acid on myelin lipids in brain of the developing rat. *Journal of Nutritional Science and Vitaminology Tokyo, 28,* 491–500.

Nakashima, Y., Yuasa, S., Hukamizu, Y., Okuyama, H., Ohhara, T., Kameyama, T., & Nabeshima, T. (1993). Effect of a high linoleate and high a-linolenate diet on general behavior and drug sensitivity in mice. *Journal of Lipid Research, 34,* 239–247.

Neuringer, M., Connor, W. E., Lin, D. S., Barstad, L., & Luck, S. (1986). Biochemical and functional effects of prenatal and postnatal omega 3 fatty acid deficiency on the retina and brain in rhesus monkeys. *Proceedings of National Academy of Science, USA, 83,* 4021–4025.

Newsholme, E. A., Calder, P., & Yaqoob, P. (1993). The regulatory, informational, and immunomodulatory roles of fat fuels. *American Journal of Clinical Nutrition, 57,* 738–751.

Noda, Y., McGeer, P. L., & McGeer, E. G. (1982). Lipid peroxides in brain during aging and vitamin E deficiency: Possible relations to changes in neurotransmitter indices. *Neurobiology of Aging, 3,* 173–178.

Nowak, T. S., & Munro, H. N. (1977). Effects of protein-calorie malnutrition on biochemical aspects of brain development. In R. J. Wurtman & J. J. Wurtman (Eds.), *Nutrition and the brain* (Vol. 2, pp. 193–260). New York: Raven Press.

Odutuga, A. A. (1982). Effects of low-zinc status and essential fatty acid deficiency on growth and lipid composition of rat brain. *Clinical Experimental of Pharmacology and Physiology, 9,* 213–221.

Oner, P., Bekpinar, S., & Oz, B. (1991). Alteration in some lipid components and $Ca2^+$ ATP_{ase} activity in brain of rats fed an atherogenic diet. *Research Communications in Chemical Pathology and Pharmacology, 72,* 337–345.

Ordonez, L. A. (1977). Control of the availability to the brain of folic acid, vitamin B_{12} and choline. In R. J. Wurtman & J. J. Wurtman (Eds.), *Nutrition and the brain* (Vol. 1, pp. 205–248). New York: Raven Press.

Perry, M. L., Gamallo, J. L., & Bernard, E. A. (1986). Effect of protein malnutrition on glycoprotein synthesis in rat cerebral cortex slices during the period of brain growth spurt. *Journal of Nutrition, 116,* 2486–2489.

Pettersen, J., & Opstvedt, J. (1992). Trans fatty acids: 5. Fatty acid composition of lipids of the brain and other organs in suckling piglets. *Lipids, 27,* 761–769.

Pitsikas, N., Carli, M., Fidecka, S., & Algeri, S. (1990). Effect of life-long hypocaloric diet on age-related changes in motor and cognitive behavior in a rat population. *Neurobiology of Aging, 11,* 417–423.

Pollitt, E., & Thomson, C. (1977). Protein-calorie malnutrition and behavior: A view from psychology. In R. J. Wurtman & J. J. Wurtman (Eds.), *Nutrition and the brain* (Vol. 2, pp. 261–306). New York: Raven Press.

Rajalakshmi, R. (1975). Effects of nutritional deficiencies on the composition and metabolic activity of the brain in the rat. In M. A. B. Brazier (Ed.), *Growth and development of the brain* (pp. 139–156). New York: Raven Press.

Rao, P. S., & Rao, K. S. (1973). Fatty acid composition of phospholipids in different regions of developing human fetal brain. *Lipids, 8,* 374–377.

Reiser, R., & Sidelman, Z. (1972). Control of serum cholesterol homeostasis by cholesterol in the milk of the suckling rat. *Journal of Nutrition, 102,* 1009–1016.

Sambuichi, E. J., Lai, A., Kido, Y., Shizuka, F., & Kishi, K. (1992). Protein deficiency and excess lipid synergistically augmented lipid peroxidation in growing rats. *Tokushima Journal of Experimental Medicine, 39,* 81–87.

Sanders, T. A., Mistry, M., & Naismith, D. J. (1984). The influence of a maternal diet rich in linoleic acid on brain and retinal docosahexaenoic acid in the rat. *British Journal of Nutrition, 51,* 57–66.

Shigenaga, M. K., Hagen, T. M., & Ames, B. N. (1994). Oxidative damage and mitochondrial decay in aging. *Proceedings of the National Academy of Science, USA, 91,* 10771–10778.

Shinitzky, M. (1984). Membrane fluidity and cellular function. In M. Shinitzky (Ed.), *Physiology of membrane fluidity* (Vol. 1, pp. 1–35). Boca Raton, FL: CRC Press.

Shukla, S. D., & Halenda, S. P. (1991). Phospholipase D in cell signalling and its relationship to phospholipase C. *Life Sciences, 48,* 851–866.

Smith, Q. R. (1990). Regulation of metal uptake and distribution within brain. In R. J. Wurtman & J. J. Wurtman (Eds.), *Nutrition and the brain* (Vol. 8, pp. 25–74). New York: Raven Press.

Soderberg, M., Edlund, C., Kristensson, K., & Dallner, G. (1991). Fatty acid composition of brain phospholipids in aging and in Alzheimer's disease. *Lipids, 26,* 421–425.

Sparks, D. L., Scheff, S. W., Hunsaker, J. C., III, Liu, H., Landers, T., & Gross, D. R. (1994). Induction of Alzheimer-like beta-amyloid immunoreactivity in the brains of rabbits with dietary cholesterol. *Experimental Neurology, 126,* 88–94.

Spector, A. A., & Yorek, M. A. (1985). Membrane lipid composition and cellular function. *Journal Lipid Research, 26,* 1015–1035.

Subramanian, C. S., & Mead, J. F. (1986). A relationship between essential fatty acid and vitamin E deficiency. *Lipids, 21,* 603–607.

Sun, G. Y., Go, J., & Sun, A. Y. (1974). Induction of essential fatty acid deficiency in mouse brain: Effects of fat deficient diet upon acyl group composition of myelin and synaptosome-rich fractions during development and maturation. *Lipids, 9,* 450–454.

Sun, G. Y., Winniczek, H., Go, J., & Sheng, S. L. (1975). Essential fatty acid deficiency: Metabolism of 20:3(n − 9) and 22:3(n − 9) of major phosphoglycerides in subcellular fractions of developing and mature mouse brain. *Lipids, 10,* 365–373.

Suzuki, H., Hayakawa, S., & Wada, S. (1989). Effect of age on the modification of brain polyunsaturated fatty acids and enzyme activities by fish oil diet in rats. *Mechanism of Ageing Development, 50,* 17–25.

Svennerholm, L., Boström, K., Helander, C. G., & Jungbjer, B. (1991). Membrane lipids in the aging human brain. *Journal of Neurochemistry, 56,* 2051–2059.

Svennerholm, L., Boström, K., Jungbjer, B., & Olsson, L. (1994). Membrane lipids of adult human brain: Lipid composition of frontal and temporal lobe in participants of age 20 to 100 years. *Journal of Neurochemistry, 63,* 1802–1811.

Tacconi, M. T., Cizza, G., Fumagalli, G., Sarzi Sartori, P., & Salmona, M. (1991). Effect of hypothyroidism induced in adult rats on brain membrane fluidity and lipid content and composition. *Research Communications in Chemical Pathology and Pharmacology, 71,* 85–103.

Tacconi, M. T., Lligona, L., Salmona, M., Pitsikas, N., & Algeri, S. (1991). Aging and food restriction: Effect on lipids of cerebral cortex. *Neurobiology of Aging, 12,* 55–59.

Thomas, M. R., & Kirksey, A. (1976). Postnatal patterns of fatty acids in brain of progeny from vitamin B-6 deficient rats before and after pyridoxine supplementation. *Journal of Nutrition, 106,* 1415–1420.

Tinoco, J., Babcock, R., Hincenbergs, I., Medwadowski, B., Miljanich, P., & Williams, M. A. (1978). Linolenic acid deficiency. *Lipids, 14,* 166–173.

Toffano, G., Leon, A., Benvegnu, D., & Cerrito, F. (1977). Effect of phospholipids on cholesterol-induced modifications in mouse brain. *Atherosclerosis, 26,* 59–66.

Torello, L. B., Yates, A. J., Hart, R., & Leon, K. S. (1986). A comparative–evolutionary study of lipids in the aging brain of mice. *Neurobiology of Aging, 7,* 337–346.

Trostler, N., Guggenheim, K., Havivi, E., & Sklan, D. (1977). Effect of thiamine deficiency in pregnant and lactating rats on the brain of their offspring. *Nutrition and Metabolism, 21,* 294–304.

Turley, S. D., Andersen, J. M., & Dietschy, J. M. (1981). Rates of sterol synthesis and uptake in the major organs of rat in vivo. *Journal of Lipid Research, 22,* 551–569.

Uauy, R., Birch, E., Birch, D., & Peirano, P. (1992). Visual and brain function measurements in studies of n-3 fatty acid requirements of infants. *Journal of Pediatrics, 120,* S168–S180.

Uauy-Dagach, R., Mena, P., & Hoffman, D. R. (1994). Essential fatty acid metabolism and requirements for LBW infants. *Acta Paediatrica, 83*(Suppl. 405), 78–85.

Umezawa, M., Ohta, A., Tojo, H., Yagi, H., Hosokawa, M., & Takeda, T. (1995). Dietary α-linolenate/linoleate balance influences learning and memory in the senescence-accelerated mouse (SAM). *Brain Research, 669,* 225–233.

Wood, R. J., Suter, P. M., & Russell, R. M. (1995). Mineral requirements of elderly people. *American Journal of Clinical Nutrition, 62,* 493–505.

Yamamoto, M., Shima, T., Uozumi, T., Sogabe, T., Yamada, K., & Kawasaki, T. (1983). A possible role of lipid peroxidation in cellular damage caused by cerebral ischemia and the protective effect of alpha-tocopherol administration. *Stroke, 14,* 977–982.

Yeh, Y. Y. (1988). Long chain fatty acid deficits in brain myelin sphingolipids of undernourished rat pups. *Lipids, 23,* 1114–1118.

Yehuda, S., & Carasso, R. L. (1993). Modulation of learning, pain thresholds, and thermoregulation in the rat by preparations of free purified α-linolenic and linoleic acids: Determination of optimal ω3-to-ω6 ratio. *Proceedings of the National Academy of Science, USA, 90,* 10345–10349.

Zhang, S., Wong, W. W., Hachey, D. L., Pond, W. G., & Klein, P. D. (1994). Dietary cholesterol inhibits whole-body but not cerebrum cholesterol synthesis in young pigs. *Journal of Nutrition, 124,* 717–725.

Appendix A

Nomenclature of Lipids

Main fatty acids
    Palmitic acid   16:0
    Palmitoleic acid   16:1
    Stearic acid   18:0
    Oleic acid   18:1n-9
    Linoleic acid   18:2n-6
    Alphalinolenic acid   18:3n-3
    Gammalinolenic acid   18:3n-6
    Arachidonic acid   20:4n-6
    Eicosapentaenoic acid   20:5n-6 if of mammalian origin
                                     20:5n-3 if of marine origin
    Docosapentaenoic acid   22:5n-3
    Docosahexaenoic acid   22:6n-3
Phospholipids
    Phosphatidylcholine
    Phosphatidylethanolamine
    Phosphatidylserine
    Phosphatidylinositol
    Phosphatidic acid
    Phosphatidylglycerol
    Diphosphatidylglycerol (cardiolipin)
    Sphingomyelin
Glycolipids
    Cerebrosides
    Gangliosides
Sulfolipids
    Cholesterol
    Cholesteryl esters
    Triglycerides

Appendix B

Water- and Lipid-Soluble Vitamins

Nomenclature allowance for adults	Biochemical function	Recommended dietary requirement
Water-soluble vitamins		
Vitamin B_1 (thiamine)	Aldehyde group transfer	0.55 mg/1,000 calories
Vitamin B_2 (riboflavin)	Hydrogen atom (electron) transfer	1.7–1.8 mg for men 1.4–1.5 mg for women
Vitamin B_3 (niacin, nicotinamide, or nicotinic acid)	Hydrogen atom (electron) transfer	6.6 mg/1,000 calories of niacin equivalents
Vitamin B_6 (pyridoxine, pyridoxal, or pyridoxamine)	Amino group transfer	2 mg for men 1.6 mg for women
Pantothenic acid	Acyl group transfer	4–7 mg
Biotin	Carboxyl transfer	10–100 µg, increasing with age
Vitamin B_{12} (cyanocobalamine)	Methyl group transfer	1–2 mg
Folic acid, folacin, pteroylglutamic acid	Methyl group transfer	200 mg
Vitamin C (ascorbic acid)	Cofactor in hydroxylation	45–60 mg
Lipid-soluble vitamins		
Vitamin A (retinol)	Visual cycle	400 of retinol equivalent
Vitamin D (calciferol)	Calcium and phosphate metabolism	5 µg daily (may be upper limit)
Vitamin E (tocopherol)	Antioxidant	10 alphatocopherol equivalents for men 8 alphatocopherol equivalents for women
Vitamin K	Prothrombin biosynthesis	50–100 µg

Note: Unless otherwise specified, all recommended dietary requirements are daily requirements.

13

Dietary Fat and Cognitive Functioning

David Benton

McLoughlin and Clarke (1989) commented "that anything which affects the balance of cerebral lipid metabolism could have profound effects on brain function" (p. 275). Because lipids account for about 50% to 60% of the dry weight of the brain (Sastry, 1985), the comment should be taken seriously.

Given the widespread attempts to lower the incidence of cardiovascular disease by decreasing the level of fat in the diet, it is surprising that the impact of these dietary changes on cognitive functioning has attracted little attention. It is particularly surprising because there is evidence that the intake of other macronutrients (Fernstrom & Wurtman, 1971) and micronutrients (Benton, 1992) influences mood and cognitive functioning. This chapter considers the possibility that the nature of dietary fat might influence cognitive functioning.

Fatty Acids

Fatty acids (FA) are aliphatic chains of 10 or more carbons, with a methyl group at one end of the molecule and a carboxyl group at the other. Figure 1 shows that *monenoic* or *monounsaturated* FA has one double bond. Those with two or more are called *polyenoic* or *polyunsaturated* FA (PUFA). Fatty acids are described using a standard nomenclature, for example, docosahexaenoic acid (DHA) is 20:6n-3. The first number is the length of the carbon chain, the number after the colon refers to the number of double bonds, and the number after the n- represents the number of carbons from the methyl end of the molecule to the first double bond. Unlike plants, animals are unable to insert double bonds at the n-3 and n-6 position and are thus unable to synthesize linoleic (18:2n-6) and alphalinolenic (18:3n-3) acid (see Figure 1). Because these FAs cannot be synthesized, they have to be obtained from the diet. They are termed *essential* FAs. If these essential FAs are provided by the diet, then the mechanisms exist to convert them to longer chain PUFAs. Oils of vegetable origin contain both linoleic and alphalinolenic acids.

We have to rely on rodent studies for most of our understanding of

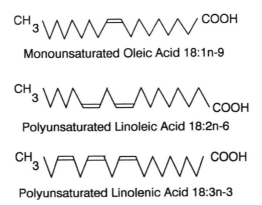

Monounsaturated Oleic Acid 18:1n-9

Polyunsaturated Linoleic Acid 18:2n-6

Polyunsaturated Linolenic Acid 18:3n-3

Figure 1. Fatty acid structure and nomenclature.

the behavioral effects of FA. In particular, there has been interest in a deficiency of either n-3 or n-6 FA. The usual way of producing an FA deficiency is to use a naturally occurring oil, such as coconut oil, that is high in saturated fats and contains minimal amounts of FA. Lard would be an alternative. Such a diet is contrasted with one that contains an oil, such as corn oil, that is low in saturated fat and high in n-6 FA. Each diet would offer equivalent caloric contents of fat, protein, and carbohydrates. The specific effects of n-3 versus n-6 FA have been addressed by comparing oils that differ in the n-3:n-6 ratio, for example, safflower oil (18:2n-6) and soybean oil (18:2n-6 and 18:3n-3).

The Significance of Fatty Acids in the Nervous System

A large proportion of lipids in the brain comprise PUFAs, particularly arachidonic acid (20:4n-6) and DHA (22:6n-3 or omega-3). In comparison with much of the rest of the body, the lipids of the gray matter of the brain, particularly the retina, contain high levels of DHA. These FAs are integral structural components of cell membranes; they interact with membrane-bound proteins and act as prostaglandin precursors. As the levels of brain PUFA increases rapidly during intrauterine and early postnatal periods, the question arises as to whether their dietary availability is important to normal structural development and ultimately cognitive ability.

The nervous systems of a wide range of species have a very similar content of DHA that suggests that it has some functional significance. In fact, a high content of DHA and a large surface area of cell membranes are two distinctive features of the central nervous system. The membranes from nonneural tissues contain phospholipids with much lower amounts of DHA than those from neural tissue. In fact, DHA is scarce in nonneural tissue. There is a remarkable similarity in the PUFA composition of mammalian brains. In all cases, the n-3:n-6 ratio is approximately 1:1. The levels of DHA differ within the brain, being high in synaptosomes and the photoreceptor cells in the retina.

Mammals are unable to synthesize DHA: It is therefore essential to consume its precursor, linolenic acid (18:3n-3) or another n-3 FA. Fish oils, high in DHA, are a particularly efficient means of reversing the influence of a diet lacking n-3 FA (Connor, Neuringer, & Lin, 1990). Our understanding of the impact of diets with varying levels of particular FA is poor. There is some concern that an excess of long-chain n-3 FA might result in pathological changes in the brain's structure (Bourne et al., 1990). A key question is whether the provision of essential FA, during a critical period when the brain is rapidly growing, has long-term implications for cognitive functioning. The brain growth spurt, in humans, takes place in the last prenatal trimester and the 1st year of life. In rodents, it is largely postnatal.

The FA composition of the brain reflects dietary FA supply (Wainwright, Huang, Bulman-Fleming, Levesque, & McCutcheon, 1994). A typical response to a diet that is n-3 deficient is the development of a brain with higher levels of n-6 FA. N-3 FA is, however, conserved, so that prolonged dietary deprivation is required before the levels decline in the brain (Bazan, 1990). A deficiency of both n-3 and n-6 FA leads to an increase in the levels of n-9 FA (Innis, 1991).

Dietary Fatty Acids and Psychological Functioning

Rodents

Many of the attempts to assess the impact of changes in the FA content of diet on behavior have examined a possible influence on learning and memory. Although there have been a series of reports that a diet low in FA is associated with decreased performance on tasks requiring learning and memory (Table 1), it should not be assumed that some other mechanism is not involved. If a low intake of FA influenced vision, then a poor learning performance may reflect defective eyesight. If, for example, the animal is less hungry, then the motivation to learn a task for a food reward would decrease.

The nature of dietary FA may influence visual perception. Because the photoreceptor cells of the retina have high concentrations of DHA, it is natural that the impact of n-3 deficiency on retinal functioning has been examined. In rodents, a diet deficient in n-3 is associated with abnormal retinal functioning (Bazan, 1990; Neuringer, Anderson, & Connor, 1988). It is possible that subtle differences in visual acuity might account for some of the reports that performance on learning tasks is influenced by diets that differ in FA makeup.

Rats eating an n-3-deficient diet displayed an increased exploration of a novel environment (Enslen, Milon, & Malnoe, 1991). Changes in activity levels can markedly influence the performance by rodents of learning tasks. A more active rat may have an increased chance of finding a reward in a maze, simply because it moves around to a greater extent. The opposite can also occur: A rat that spends time exploring may not spend so much time trying to perform a learning task.

Table 1. The Influence of Dietary Provision of Fatty Acids on the Learning of Rodents

Authors	Dietary fat	Stage	Test	Effect
		Food-motivated learning		
Lamptey & Walker (1976)	Safflower vs. soybean oil	G, L, PW	Y maze	n-3 increased correct responses
Lamptey & Walker (1978)	Corn vs. coconut oil	G, L, PW	Y maze	Coconut oil during gestation decreased correct responses
Fujimoto et al. (1989)	DHA vs. safflower and olive oil	PW	Y maze	n-3 increased correct responses
Greenwood & Winocur (1990)	Soybean oil vs. lard vs. chow	PW	Hebb–Williams maze	Soybean oil superior to lard, inferior to chow
Caldwell & Churchill (1966)	Fat free vs. chow	G	Lashley maze	Chow better performance
Wong et al. (1989)	Coconut vs. olive vs. corn oil	PW	Radial maze	Corn oil better performance than others
Yamamoto et al. (1987)	Safflower vs. perilla oil	G, L, PW	Brightness discrimination	n-3 better performance
Yamamoto et al. (1988)	Safflower vs. perilla oil vs. chow	G, L, PW	Brightness discrimination	n-3 better performance
Yamamoto et al. (1991)	Safflower vs. perilla oil	G, L, PW	Brightness discrimination	n-3 better performance
Winocur & Greenwood (1993)	Lard vs. chow vs. soybean oil	PW	Discrimination learning	Low levels of soybean oil better performance; high levels of lard and soybean oil disruptive

Study	Comparison	Timing	Task	Result
			Shock-avoidance-motivated behavior	
Bourne et al. (1989)	Sunflower vs. soybean oil	G, L, PW	Shuttlebox	n-3 better performance
Galli et al. (1975)	Fat free vs. corn oil	G	Shuttlebox	Corn oil better performance
Paoletti & Galli (1972)	Fat free vs. corn oil	G, L, PW	Shuttlebox	Corn oil better performance
Mills et al. (1988)	Osmotic pumps FFA n-6, n-3, vs. olive oil	G, L	Shock avoidance	n-3 better performance
Morgan et al. (1981)	Maize oil vs. coconut oil	G, L	Y maze	Coconut oil slower learning
Ruthrich et al. (1984)	Sunflower vs. palmkernel oil	G, L, PW	Brightness discrimination	Sunflower oil better retention
			Water maze	
Coscina et al. (1986)	Soybean oil vs. lard vs. chow	PW	Morris water maze	Soybean oil better performance
Yeduda (1989)	Soybean vs. sunflower vs. lard vs. chow	PW	Morris water maze	Soybean oil better performance
Wainwright et al. (1994)	Coconut vs. olive vs. linseed vs. safflower oil	G, L, PW	Morris water maze	n-3 faster learning than saturated fatty acids

Note: Coconut oil and lard have minimal fatty acids. Corn oil and safflower oil are high in n-6. Soybean oil, linseed oil, and perilla oil contain both n-3 and n-6 fatty acids. Olive oil is high in monounsaturated fatty acids. DHA = docosahexaenoic acid, FFA = free fatty acid, G = gestation, L = lactation, PW = postweaning.

There are several reports that the consumption of diets differing in their FA content is associated with the differential performance of rodents in mazes of various types (see Table 1). In a Y maze, rats have to learn to run to one arm, perhaps one that is white rather than black, to receive a food reward. Using such a task, Lamptey and Walker (1976) found that the consumption of a diet containing n-3 FA was associated with better performance. The problem of interpretation is obvious. The rat is asked to distinguish a black from a white arm. Is an improved performance a reflection of better learning and memory or better visual acuity?

The use of the Morris water maze might allow the importance of visual cues to be established. In this task, an animal is placed in a baby pool and has to swim until a platform hidden under the water is found and the animal can rest. The task can be viewed as a measure of spatial learning, although the use of visual cues in a room cannot be excluded. Weanling rats fed soybean oil were more able to learn to find the platform in the water maze (Coscina, Yehuda, Dixon, Kish, & Lephron-Greenwood, 1986; Yehuda, 1989).

Table 1 shows that a number of studies have found that the composition of the FA in the diet influences various tasks motivated by electric shock. Because soybean oil in the diet has been found to increase the pain threshold (Yehuda, Leprohon-Greenwood, Dixon, & Coscina, 1986), it is unclear to what extent the effects are due to this mechanism rather than learning or memory.

Although every measure of rodent learning brings with it problems of interpretation, Table 1 summarizes a body of findings that point in the same direction. Irrespective of the learning task, be it a water maze, food-motivated maze learning, or shock avoidance, the FA offered by the diet influenced performance. Although the impact on learning cannot be distinguished from other behavioral effects, the consistency of findings, using different paradigms, suggests that we should take seriously the possibility that the FA content of the diet influences learning and memory.

Although there has been no attempt, to date, to systematically examine dietary impact at different stages of development, the impression created by Table 1 is that it can have an impact during gestation, lactation, and in the postweaning period.

When the impact of a diet with low levels of n-3 FA has been examined, repeatedly there have been suggestions that they are associated with a deficiency in cognitive capacity (Bourne et al., 1989; Lamptey & Walker 1976; Nakashima et al., 1993; Yamamoto et al., 1988, 1991; Yamamoto, Saitoh, Moriuchi, Nomura, & Okuyama, 1987). There is, however, still no definitive answer to this question. The data of Wainwright, Huang, Bulman-Fleming, Levesque, and McCutcheon (1994) are interesting. Although they did not find that animals fed a diet deficient in n-3 FA differed from a group containing n-3 FA, the latter learned a water maze more rapidly than animals who received saturated FA. However, when the levels of brain n-3 FA were measured, those who had received the saturated FA had the lowest levels of n-3 FA, in fact, 80% lower than the controls, who received an n-3-FA-containing diet. No differences were found when reversal learning was examined. If there were cognitive effects of a diet low in n-3 FA, then they were subtle. It is possible that the Morris water maze does not offer a sufficiently demanding task to allow subtle aspects of diet to be demonstrated.

Winocur and Greenwood (1993) pointed to additional complications. A diet with high levels of PUFA (soybean oil) was associated with better discrimination learning than one containing saturated fat (lard). This superiority occurred only when fat was 5% weight/weight (w/w) of the diet. If fat was 20% w/w of the diet, then performance was disrupted, irrespective of whether the fat was saturated or polyunsaturated. These data suggest that high-fat diets can adversely affect learning and memory, irrespective of their nature. In summary, there is good evidence that the fat composition of the diet influences the performance of rodents on various tests of cognitive performance. We cannot, however, be certain if the effect is mediated through improved learning and memory capacities as such, rather than other mechanisms.

Humans

The possibility that n-3 FA is necessary for the optimal development of the nervous system has led to concern that the formulas that are offered to infants may be deficient in fatty acids (Carlson, 1993). Docosahexaenoic acid is found in human milk (Koletzko & Bremer, 1989), and the levels can be increased by supplementing the maternal diet with fish oils (Harris, Connor, & Lindsey, 1984). A recent trend is to add essential FAs to cow-milk-based infant formulas, to make them more similar to human milk, although its impact has not as yet been fully established.

There are preliminary reports of a correspondence between DHA status in human infants and visual acuity (Uauy, Birch, Birch, Tyson, & Hoffman, 1990). Carlson, Werkman, Rhodes, and Tolley (1993) found that human infants who received marine oil supplements (high in n-3 FA) had better visual acuity at 2 and 4 months, although not at later stages. Monkeys deprived of n-3 FA also were reported to have poorer visual acuity (Neuringer, Connor, Van Petten, & Barstad, 1984).

Lucas, Morely, Cole, Lister, and Leeson-Payne (1992) found that breast-fed premature babies had 10.2-point higher IQ scores at 7 to 8 years of age than did those who had taken a cows-milk-based formula. Necessarily, such a finding leads to speculation concerning the possible mechanism. Although the origin of the change is unclear, a leading candidate is that the essential FAs, offered by human milk, had influenced the development of the brain and, hence, later performance on intelligence tests. At present, this suggestion is little more than speculation, although further data are awaited with some anticipation.

Fatty Foods and Reaction Times

In humans, the impact on cognitive functioning of the level and the nature of fat in the diet has been little examined. Reaction times offer an important measure of cognitive functioning that may be used in a large-scale epidemiological study. The theory that mental speed is fundamental to cognitive functioning has a long history. Although for a period it fell into disrepute, in recent years, the suggestion that intelligence and speed of mental processing are related has attracted renewed interest (Vernon, 1987). Reviews of the topic quote correlations from $-.30$ to $-.50$ between intelligence and speed of reaction (Jenson, 1982). Eysenck (1987) asserted that of the factors that underlie intelligence, mental speed is the most fundamental, and that choice reaction time offers a convenient index.

The Health and Lifestyle Survey (1987) used the British electoral register to obtain a representative sample of 7,076 randomly chosen adults. A range of information on health-related behaviors was collected, including diet and speed of reaction times. Reaction times were measured with a portable machine. The second and third fingers of each hand were placed on four buttons labeled *one* to *four*. When the digit 1, 2, 3, or 4 appeared on a screen, the participant pressed the corresponding key.

The participants also responded to a list of 31 types of food, by stating the frequency with which it was eaten. The range of responses were (a) *Never or on very rare occasions*, (b) *Rarely / sometimes but less than once or twice a week*, (c) *Once or twice a week*, (d) *Most days, 3–6 days a week*, (e) *Daily*, and (f) *More than once a day*. The responses to the food-frequency questionnaire were factor analyzed. The factors that resulted could be readily interpreted in dietary terms, for example, the frequency that vegetables were eaten clustered together, as did the eating of fruit and salad. In the present context, only data from a factor labeled Fatty Foods (eating of crisps [potato chips], chips [french fries], fried foods, and sausage and meat products) are reported: This dietary factor was uniquely and very strongly associated with the speed of reaction times. The population was divided into approximate thirds and described as consuming low, medium, and high amounts of fatty foods. The population was categorized by gender, age (18 to 39, 40 to 59, 60 or over) and socioeconomic grouping (1/2: managerial/professional, 3: clerical/administrative, 4: skilled manual, 5: semiskilled manual, 6: unskilled manual).

Figure 2 shows the association between the amount of fatty food in the diet and reaction times. The data reported are the mean reaction times in milliseconds for 40 trials. The more fatty food in the diet, the faster were reaction times. This association was very large and extremely statistically significant. The difference between those eating high and low levels of fatty foods was as much as 150 ms. The association between the eating of greater amounts of fatty foods and reaction times was a robust phenomenon. It was found in both genders and all ages, irrespective of socioeconomic background, $F(2, 6990) = 12.49$, $p < 0.0001$.

These data should be interpreted with the greatest of caution. Although the label *fatty foods* has been used, there was no measure of the fat content of the diet. If one consumes a diet low in fat, then the calories need to be made up with other food items. Is it the presence or absence of

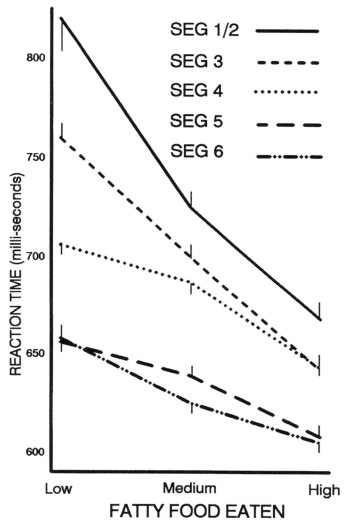

Figure 2. The relationship between the eating of fatty foods and reaction times. The data are mean reaction times + standard errors of measurement for Socioeconomic Group (SEG) 1/2: professional/managerial, SEG 3: clerical/administrative, SEG 4: skilled manual, SEG 5: semiskilled manual, SEG 6: unskilled manual workers.

fatty foods that is important? Or, rather, is it the foods that are added or removed from the diet, depending on the amount of fat consumed, that are important? There was, however, no obvious relationship between reaction times and other measures of diet. The powerful relationship was uniquely between fatty foods and reaction times.

The data in Figure 2 are correlational. It follows that a causal relationship between diet and reaction times cannot be inferred. There are, however, good reasons to further consider the possibility that such a relationship exists. Hill (1965) listed aspects of a correlation coefficient that would lead one to suspect that a causal relationship did exist.

A very strong and consistent association suggests causality. In the present context, the association between the eating of fatty food and reaction times was very large and was found consistently, irrespective of gender, age, and social background. Dose–response curves add additional weight to the suggestion that causality exists.

If the association is causal, then the relationship must be specific to the factors in question. Although it is not logically possible to exclude the possibility that a factor associated with diet, rather than diet as such, was the causal agent, there are no obvious alternative mechanisms. The eating of fatty food is associated with a range of other characteristics, such as an increased likelihood to smoke, drink, or consume particular foods. For example, people who drink are likely to have slower and not faster reaction times. When the intake of other food groups was examined, only fatty food showed this strong and consistent relationship.

Another criterion suggested by Hill (1965) was plausibility: Is it reasonable to suggest that dietary fat influences neural functioning? The animal data reviewed above demonstrated that fatty acids derived from diet penetrate the brain and influence behavior (see Table 1). In humans, consumption of a high-fat diet has been reported to alter the cerebral metabolism of glucose leading to the elevation of the electroconvulsive threshold (Appleton & DeVino, 1974). With epileptics, a high-fat diet is a useful adjunct when medication alone is unable to control seizures (Millichap, Jones, & Rudis, 1964). It seems reasonable to further consider the possibility that dietary fat has an impact on cognition.

A final test suggested by Hill (1965) was that the experimental manipulation of dietary fat should be associated with a change in reaction times that should postdate the change in diet. The acute and chronic impact of dietary fat has been little studied. An exception is Lloyd, Green, and Rogers (1994), who compared lunches that offered low-fat and high-carbohydrate, high-fat and low-carbohydrate, or medium-fat and medium-carbohydrate meals. Those eating the medium-fat and medium-carbohydrate lunches had faster reaction times than those eating either of the other two meals. In addition, medium levels of these macronutrients were associated with reports of feeling more alert, certain, and cheerful.

Too much weight should not be placed on a single isolated study. Much more information is needed. The Lloyd et al. (1994) study examined the acute response to variations in the level of fat in a meal. The chronic impact of a diet consistently containing higher levels of fat may well be different, because animal studies suggest that over time, the structure of the brain is modified (Wainwright et al., 1994). In conclusion, the systematic examination of Hill's (1965) criteria suggests that we should take very seriously the hypothesis that decreasing the amount of fat in the diet is associated with alterations in cognitive functioning. In drawing this conclusion, the limitations of the present data should be kept in mind. Firm conclusions await further data.

Cholesterol Levels and Mental Processing

On the basis of animal studies, Yehuda (1987) proposed that dietary manipulation may alter behavior by changing brain cholesterol levels and neuronal membrane fluidity. Kessler and Yehuda (1985) found that learning per se significantly changed cholesterol levels in the hippocampus and cortex of rats, with corresponding increases in membrane fluidity. Although cholesterol as such does not enter the brain from the blood, it offers one index of FA metabolism. Benton (1995) related serum cholesterol levels to reaction times.

The plasma cholesterol levels of 123 male and 151 female undergraduates, consuming freely chosen diets, were measured (Benton, 1995). Eight lamps, each with a button below it, were arranged in a semicircle 5.5 in. from a central button. The participant depressed the central button with his or her dominant index finger. When one of the eight lights lit up, the participant pressed a button in front of it. Reaction times were monitored under four conditions, when it was possible for one, two, four, or eight lamps to be illuminated. The reaction times were divided into decision time (the time taken to raise the finger from the home button) and move-

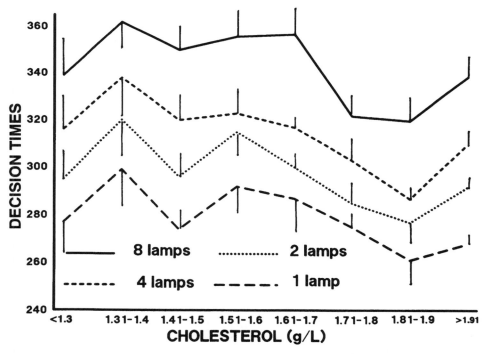

Figure 3. The relationship between plasma cholesterol levels and decision and movement times in female participants. The data are decision times + standard errors, in milliseconds. Decision times reflect the time taken to attend and plan a response. From "Do Low Cholesterol Levels Slow Mental Processing?" by D. Benton, 1995, *Psychosomatic Medicine, 57*, p. 51. Copyright 1995 by Williams & Wilkins. Reprinted with permission.

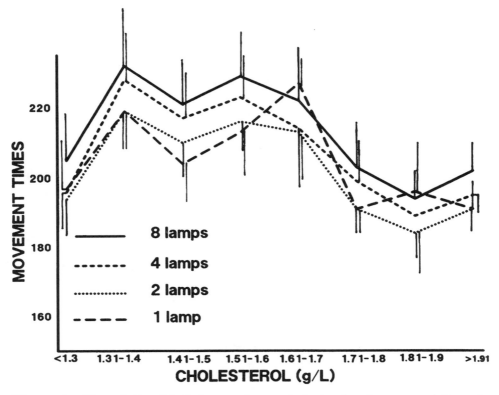

Figure 4. The relationship between plasma cholesterol and movement times in female participants. The data are movement times + standard errors, in milliseconds. Movement times reflect the degree of motor control. From "Do Low Cholesterol Levels Slow Mental Processing?" by D. Benton, 1995, *Psychosomatic Medicine, 57*, p. 51. Copyright 1995 by Williams & Wilkins. Reprinted with permission.

ment time (the time taken from leaving the home key to pushing the key corresponding to the illuminated lamp). Decision time is a measure of the time required to attend to the situation and plan appropriate action. Movement times reflect motor control (Jensen, 1982).

For female participants, the relationship between cholesterol values and reaction time variables was examined by the calculation of linear regression equations. Lower cholesterol values were associated with slower decision times (see Figure 3) and slower movement times (see Figure 4). For male participants, the relationship between plasma cholesterol levels and decision time was not linear. Figure 5 shows that both low and high cholesterol levels were associated with slower decision times in both the four- and eight-light conditions. A comparable analysis of the movement times of male participants failed to find statistically significant relationships.

The Benton (1995) study reported a relationship between plasma cholesterol values and cognitive efficiency. Although the association accounted only for a small amount of the variance, the phenomenon was demon-

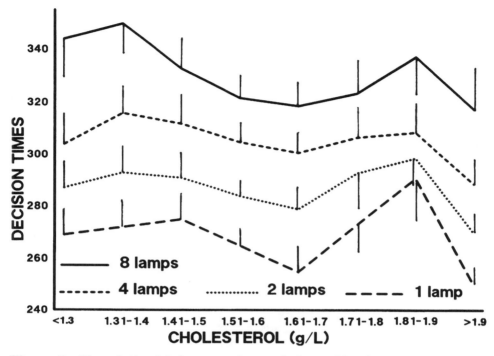

Figure 5. The relationship between plasma cholesterol levels and decision times in male participants. The data are decision times + standard errors, in milliseconds. From "Do Low Cholesterol Levels Slow Mental Processing?" by D. Benton, 1995, *Psychosomatic Medicine, 57,* p. 52. Copyright 1995 by Williams & Wilkins. Reprinted with permission.

strated in a sample several orders of magnitude smaller than needed to relate cholesterol levels to the incidence of suicide (Engelberg, 1992; Lindberg, Rastam, Gullberg, & Eklund, 1992; Muldoon, Manuck, & Matthews, 1990). The association was linear and more consistent in women, rather than in men, suggesting that several underlying mechanisms may have been involved.

It is important to distinguish low cholesterol values from the impact of lowering cholesterol by changes in diet. The Benton (1995) study examined low rather than lowered cholesterol levels. It is known that serum cholesterol, to a large extent, reflects genetic factors, and there was nothing in the Benton (1995) findings that precluded the possibility that individual differences in hormonal or biochemical variables independently influenced both plasma cholesterol and brain functioning.

The Benton (1995) data are correlational in nature, and a causal relationship cannot be inferred. Attempts to decrease plasma cholesterol levels may also influence neural functioning. A major function of cholesterol in the body is as a part of cell membranes. Although cholesterol, as such, does not cross the blood–brain barrier, FA derived from diet penetrates the brain and modifies the composition of neuronal membranes, alters membrane fluidity, and changes the functional state of membrane-bound proteins that are important in neural transmission.

Although dietary diaries were not kept in the Benton (1995) study, it seems improbable that the findings reflected systematic variations in diet. When extremely low fat diets are taken by those with high plasma cholesterol levels, with the aim of decreasing heart disease, levels typically fall about 15%. There is no reason to expect that in the young, healthy sample, even a minority would have been consuming extremely low fat diets; hence, the impact of diet on cholesterol values would be expected to be limited.

Until the experimental manipulation of cholesterol levels has been related to changes in decision times, we should not claim a causal relationship. We await these critical data, although the previous reports that the experimental manipulations of fat intake and cholesterol levels are associated with changes in the behavior of both human beings (Muldoon et al., 1990) and animals (see Table 1) support the hypothesis that the intake of dietary fat may influence cognitive functioning. In fact, there is one report that a reduction in cholesterol levels in men over, but not under, the age of 40 was associated with improved performance on a series of cognitive tests (Reitan & Shipley, 1963). In contrast, Harrison and Ashton (1994) found that cholesterol-lowering drugs did not influence electroencephalograph-evoked potentials and mood scales.

Conclusion

The present chapter reviewed the evidence that the amount and nature of fat in the diet influence cognitive functioning. From animal literature there is clear evidence that the amount and the nature of FA in the diet influence the structure of the brain. Equally, there are numerous reports that these diets influence the performance of rodents on a variety of learning tasks. We cannot, however, be certain that these effects are always mediated through changes in cognitive ability as opposed to other aspects of behavior. The data in humans are extremely limited and preclude even a tentative conclusion. The data are, however, sufficient to justify more systematic examination of the topic.

References

Appleton, D. B., & DeVino, D. C. (1974). An animal model for the ketogenic diet. *Epilepsia*, *15*, 211–227.

Bazan, N. G. (1990). Supply of n-3 polyunsaturated fatty acids and their significance in the central nervous system. In R. J. Wurtman & J. J. Wurtman (Eds.), *Nutrition and the brain* (Vol. 8, pp. 1–24). New York: Raven Press.

Benton, D. (1992). Vitamin–mineral supplements and intelligence. *Proceedings of the Nutrition Society*, *51*, 295–302.

Benton, D. (1995). Do low cholesterol levels slow mental processing? *Psychosomatic Medicine*, *57*, 50–53.

Bourne, J. M., Bonneil, M., Dumont, O., Piciotti, M., Calaf, R., Portugal, H., Nalbone, G., & Lafont, H. (1990). Effect of increasing amounts of dietary fish oil on brain and liver fatty composition. *Biochimica Biophysica Acta, 1043*, 149–152.

Bourne, J. M., Francois, M., Youyou, A., Dumont, O., Piciotti, M., Pascal, G., & Durand, G. (1989). The effects of dietary-linolenic acid on the composition of nerve membranes, enzymatic activity, amplitude of electrophysiological parameters, resistance to poisons and performance of learning tasks in rats. *Journal of Nutrition, 119*, 1880–1892.

Caldwell, D. F., & Churchill, J. A. (1966). Learning impairment in rats administered a lipid free diet during pregnancy. *Psychological Reports, 19*, 99–102.

Carlson, S. E. (1993). Lipid requirements of very-low-birth-weight infants for optimal growth and development. In *Lipids, learning and the brain: Fats in infant formulas* (pp. 188–207). Report of the 103rd Ross Conference on Pediatric Research, Ross Laboratories, Columbus, Ohio.

Carlson, S. E., Werkman, S. H., Rhodes, P. G., & Tolley, E. A. (1993). Visual acuity development in healthy preterm infants: Effects of marine oil supplementation. *American Journal of Clinical Nutrition, 58*, 35–42.

Connor, W. E., Neuringer, M., & Lin, D. S. (1990). Dietary effects in brain fatty acid composition: The reversibility of n-3 fatty acid deficiency and turnover of docosahexaenoic acid in the brain, erthrocytes and plasma of rhesus monkeys. *Journal of Lipid Research, 31*, 237–247.

Coscina, D. V., Yehuda, S., Dixon, L. M., Kish, S. J., & Lephron-Greenwood, C. E. (1986). Learning is improved by a soybean oil diet in rats. *Life Science, 38*, 1789–1794.

Engelberg, H. (1992). Low serum cholesterol and suicide. *The Lancet, 339*, 727–729.

Enslen, M., Milon, H., & Malnoe, A. (1991). Effect of low intake of n-3 fatty acids during development on brain phospholipids fatty acid composition and exploratory behaviour in rats. *Lipids, 26*, 203–208.

Eysenck, H. J. (1987). Speed of information processing reaction time and the theory of intelligence. In P. A. Vernon (Ed.), *Speed of information processing and intelligence* (pp. 21–67). Norwood, NJ: Ablex.

Fernstrom, J. D., & Wurtman, R. J. (1971). Brain serotonin content: Increase following ingestion of carbohydrate diet. *Science, 174*, 1023–1025.

Fujimoto, K., Yao, K., Miyazawa, T., Hironto, H., Nishikawa, M., Kimura, S., Maruyama, K., & Nonaka, M. (1989). The effect of dietary docosahexaeoate on the learning ability of rats. In R. K. Chandra (Ed.), *Health effects of fish and fish oils* (pp. 275–284). St. John's, Newfoundland, Canada: ARTS Biomedical.

Galli, C., Messeri, P., Oliverio, A., & Paoletti, R. (1975). Deficiency of essential fatty acids during pregnancy and avoidance learning in the progecy. *Pharmacological Research Communications, 7*, 71–80.

Greenwood, C. E., & Winocur, G. (1990). Learning and memory impairment in rats fed a high saturated fat diet. *Behavioral Neural Biology, 53*, 74–87.

Harris, W. S., Connor, W. E., & Lindsey, S. (1984). Will dietary w-3 fatty acids change the composition of human milk? *American Journal of Clinical Nutrition, 40*, 780–785.

Harrison, R. W. S., & Ashton, C. H. (1994). Do cholesterol lowering agents affect brain activity—A comparison of simvastatin, pravastatin and placebo in healthy volunteers. *British Journal of Clinical Pharmacology, 37*, 231–236.

Health and Life Style Survey. (1987). London: Health Promotion Research Trust.

Hill, A. B. (1965). The environment and disease: Association or causation? *Proceedings of the Royal Society of Medicine, 58*, 295.

Innis, S. M. (1991). Essential fatty acids in growth and development. *Progress in Lipid Research, 30*, 39–103.

Jensen, A. R. (1982). Reaction time and psychometric g. In H. J. Eysenck (Ed.), *A model for intelligence* (pp. 93–132). Berlin: Springer-Verlag.

Kessler, R. A., & Yehuda, S. (1985). Learning-induced changes in brain cholesterol and fluidity: Implication for brain aging. *International Journal of Neuroscience, 28*, 73–82.

Koletzko, B., & Bremer, H. J. (1989). Fat content and fatty acid composition of infant formulas. *Acta Paediatrica Scandinavica, 78*, 513–521.

Lamptey, M. S., & Walker B. L. (1976). A possible essential role for dietary linolenic acid in the development of the young rat. *Journal of Nutrition, 106*, 89–93.

Lamptey, M. S., & Walker, B. L. (1978). Learning behavior and brain lipid composition in rats subjected to essential fatty acid deficiency during gestation lactation and growth. *Journal of Nutrition, 108,* 358–367.

Lindberg, G., Rastam, L., Gullberg, B., & Eklund, G. A. (1992). Low serum cholesterol concentration and short term mortality from injury in men and women. *British Medical Journal, 305,* 277–279.

Lloyd, H. M., Green, M. W., & Rogers, P. J. (1994). Mood and cognitive performance effects of isocaloric lunches differing in fat and carbohydrate content. *Physiology and Behavior, 56,* 51–57.

Lucas, A., Morely, R., Cole, T. J., Lister, G., & Leeson-Payne, C. (1992). Breast milk and subsequent intelligence quotient in children born preterm. *The Lancet, 339,* 261–264.

McLoughlin, I., & Clarke, P. (1989). Lipid lowering drugs. *British Journal of Psychiatry, 154,* 275–276.

Millichap, J. C., Jones, J. C., & Rudis, B. P. (1964). Mechanisms of anticonvulsant action of ketogenic diet. *American Journal of Disorders of Childhood, 107,* 593–604.

Mills, D. E., Ward, R. P., & Young, C. (1988). Effects of prenatal and early postnatal fatty acid supplementation on behavior. *Nutrition Research, 8,* 273–286.

Morgan, B. L. G., Oppenheimer, J., & Winick, M. (1981). Effects of essential fatty acid deficiency during late gestation on brain N-acetylneuraminic acid metabolism and behaviour in the progency. *British Journal of Nutrition, 46,* 223–230.

Muldoon, M. F., Manuck, S. B., & Matthews, K. A. (1990). Lowering cholesterol concentrations and mortality: A quantitative review of primary preventive trials. *British Medical Journal, 301,* 309–314.

Nakashima, Y., Yuasa, S., Hakamizu, Y., Okuyama, H., Ohhara, T., Kameyama, T., & Nabeshima, T. (1993). Effect of a high linoleate and a high alpha-linolenate diet on general behavior and drug sensitivity. *Journal of Lipid Research, 34,* 239–247.

Neuringer, M., Anderson, G. J., & Connor, W. E. (1988). The essentiality of n-3 fatty acids in the development and function of the retina and brain. *Annual Review of Nutrition, 8,* 517–541.

Neuringer, M., Connor, W. E., Van Petten, C., & Barstad, L. (1984). Dietary omega-3 fatty acid deficiency and visual loss in infant rhesus monkeys. *Journal of Clinical Investigation, 73,* 272–276.

Paoletti, R., & Galli, C. (1972). Effects of essential fatty acid deficiency on the central nervous system in the growing rat. In K. Elliot & J. Knight (Eds.), *Lipids, malnutrition and the developing brain* (pp. 121–140). A Ciba Foundation and Nestlé Foundation joint symposium. New York: Associate Scientific.

Reitan, R. M., & Shipley, R. E. (1963). The relationship of serum cholesterol changes to psychological abilities. *Journal of Gerontology, 18,* 350–357.

Ruthrich, H.-L., Hoffman, P., Matthies, H., & Forster, W. (1984). Perinatal linoleate deprivation impairs learning and memory in adult rats. *Behavioral Neural Biology, 40,* 205–212.

Sastry, P. S. (1985). Lipids of nervous tissue: Composition and metabolism. *Progress in Lipid Research, 24,* 169–176.

Uauy, R. D., Birch, D. G., Birch, E. E., Tyson, J. E., & Hoffman, D. R. (1990). Dietary omega-3 fatty acids in retinal function of very-low-birth-weight neonates. *Pediatric Research, 28,* 485–492.

Vernon, P. A. (1987). *Speed of information processing and intelligence.* Norwood, NJ: Ablex.

Wainwright, P. E., Huang, Y.-S., Bulman-Fleming, B., Levesque, S., & McCutcheon, D. (1994). The effects of dietary fatty acid composition combined with environmental enrichment on brain and behavior in mice. *Behavioral Brain Research, 60,* 125–136.

Winocur, G., & Greenwood, C. E. (1993). High-fat diets impair conditional discrimination learning in rats. *Psychobiology, 21,* 286–292.

Wong, K. L., Murakami, K., & Routtenberg, A. (1989). Dietary cis-fatty acids that increase protein F_1 phosphorylation enhance spatial memory. *Brain Research, 505,* 302–305.

Yamamoto, N., Hashimoto, A., Takemoto, Y., Okuyama, H., Nomura, M., Kitajima, R., Togashi, T., & Tamai, Y. (1988). Effect of the dietary-linolenate/linoleate balance on lipid composition and learning ability of rats: II. Discrimination process, extinction process and glycolipid composition. *Journal of Lipid Research, 29,* 1013–1021.

Yamamoto, N., Okaniwa, Y., Mori, S., et al. (1991). Effects of a high-linoleate and a high-linoleate diet on the learning ability of aged rats: Evidence against an auto-oxidation-related lipid peroxide theory of aging. *Journal of Gerontology, 46*, B17.

Yamamoto, N., Saitoh, M., Moriuchi, A., Nomura, M., & Okuyama, H. (1987). Effect of dietary-linolenate/linoleate balance on brain lipid composition and learning ability of rats. *Journal of Lipid Research, 28*, 144–151.

Yeduda, S. (1987). Nutrients, brain chemistry and behavior: A possible role for the neuronal membrane. *International Journal of Neuroscience, 35*, 21–36.

Yehuda, S. (1989). Behavioral effects of dietary fats. In R. K. Chandra (Ed.), *Health effects of fish and fish oils* (pp. 327–335). St. Johns, Newfoundland, Canada: ARTS Biomedical.

Yehuda, S., Leprohon-Greenwood, C. E., Dixon, L. M., & Coscina, D. V. (1986). Effects of dietary fat on pain threshold thermoregulation and motor activity in rats. *Pharmacology Biochemistry and Behavior, 24*, 1775–1777.

Part V

Public Health Perspectives

14

Hypocholesterolemia, Hypolipoproteinemia, and Risk of Death

Roy B. Verdery

Although it is well established that high levels of cholesterol and certain lipoproteins are strongly associated with increased risk for coronary artery disease, cerebrovascular disease, and death from myocardial infarction and stroke, the association of low levels of cholesterol and certain lipoproteins with increased prevalence of other diseases and risk of death from these diseases has been equally well established. The earliest reports of association of low cholesterol levels with disease, particularly malnutrition and cancer, are from the 1930s (G. L. Muller, 1930). Reports from the 1940s describe the association between low cholesterol levels and acute febrile illnesses (Nishita, 1941).

Since these early studies on low blood lipid levels in chronic and acute disease, there have been significant changes in both our understanding of the biochemistry of lipids and lipoproteins and the methodology used to measure blood lipids and lipoproteins. Initially, blood lipid levels measured included only total cholesterol, triglyceride, and phospholipid. In the 1950s, lipoproteins were discovered to be the carriers of these lipids, and measurements of specific lipoproteins, primarily chylomicrons, very low density lipoproteins (VLDLs), low density lipoproteins (LDLs), and high density lipoproteins (HDLs), became necessary to understand the characteristics of dyslipoproteinemias. More recently, the proteins associated with lipoproteins, apolipoproteins, have been exhaustively studied. Each lipoprotein species has specific apolipoproteins that are important structural elements and help regulate the metabolism of the lipids that are carried.

Careful metabolic studies of synthesis and turnover rates of apolipoproteins have shown that to a great extent, levels of cholesterol and other lipids and of specific lipoproteins are regulated by synthesis and turnover rates of associated apolipoproteins and levels of certain enzymes, including lipoprotein lipase (LPL), hepatic triglyceride lipase (HTGL), lecithin cho-

This work was supported in part by National Institute on Aging Grant SERCA K01-AG00414 and the Arizona Center on Aging, University of Arizona School of Medicine.

lesterol acyltransferase (LCAT), and cholesteryl ester transfer protein
(CETP). The molecular biological processes that control the levels of these
structural and regulatory proteins are just now being understood, with
the help of genetically engineered regulatory and structural proteins with
altered amino acid sequences and the development of transgenic and
knockout mice, which have had their apolipoprotein levels artificially ma-
nipulated. These points are important in the following discussion, because
the association of hypocholesterolemia and hypolipoproteinemia with risk
of death needs to be tied to an understanding of the biological and biochemical processes that regulate levels of cholesterol and lipoproteins in
the blood.

This chapter reviews the epidemiological connections among hypocholesterolemia, death, lipid abnormalities, metabolic problems, and disease.
Mechanisms that may underlie hypocholesterolemia and its relationship
to aging and affect are then discussed.

Epidemiological Connections Between Death and Hypocholesterolemia

A connection between low cholesterol levels and increased risk of death
has been seen in almost all population-based studies of cholesterol. Studies
of large numbers of young and middle-aged people have demonstrated that
the risk of death is a J-shaped function of the cholesterol level. The Whitehall Study (Rose & Shipley, 1980); the Pooling Project Research Group
(Oliver, 1981); Multiple Risk Factor Intervention Trial (Martin, Hulley,
Broconer, Koller, & Wentworth, 1986); the Helsinki Heart Study (Frick
et al., 1987); and the Lipid Research Clinics clinical trial (Cowan et al.,
1990), among others, have all shown similar results (Criqui, 1991; Muldoon, Manuck, & Matthews, 1990). In addition to the widely discussed
relationship between *hyper*cholesterolemia and risk of death in people
with plasma cholesterol greater than 180–220 mg/dl, there is increased
risk of death at cholesterol levels less than 150–220 mg/dl (see Figure 1).

Disease-specific analysis of risk of death shows that a large part of
the positive correlation between cholesterol levels and risk of death is due
to increased risk for cardiovascular artery and cerebrovascular disease in
people with high cholesterol levels. Deaths due to most other diseases are
associated with low cholesterol levels, as described later in this chapter.

In elderly people in nursing homes, the relationship between hypocholesterolemia and risk of death is especially striking (see Figure 2). Prospective studies of several different nursing homes in several different
countries showed that cholesterol levels less than 150 mg/dl are associated
with two to three or more times the risk of death than normal cholesterol
levels (180–220 mg/dl) (Forette, Tortrat, & Wolmark, 1989; Rudman et al.,
1987; Verdery & Goldberg, 1991). It has been proposed that cholesterol, in
combination with hematocrit, can be used to create a mortality risk index
that is useful in predicting which patients in a nursing home are at most
risk of dying within 1 year (Rudman, Mattson, Feller, & Nagraj, 1989).

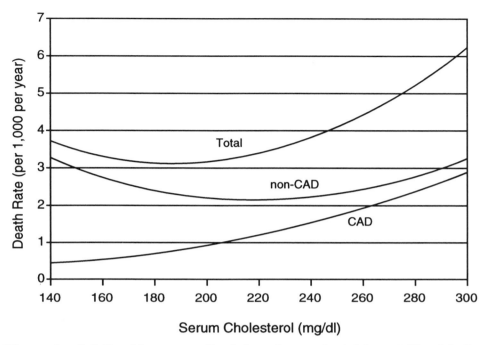

Figure 1. Relationships among the J-shaped curve for total mortality risk, the monotonically increasing curve for coronary artery disease (CAD) mortality risk, and the asymptotic curve for non–coronary artery disease (non-CAD) risk of death. Data from Martin, Hulley, Broconer, Koller, & Wentworth, 1986.

Hypocholesterolemia that develops in acutely hospitalized people is also a predictor of mortality and morbidity (Noel, Smith, & Ettinger, 1991). Patients whose cholesterol levels fall by more than 40 mg/dl have a longer length of stay, more complications, and are more likely to die than patients whose cholesterol levels remain constant during hospitalization. These patients are also more likely to be those who had surgery during their hospitalization or a period of in-hospital starvation.

In population-based studies in Japan and among people of Japanese descent who immigrated to the United States, low cholesterol levels have been associated with increased risk of hemorrhagic stroke and death from strokes or other cerebrovascular diseases (Kagan, Popper, & Rhoads, 1980; Tanaka et al., 1982). This observation was not supported in a Chinese cohort with an especially high incidence of strokes (Chen, Collins, Peta, & Li, 1989; Li 1979). On the other hand, there are reports of people with acutely reduced cholesterol levels taking cyclosporin, with unexpectedly high stroke rates (Cooper et al., 1989). The mechanism for an association of strokes with hypocholesterolemia is unknown, but it has been speculated that because cholesterol plays a role in plasma membrane structure, people with low cholesterol levels have impaired capillary permeability or increased arteriolar fragility (Konishi et al., 1993), which might predispose

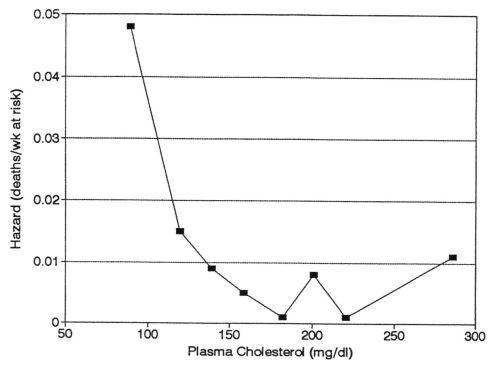

Figure 2. Risk of death in a nursing home, showing the markedly increased mortality in people with low cholesterol levels. This graph can be thought of as the left-hand side of a mortality–cholesterol graph, as depicted in Figure 1. wk = week. Data are from Verdery & Goldberg, 1991.

them to platelet aggregation and subsequent strokes. A contributing factor is that low cholesterol levels occur in people with hypertension, perhaps due to high salt content of some low cholesterol diets and that it may be hypertension that increases risk for stroke in people with hypocholesterolemia.

Lipid Abnormalities and Dyslipoproteinemias

Most of the epidemiological studies listed in the previous section showed associations of low cholesterol levels with increased risk of death but did not address the question of which lipoproteins were low and whether there were differential effects of low levels of LDL or HDL, the two principal lipoproteins containing cholesterol. In hospitalized patients who developed hypocholesterolemia, both cholesterol and triglyceride levels were decreased (Noel et al., 1991). In this study, all of the lipoproteins—VLDL, LDL, and HDL—were decreased in concentration in the people who had low cholesterol levels.

Population- and institution-based epidemiological studies of hypocholesterolemia, like those of hypercholesterolemia, included people with a variety of genetic differences in lipid and lipoprotein metabolism. Several well-known genetic variants lead to low levels of HDL or LDL (Granot & Decklebaum, 1989; Malloy & Kane, 1982). These low lipoprotein levels are associated with increased risk of death in some instances, such as Tangier disease, LCAT deficiency, and abetalipoproteinemia. In some instances, particularly A-1 Milano disease, the genetic defect is associated with increased survival. In one population-based study, hypocholesterolemia was found to be attributable to increased frequency of the apolipoprotein E-2 phenotype and decreased frequency of the apolipoprotein E-4 phenotype and relatively unrelated to prevalence of disease or differences in diet (Snyder et al., 1993).

Because these genetic variations are widely distributed in the population and undoubtedly were present in population-based and institution-based studies referred to previously, many of the results of these epidemiological studies may be due, in part, to genetic variability in apolipoproteins and enzymes controlling lipid and lipoprotein metabolism.

Metabolic Problems Associated With Hypocholesterolemia

An association between hypocholesterolemia and life-threatening anemia from a variety of causes has been known for more than 60 years (G. L. Muller, 1930). As described in subsequent sections, much of this association is due to associations between hypocholesterolemia and hematologic malignancies. Nonetheless, anemia due to other causes, particularly nutritional deficiency, vitamin B_{12} deficiency, and iron deficiency, has also been described (Elwood, Mahler, Sweetnam, & Moore, 1970; G. L. Muller, 1930; Rifkind & Gale, 1967). Additionally, genetic variants in hematopoiesis and hemoglobin synthesis, primary causes of anemia, are also associated with hypocholesterolemia (G. L. Muller, 1930; Rifkind & Gale, 1967). Many of these causes of anemia are associated with a shortened life span. Hence, hypocholesterolemia, in turn, is associated with increased risk of death in anemia. As described earlier, the nursing-home-based studies of Rudman and colleagues suggest that anemia (regardless of etiology) and hypocholesterolemia, to some extent, are additive in predicting bad outcomes (Rudman et al., 1989).

Two other problems associated with hypocholesterolemia that are also perhaps linked to anemia are hypoalbuminemia and weight loss. It is well established that people with low levels of albumin also have low levels of HDL cholesterol (Nanji & Reddy, 1983). Weight loss, in addition, is closely associated with hypocholesterolemia, hypoalbuminemia, and anemia, and it is well established that hypocholesterolemia, hypoalbuminemia, and anemia are markers of malnourished states whether due primarily to starvation or secondarily to increased utilization of calories and protein by people in catabolic states. These catabolic states, in turn, are associated with increased risk of death.

Table 1. Clinical Conditions Causing Hypocholesterolemia

Condition	VLDL	LDL	HDL	Enzymes[a]
Fever	↑	↓↓	↓↓	↓
Infection	↑	↓↓	↓↓	↓
Sepsis	↑	↓↓	↓↓	↓
HIV infection		↓	↓	
Trauma		↓	↓↓	
Surgery	↑	↓	↓↓	
Burns		↓	↓↓	
Myocardial infarction		↓	↓	↓
Rheumatoid arthritis		↓	↓	
Cancer		↓	↓	
Cirrhosis			↓↓	
Drug abuse			↓	

Note: VLDL = very low density lipoprotein; LDL = low density lipoprotein; HDL = high density lipoprotein; ↑ = modest increase; ↓ = modest decrease; ↓↓ = significant decrease.
[a]Enzymes include lipoprotein lipase, hepatic triglyceride lipase, lecithin cholesterol acyl-transferase, and cholesteryl ester transfer protein.

Hypocholesterolemia and Disease

Many acute and chronic diseases are associated with hypocholesterolemia. Most of these are serious diseases or medical conditions that have high rates of death as consequences. Table 1 gives a list of these diseases and the lipoproteins that have been shown to be decreased.

The first group of diseases associated with hypocholesterolemia is those involving fever and infection (Alvarez & Ramos, 1986; Beisel & Fiser, 1970; Gallin, Kaye, & O'Leary, 1969; Lanza-Jacoby, Wong, Tabares, Baer, & Schneider, 1992; Nishita, 1941; Page, 1954; Sammalkorpi, Valtonen, Kertula, Nikkilä, & Taskinen, 1988). Essentially, all febrile illnesses and bacterial infections are associated with hypocholesterolemia. In these diseases, both LDL and HDL are markedly reduced. Very low density lipoprotein is sometimes decreased and sometimes increased. Generally, however, the principal lipoprotein that is lowered is LDL, which can be reduced to less than half of its baseline level. These infectious diseases are associated also with decreased levels of all of the enzymes regulating lipoprotein metabolism, including LCAT, LPL, HTGL, and CETP.

Certain viral infections also cause decreased levels of LDL and HDL. Most notably, HIV infection is associated with hypocholesterolemia and decreased LDL and HDL (Coodley & Coodley, 1991; Shor-Posner et al., 1993). Association of hypocholesterolemia with HIV infection is seen whether or not the diagnostic criteria for AIDS are present. This association is also independent of illegal drug use.

A second large category of medical problems associated with hypocholesterolemia is trauma and surgery (Hailer, Adolph, Eckart, & Wolfram, 1982; Lindholm, Eklund, & Rössner, 1982; Malmendier, Amerijckx, Bihain, & Fischer, 1985). Both trauma and surgery, particularly polytrauma and major invasive surgery, are associated with profound drops in cholesterol and decreased LDL and HDL levels. In polytrauma and major surgery, HDL appears to be more markedly affected than is LDL, dropping in some people to 20% of the baseline level.

Burns are also associated with hypocholesterolemia (Birke, Carlson, & Liljedahl, 1965). Recovery from burns typically involves both infection and surgery because of the vigorous debridement necessary for their treatment. It is, therefore, not clear whether burns are associated with hypocholesterolemia independent of these other factors. Nonetheless, burns and their associated mortality are important causes in the link between hypocholesterolemia and death.

The link between cancer and hypocholesterolemia and the link between hypocholesterolemia and death from cancer have been known since the 1930s (G. L. Muller, 1930). One of the strongest links is between hematologic malignancies, particularly myeloproliferative malignancies, including leukemia, lymphomas, and primary erythropoietic malignancies and hypocholesterolemia (Gilbert, Ginsberg, Fagerstrom, & Brown, 1981; Reverter et al., 1988; Shokunbi, Ahaneku, & Okpala, 1991; Spiegel, Schaefer, Magrath, & Edwards, 1982; Zyada, Hassan, Rees, & Ragab, 1990). The link between solid tumors and hypocholesterolemia is less certain, although there have been numerous reports of an association between hypocholesterolemia and risk of cancer death, particularly in late stages of cancer (Bayerdörffer et al., 1993; Nomura, Stemmerman, & Chyou, 1991; Umeki, 1993). The progressive development of hypocholesterolemia in untreated cancer patients has been proposed as a way to predict imminent death (Chao, Efron, & Wolf, 1975; C. P. Muller, Trilling, & Steinke, 1992).

Among the more controversial links between cancer and hypocholesterolemia is the link between colon cancer and hypocholesterolemia. Many of the population-based studies that were focused on exploring the link between hypercholesterolemia and atherosclerotic death showed that hypocholesterolemia was especially associated with increased risk of death due to colorectal cancer (Kritchevsky, Wilcosky, Morris, Truong, & Tyroler, 1991; Schatzkin et al., 1987). This raised the question of whether hypocholesterolemia was a cause or consequence of colon cancer. Subsequent studies have generally concluded that many people with hypocholesterolemia had undetected colon cancer (Feinleib, 1983; Jacobs et al., 1992; Kritchevsky et al., 1991; Miller, Tartter, Papatestas, Slater, & Aufsas, 1981; Nomura et al., 1991). Studies showing an absence of links between colonic polyps, precursors of colon cancer, and cholesterol levels can also be cited as evidence that hypocholesterolemia does not cause colon cancer but, more likely, is a consequence of colon cancer (Bayerdörffer et al., 1993; Miller et al., 1981).

Another medical problem that has been associated with hypocholesterolemia for many years is acute myocardial infarction (Moriguchi, Fusegawa, Tamachi, & Goto, 1991; Stubbe, Gustafason, & Nilsson-Ehle, 1982; Watson, Buchanan, & Dickson, 1963). Levels of cholesterol decrease markedly after myocardial infarction; so, to assess cardiovascular risk postinfarction, it is necessary to wait up to 6 months for reestablishment of the baseline. Low density lipoprotein and HDL, along with LPL, HTGL, and LCAT, are also decreased after myocardial infarction (Moriguchi et al., 1991). In the case of myocardial infarction, it is quite clear that the hypocholesterolemia is a consequence of this life-threatening condition rather than a cause.

Several chronic conditions also cause hypocholesterolemia. The best studied of them is rheumatoid arthritis. People with active rheumatoid arthritis typically have hypocholesterolemia (Oren & Rachmilewitz, 1992; Svenson, Lithell, Hällgren, Selinus, & Vessby, 1987). Systemic lupus erythmatosis and Crohn's disease also may be associated with hypocholesterolemia (Anonymous, 1989). The hypocholesterolemia of rheumatoid arthritis parallels the elevations of acute-phase reactants such as C-reactive protein and other evidence of active inflammation.

Cirrhosis is another life-threatening condition that is associated with hypocholesterolemia (Levesque, Gancel, Pertuet, Czernichow, & Courtois, 1991; Nanji & Reddy, 1983; Page, 1954). The case of cirrhosis, however, is unique in that the hypocholesterolemia is generally associated with low levels of HDL and, particularly, the development of abnormal HDL due to circulating bile salts. Nonetheless, in a focus on hypocholesterolemia and risk of death, this disease has to be kept in mind as a potential mediator.

Finally, it has recently been shown that substance abusers, particularly abusers of injectable narcotics, have hypocholesterolemia (Gettler, 1991; Maccari, Bassi, Zanoni, & Plancher, 1991). This association is present even in the absence of HIV infection.

In all of these diseases, with the exception of cancer and infection, it can generally be stated that hypocholesterolemia is a consequence of the disease rather than the cause of the disease. The role of hypocholesterolemia in causing infection is theoretical but may be operative in elderly people. In general, hypocholesterolemia has been shown to be associated with decreased immune function, particularly a decrease in the ability of lymphocytes to proliferate (Cuthbert & Lipsky, 1984, 1986). It can be argued that hypocholesterolemia, which occurs due to malnutrition or other causes, might, in turn, cause a relative immunodeficiency and increase the susceptibility to bacterial or viral infection.

Mechanisms Underlying Hypocholesterolemia

Hypocholesterolemia must be caused by either decreased production of cholesterol or increased removal. Data suggest that both of these mechanisms occur in different circumstances.

The production of LDL is closely linked to triglyceride metabolism, particularly the synthesis and clearance of VLDL, the principal endogenous transporter of lipid from the liver to peripheral tissues. In many circumstances, infections are associated with increased VLDL and decreased levels of LPL, the principal enzyme responsible for VLDL clearance (Heller, Reynaert, & Harvengt, 1985). Because LPL activity is reduced, hypertriglyceridemia associated with infection is associated with decreased LDL and elevated VLDL levels. Elevated VLDL levels second-

Table 2. Cytokines Causing Hypocholesterolemia

Cytokine	VLDL	LDL	HDL	Enzymes[a]
IL-1β		↓	↓?	
IL-2		↓	↓	
IL-6		↓	↓	↓
TNFα	↑	↓	↓	↓
Interferon-γ		↓?	↓?	
Interferon-β		↓		

Note: VLDL = Very low density lipoprotein; LDL = low density lipoprotein; HDL = high density lipoprotein; IL = interleukin; TNF = tumor necrosis factor; ↑ = modest increase; ↓ = modest decrease; ↓? = possible modest decrease.
[a]Enzymes include lipoprotein lipase, hepatic triglyceride lipase, lecithin cholesterol acyltransferase, and cholesteryl ester transfer protein.

arily lower HDL cholesterol levels. The end result is hypocholesterolemia with both low LDL and low HDL levels.

In myeloproliferative diseases, on the other hand, decreased LDL is associated with increased clearance of LDL (Ginsberg, Le, Gilbert, Le, & Brown, 1986; Vallabhajosula et al., 1989). Lymphomas, leukemia, and other malignancies have increased levels and increased activity of LDL receptors, which avidly bind and take up LDL, thus reducing their concentration.

High density lipoprotein kinetics in acquired hypolipoproteinemia have not been studied. The production of apolipoprotein A-I, the major HDL apolipoprotein, however, is downregulated by many of the cytokine mediators of inflammation (Ettinger et al., 1994; Morrone et al., 1988; Morrone, Cortese, & Sorrentino, 1989).

Cytokine mediators of inflammation may underlie most hypocholesterolemia. Several cytokines, including tumor necrosis factor-α, interleukin (IL)1-β, IL-2, IL-6, interferon-γ, and interferon-β, are associated with hypocholesterolemia (Boue et al., 1990; Ettinger, Harris, Verdery, Tracy, & Kouba, 1995; Hermus et al., 1992; Schectman et al., 1992). Tumor necrosis factor decreases LPL activity, leading to increased triglyceride and VLDL levels and decreased LDL and HDL cholesterol levels. In both experimental animals and humans, infusion of cytokines decreases the cholesterol level, generally causing profound decreases in HDL levels and a lesser decrease in LDL levels. One of the molecular mechanisms underlying cytokine-induced hypocholesterolemia appears to be a direct effect of cytokines on the production of apolipoprotein B and apolipoproteins A-I and A-II by the hepatocyte (Ettinger et al., 1994; Morrone et al., 1988, 1989; Stopeck, Nicholson, Mancini, & Hajjar, 1993). This decreased synthesis appears to be due to decreased production of the associated messenger ribonucleic acid (mRNA), suggesting that the effect of cytokines on production of lipoproteins occurs at the level of transcription. Table 2 lists cytokines that have been studied and the effects on lipoprotein secretion.

Although cytokine elevation and transcriptional regulation of apolipoprotein production may play a role in many cases of hypocholesterolemia, other factors that may cause hypocholesterolemia have not been exhaustively studied. Turnover of LDL and HDL has been measured in only a few clinical diseases, although much is known about their turnover in normal people and healthy people with genetic variants in lipoprotein metabolism. It is, therefore, quite possible that in circumstances besides malignancies, hypocholesterolemia is caused by increased rates of LDL and HDL clearance.

Effects of Aging

There have been few population-based studies of elderly people, looking at risk of death in relationship to cholesterol levels (Fagard, 1991; Ives, Bonino, Traven, & Kuller, 1993). Those studies that have been reported show that the increased risk of death at low cholesterol levels is more pronounced than at high cholesterol levels. It is not clear, however, whether that is simply due to the increased numbers of older people with low cholesterol levels or whether age independently impacts on the relationship between hypocholesterolemia and increased risk of death.

Aging is also associated with acquired hypocholesterolemia and increased risk of death. Cross-sectional and longitudinal studies of changes in cholesterol level with age show that after the age of 65, cholesterol levels decrease, in general (Herschkopf et al., 1982). An additional complication in the association between age and hypocholesterolemia is that elderly people in acute- and chronic-care settings show more pronounced decreases in their cholesterol levels in response to infections, trauma, and other inflammatory conditions (Noel, Smith, & Ettinger, 1991).

As risk of death increases due to age-associated disease, the level of cholesterol drops in association with age. With age, the prevalence of infectious disease; chronic inflammatory conditions such as rheumatoid arthritis, cancer, and acute myocardial infarction; and certain affective disorders, including depression, increases. As described earlier, these, in turn, are associated with hypocholesterolemia presumably caused by the mechanisms previously outlined. Thus, with age, the prevalence of diseases causing hypocholesterolemia increases, and the degree of hypocholesterolemia caused by these diseases increases as well, resulting in much more pronounced hypocholesterolemia in elderly people. Thus the association of hypocholesterolemia with aging is probably a combination of increased prevalence of age-associated diseases, longitudinal changes in diet and dietary preference, and perhaps changes in physiological mechanisms regulating immune function and lipoprotein metabolism that occur with age.

Relationship With Affect

Hypocholesterolemia has been associated with depression, suicide, and affective disorders, as described elsewhere in this book (see also Glueck, Kuller, et al., 1994; Glueck, Tieger, et al., 1994). These affective disorders are often associated with acute and chronic medical illness (Andrykowski, 1994; Clark & Steer, 1994; Gregory, Jimerson, Walton, Daley, & Paulsen, 1992). Given the well established causal relationship between acute and chronic illness and hypocholesterolemia, the association between hypocholesterolemia and affective disorders may be secondary to the association between affective disorders and illness. An alternative mechanism connecting affective disorder and hypocholesterolemia may be more direct, however. Cytokine mediators of inflammation both are produced by the brain and, in turn, cause changes in the brain and behavior. Hypocholesterolemia may be caused directly by disorders in the central nervous system, mediated by centrally produced cytokines. Alternatively, affective disorders and hypocholesterolemia may be caused by primary disorders in the immune system resulting in production of cytokines. In this way, the epidemiologic connection between hypocholesterolemia and increased risk of death may be mediated by death (e.g., suicide) due to affective disorders as much as it is mediated by prevalence of cancer, infection, or other somatic conditions.

Summary and Conclusion

Clearly, hypocholesterolemia is associated with increased risk of death. This has been shown both in population-based epidemiological studies and in clinical epidemiological studies of groups in acute- and long-term care settings. This association between hypocholesterolemia and risk of death is actually a very old observation and is related to the observation that hypocholesterolemia is associated with a number of life-threatening diseases, including cancer, infection, burns, trauma, surgery, myocardial infarction, arthritis, substance abuse, and affective disorders, including depression. Several mechanisms underlie hypocholesterolemia, including decreased synthesis of cholesterol and cholesterol-carrying lipoproteins and increased removal of cholesterol and cholesterol-carrying lipoproteins. There are at least two different mechanisms at the cellular level that are responsible for these changes in plasma levels: increased removal of lipids and lipoproteins by certain cells and decreased production of lipids and lipoproteins by the liver. This second mechanism, the decreased production of lipids and lipoproteins by the liver, is mediated, at least in part, by inflammatory cytokines. Elevated levels of inflammatory cytokines may very well be a major mechanism underlying the hypocholesterolemia seen in a majority of the diseases listed above.

In many instances, hypocholesterolemia is a secondary effect of diseases that independently cause death by a variety of mechanisms. However, the inverse situation, in which hypocholesterolemia is the cause of disease, cannot be ruled out in many instances. There are no data, however, that suggest that deliberate reduction of cholesterol levels in hypercholesterolemic persons at increased risk for atherosclerosis increases the risk of death due to these other conditions.

References

Alvarez, C., & Ramos, A. (1986). Lipids, lipoproteins, and apolipoproteins in serum during infection. *Clinical Chemistry, 32,* 142–145.

Andrykowski, M. A. (1994). Psychiatric and psychosocial aspects of bone marrow transplantation. *Psychosomatics, 35,* 13–24.

Anonymous. (1989). Severe acquired hypocholesterolemia: Two case reports. *Nutrition Reviews, 47,* 202–207.

Bayerdörffer, E., Mannes, G. A., Richter, W. O., Ochsenkühn, T., Seeholzer, G., Köpcke, W., Wiebecke, B., & Paumgartner, G. (1993). Decreased high-density lipoprotein cholesterol and increased low-density cholesterol levels in patients with colorectal adenomas. *Annals of Internal Medicine, 118,* 481–487.

Beisel, W. R., & Fiser, R. H. (1970). Lipid metabolism during infectious illness. *American Journal of Clinical Nutrition, 23,* 1069–1079.

Birke, G., Carlson, L. A., & Liljedahl, S. (1965). Lipid metabolism and trauma: III. Plasma lipids and lipoproteins in burns. *Acta Medica Scandinavica, 178,* 337–350.

Boue, F., Pastran, Z., Spielmann, M., Le Chevalier, T., Subirana, R., Sevin, D., Paoletti, C., Brandely, M., Avril, M. F., & Sancho-Garnier, H. (1990). A phase I trial with recombinant interferon gamma (Roussel UCLAF) in advanced cancer patients. *Cancer Immunology and Immunotherapy, 32,* 67–70.

Chao, F., Efron, B., & Wolf, P. (1975). The possible prognostic usefulness of assessing serum proteins and cholesterol in malignancy. *Cancer, 35,* 1223–1229.

Chen, Z., Collins, R., Peto, R., & Li, W. (1989). Serum cholesterol levels and stroke mortality [letter to the editor]. *New England Journal of Medicine, 321,* 1339.

Clark, D. A., & Steer, R. A. (1994). Use of nonsomatic symptoms to differentiate clinically depressed and nondepressed hospitalized patients with chronic medical illnesses. *Psychological Reports, 75,* 1089–1090.

Coodley, G., & Coodley, M. K. (1991). Hypocholesterolemia and malabsorption in HIV infection [Letter to the editor]. *Western Journal of Medicine, 154,* 735.

Cooper, D. K. C., Novitzky, D., Davis, L., Juff, J. E., Parker, D., Schlesinger, R., Sholer, C., & Zuhdi, N. (1989). Does central nervous system toxicity occur in transplant patients with hypocholesterolemia receiving cyclosporine? *Journal of Heart Transplantation, 8*(3), 221–224.

Cowan, L., O'Connell, D. L., Criqui, M., Barrett-Connor, E., Bush, T. L., & Wallace, R. B. (1990). Cancer mortality and lipid and lipoprotein levels: The Lipid Research Clinics Program Mortality Follow-Up Study. *American Journal of Epidemiology, 131,* 468–482.

Criqui, M. H. (1991). Cholesterol, primary and secondary prevention, and all-cause mortality. *Annals of Internal Medicine, 115,* 973–976.

Cuthbert, J. A., & Lipsky, P. E. (1984). Modulation of human lymphocyte responses by low density lipoproteins (LDL): Enhancement but not immunosuppression is mediated by LDL receptors. *Proceedings of the National Academy of Sciences, USA, 81,* 4539–4543.

Cuthbert, J. A., & Lipsky, P. E. (1986). Promotion of human T lymphocyte activation and proliferation by fatty acids in low density and high density lipoproteins. *Journal of Biological Chemistry, 261,* 3620–3627.

Elwood, P. C., Mahler, R., Sweetnam, P., & Moore, F. (1970). Association between circulating hæmoglobin level, serum-cholesterol, and blood pressure. *The Lancet, 1,* 589–591.

Ettinger, W. H., Harris, T., Verdery, R. B., Tracy, R., & Kouba, E. (1995). Evidence for inflammation as a cause of hypocholesterolemia in older people. *Journal of the American Geriatrics Society, 43,* 264–266.

Ettinger, W. H., Varma, V. K., Sorci-Thomas, M., Parks, J. S., Sigmon, R. C., Smith, T. K., & Verdery, R. B. (1994). Cytokines decrease apolipoprotein accumulation in medium from Hep G2 cells. *Arteriosclerosis and Thrombosis, 14*(1), 8–13.

Fagard, R. (1991). Serum cholesterol levels and survival in elderly hypertensive patients: Analysis of data from the European Working Party on High Blood Pressure in the Elderly. *American Journal of Medicine, 90*(Suppl. 3A), 625–635.

Feinleib, M. (1983). Review of the epidemiological evidence for a possible relationship between hypocholesterolemia and cancer. *Cancer Research, 43,* 2503s–2507s.

Forette, B., Tortrat, D., & Wolmark, Y. (1989). Cholesterol as risk factor for mortality in elderly women. *The Lancet, 1,* 868–870.

Frick, M. H., Haapa, K., Heinonen, O. P., Helo, P., et al. (1987). Helsinki Heart Study: Primary prevention trial with gemfibrozil in middle-aged men with dyslipoproteinemia. *New England Journal of Medicine, 317,* 1237–1245.

Gallin, J. I., Kaye, D., & O'Leary, W. M. (1969). Serum lipids in infection. *New England Journal of Medicine, 281,* 1081–1086.

Gettler, J. F. (1991). Hypocholesterolemia in substance abusers [Letter to the editor]. *Southern Medical Journal, 84,* 937.

Gilbert, H. S., Ginsberg, H., Fagerstrom, R., & Brown, W. V. (1981). Characterization of hypocholesterolemia in myeloproliferative disease: Relation to disease manifestations and activity. *American Journal of Medicine, 71,* 595–602.

Ginsberg, H. N., Le, N. A., Gilbert, H. S., Le, N., & Brown, W. V. (1986). Altered high density lipoprotein metabolism in patients with myeloproliferative disorders and hypocholesterolemia. *Metabolism, 35,* 878–882.

Glueck, C. J., Kuller, F. E., Hamer, T., Rodriguez, R., Sosa, F., Sieve-Smith, L., & Morrison, J. A. (1994). Hypocholesterolemia, hypertriglyceridemia, suicide, and suicide ideation in children hospitalized for psychiatric diseases. *Pediatric Research, 35,* 602–610.

Glueck, C. J., Tieger, M., Kunkel, R., Hamer, T., Tracy, T., & Speirs, J. (1994). Hypocholesterolemia and affective disorders. *American Journal of Medical Sciences, 308*(4), 218–225.

Granot, E., & Deckelbaum, R. J. (1989). Hypocholesterolemia in childhood. *Journal of Pediatrics, 115*(2), 171–185.

Gregory, R. J., Jimerson, D. C., Walton, B. E., Daley, J., & Paulsen, R. H. (1992). Pharmacotherapy of depression in the medically ill: Directions for future research. *General Hospital Psychiatry, 14,* 36–42.

Hailer, S., Adolph, M., Eckart, J., & Wolfram, G. (1982). Apolipoprotine und Lipide im Serum von Schwerverletzten in Abhängigkeit von der Ernährung [The relation between nutritional state and lipoprotein and lipid levels in the blood serum of gravely injured patients]. *Infusionstherapie, 9,* 302–309.

Heller, F., Reynaert, M., & Harvengt, C. (1985). Plasma activities of lipoprotein lipase, hepatic lipase, and lecithin:cholesterol acyltransferase in patients considered for parenteral nutrition with fat emulsion. *American Journal of Clinical Nutrition, 41,* 748–752.

Hermus, A. R., Sweep, C. G., Demacker, P. N., van der Meer, M. J., Kloppenborg, P. W., & van der Meer, J. W. (1992). Continuous infusion of interleukin-1 beta in rats induces a profound fall in plasma levels of cholesterol and triglycerides. *Arteriosclerosis Thrombosis, 12,* 1036–1043.

Herschkopf, R. J., Elahi, D., Andres, R., Baldwin, H. L., Raizes, G. S., Schocken, D. D., & Tobin, J. D. (1982). Longitudinal changes in serum cholesterol in man: An epidemiological search for an etiology. *Journal of Chronic Disease, 35,* 101–114.

Ives, D. G., Bonino, P., Traven, N. D., & Kuller, L. H. (1993). Morbidity and mortality in rural community-dwelling elderly with low total serum cholesterol. *Journal of Gerontology, 48*(3), M103–M107.

Jacobs, D., Blackburn, H., Higgins, M., Reed, D., Iso, H., Gardner, M., Neaton, H., Nelson, J., Potter, J., Rifkind, B., Rossouw, H., Shekelle, R., Yosuf, S., for participants in the Conference on Low Cholesterol:Mortality Association. (1992). Report of the Conference on Low Blood Cholesterol:Mortality Association. *Circulation, 86,* 1040–1060.

Kagan, A., Popper, J. S., & Rhoads, G. G. (1980). Factors related to stroke incidence in Hawaiian Japanese men. *Stroke, 11*(1), 14–21.

Konishi, M., Iso, H., Komachi, Y., Shimamoto, L. M., Jacobs, D. R., Terau, A., Baba, S., & Ito, M. (1993). Associations of serum cholesterol, different types of stroke and stenosis distribution of cerebral arteries: The Akita Pathology Study. *Stroke, 24,* 954–964.

Kritchevsky, S. B., Wilcosky, T. C., Morris, D. L., Truong, K. N., & Tyroler, H. A. (1991). Changes in plasma lipid and lipoprotein cholesterol and weight prior to the diagnosis of cancer. *Cancer Research, 51,* 3198–3203.

Lanza-Jacoby, S., Wong, S. H., Tabares, A., Baer, D., & Schneider, T. (1992). Disturbances in the composition of plasma lipoproteins during gram-negative sepsis in the rat. *Biochimica Biophysica Acta, 1124,* 233–240.

Levesque, H., Gancel, A., Pertuet, S., Czernichow, P., & Courtois, H. (1991). Hypocholestér-
olémie: prévalence, intérêt diagnostique et prognostique: etude dans un service de méd-
icine interne [Hypocholesterolemia: Prevalence, diagnostic and prognostic value]. *Presse
Medicale, 20,* 1935–1938.

Li, W. (1979). Coronary heart disease survey in factories and countryside. *Acta Medica Pri-
mae Shanghai, 6,* 65–75.

Lindholm, M., Eklund, J., & Rössner, S. (1982). Pronounced dyslipoproteinemia in intensive
care patients. *Journal of Parenteral and Enteral Nutrition, 6,* 432–438.

Maccari, S., Bassi, C., Zanoni, P., & Plancher, A. C. (1991). Plasma cholesterol and triglycerides in heroin addicts. *Drug and Alcohol Dependency, 29*(2), 183–187.

Malloy, M. J., & Kane, J. P. (1982). Hypolipidemia. *Medical Clinics of North America, 66,*
469–483.

Malmendier, C. L., Amerijckx, J. P., Bihain, B. E., & Fischer, M. L. (1985). Changes in
apolipoprotein and lipids in patients after surgery. *Biomedical Pharmacology, 39,* 192–
195.

Martin, M. J., Hulley, S. B., Broconer, W. S., Koller, L. H., & Wentworth, D. (1986). Serum
cholesterol, blood pressure, and mortality: Implications from a cohort of 301,602 men.
The Lancet, 2, 933–936.

Miller, S. R., Tartter, P. I., Papatestas, A. E., Slater, G., & Aufsas, A. H. (1981). Serum
cholesterol and human colon cancer. *Journal of the National Cancer Institute, 67,* 297–
300.

Moriguchi, E. H., Fusegawa, Y., Tamachi, H., & Goto, Y. (1991). Low lipase activities and
large HDL particles in patients with myocardial infarction. *Asian Medical Journal,
34*(2), 104–115.

Morrone, G., Ciliberto, G., Oliviero, S., Arcone, R., Dente, L., Content, J., & Cortese, R.
(1988). Recombinant interleukin 6 regulates the transcriptional activation of a set of
human acute phase genes. *Journal of Biological Chemistry, 263,* 12554–12558.

Morrone, G., Cortese, R., & Sorrentino, V. (1989). Post-transcriptional control of negative
acute phase genes by transforming growth factor beta. *European Molecular Biology
Organization, 8,* 3767–3771.

Muldoon, M. F., Manuck, K. M., & Matthews, K. A. (1990). Lowering cholesterol concentrations and mortality: A quantitative review of primary prevention trials. *British Medical
Journal, 301,* 309–314.

Muller, C. P., Trilling, B., & Steinke, B. (1992). The prognostic significance of total serum
cholesterol in patients with Hodgkin's disease. *Cancer, 69,* 1042–1046.

Muller, G. L. (1930). The cholesterol metabolism in health and anemia. *Medicine, 9*(2),
119–174.

Nanji, A. A., & Reddy, S. (1983). Use of total cholesterol/albumin ratio as an alternative to
high density lipoprotein cholesterol measurement. *Journal of Clinical Pathology, 36,*
716–718.

Nishita, S. (1941). Studies on the fluctuation of the lipid content of the blood in the fever
period. *Japanese Journal of Experimental Medicine, 19,* 97–107.

Noel, M. A., Smith, T. K., & Ettinger, W. H. (1991). Characteristics and outcomes of hospitalized older patients who develop hypocholesterolemia. *Journal of the American Geriatrics Society, 39,* 455–461.

Nomura, A. M. Y., Stemmerman, G. N., & Chyou, P. (1991). Prospective study of serum
cholesterol levels and large-bowel cancer. *Journal of the National Cancer Institute, 83,*
1403–1407.

Oliver, M. F. (1981). Serum cholesterol—The knave of hearts and the joker. *The Lancet, 2,*
1090–1095.

Oren, R., & Rachmilewitz, D. (1992). Preoperative clues to Crohn's disease in suspected,
acute appendicitis. *Journal of Clinical Gastroenterology, 15,* 306–310.

Page, I. H. (1954). Atherosclerosis, an introduction. *Circulation, 10*(1), 1–27.

Reverter, J. C., Sierra, J., Marti-Tutusaus, J. M., Montserrat, E., Granena, A., & Rozman,
C. (1988). Hypocholesterolemia in acute myelogenous leukemia. *European Journal of
Haematology, 41,* 317–320.

Rifkind, B. M., & Gale, M. (1967). Hypolipidæmia in anæmia. *The Lancet, 2,* 640–642.

Rose, G., & Shipley, M. J. (1980). Plasma lipids and mortality: A source of error. *The Lancet*, *1*, 523–526.

Rudman, D., Mattson, D. E., Feller, A. G., & Nagraj, H. S. (1989). A mortality risk index for men in a Veterans Administration extended care facility. *Journal of Parenteral and Enteral Nutrition*, *13*, 189–195.

Rudman, D., Mattson, D. E., Nagraj, H. S., Caindec, N., Rudman, I. W., & Jackson, D. L. (1987). Antecedents of death in men of a Veterans Administration nursing home. *Journal of the American Geriatrics Society*, *35*, 496–502.

Sammalkorpi, K., Valtonen, V., Kertula, Y., Nikkilä, E., & Taskinen, M. (1988). Changes in serum lipoprotein pattern induced by acute infection. *Metabolism*, *37*, 859–865.

Schatzkin, A., Hoover, R. N., Taylor, P. R., Ziegler, R. G., Carter, C. L., Larson, D. B., & Licitra, L. M. (1987). Serum cholesterol and cancer in the NHANES I epidemiologic followup study. *The Lancet*, *2*, 298–301.

Schectman, G., Kaul, S., Mueller, R. A., Borden, E. C., & Kissebah, A. H. (1992). The effect of interferon on the metabolism of LDLs. *Arteriosclerosis and Thrombosis*, *12*, 1053–1062.

Shokunbi, W. A., Ahaneku, J. E., & Okpala, I. E. (1991). Cholesterol, lipoprotein and phospholipid levels in acute lymphoblastic leukaemia [Letter to the editor]. *European Journal of Haematolology*, *46*, 59–61.

Shor-Posner, G., Basit, A., Lu, Y., Cabrejos, C., Chang, J., Fletcher, M., Mantero-Atienza, E., & Baum, M. K. (1993). Hypocholesterolemia is associated with immune dysfunction in early human immunodeficiency virus-1 infection. *American Journal of Medicine*, *94*, 515–519.

Snyder, S. M., Terdiman, J. F., Cann, B., Feingold, K. R., Hubl, S. T., Smith, R. S., & Young, S. G. (1993). Relationship of apolipoprotein E phenotypes to hypocholesterolemia. *American Journal of Medicine*, *95*, 480–488.

Spiegel, R. J., Schaefer, E., Magrath, I. T., & Edwards, B. K. (1982). Plasma lipid alterations in leukemia and lymphoma. *American Journal of Medicine*, *72*, 775–782.

Stopeck, A. T., Nicholson, A. C., Mancini, F. P., & Hajjar, D. P. (1993). Cytokine regulation of low density lipoprotein receptor gene transcription in HepG$_2$ cells. *Journal of Biological Chemistry*, *268*, 17489–17494.

Stubbe, I., Gustafason, A., & Nilsson-Ehle, P. (1982). Alterations in plasma proteins and lipoproteins in acute myocardial infarction: Effects of lipoprotein lipase. *Scandinavian Journal of Laboratory and Clinical Investigation*, *42*, 437–444.

Svenson, K. L. G., Lithell, H., Hällgren, R., Selinus, I., & Vessby, B. (1987). Serum lipoprotein in active rheumatoid arthritis and other chronic inflammatory arthritides. *Archives of Internal Medicine*, *147*, 1912–1916.

Tanaka, H., Tanaka, Y., Hayashi, M., Ueda, Y., Date, C., Baba, T., Hironobu, S., Horimoto, T., & Owada, K. (1982). Secular trends in mortality for cerebrovascular diseases in Japan, 1960 to 1979. *Stroke*, *13*, 574–581.

Umeki, S. (1993). Decreases in serum cholesterol levels in advanced lung cancer. *Respiration*, *60*(3), 178–181.

Vallabhajosula, S., Gilbert, H. S., Goldsmith, S. J., Paidi, M., Hanna, M. M., & Ginsberg, H. N. (1989). Low density lipoprotein (LDL) distribution shown by [99m]technetium-LDL imaging in patients with myeloproliferative diseases. *Annals of Internal Medicine*, *110*, 208–213.

Verdery, R. B., & Goldberg, A. P. (1991). Hypocholesterolemia as a predictor of death: A prospective study of 224 nursing home residents. *Journal of Gerontology*, *46*(3), M84–M90.

Watson, W. C., Buchanan, K. D., & Dickson, C. (1963). Serum cholesterol levels after myocardial infarction. *British Medical Journal*, *2*, 709–712.

Zyada, L. E., Hassan, H. T., Rees, J. K., & Ragab, M. H. (1990). The relation between hypocholesterolemia and degree of maturation in acute myeloid leukemia. *Hematology and Oncology*, *8*(1), 65–69.

15

Low Serum Total Cholesterol and Mortality From Accidents and Suicide

Albertine J. Schuit, Jacqueline M. Dekker, and
Evert G. Schouten

In many industrialized countries, preventive trials are conducted to study the protective effect of cholesterol-lowering drugs or diet on coronary heart disease incidence and mortality. Although these trials are effective in reducing coronary heart disease incidence, a coherent reduction of total mortality is not always apparent. Participants in the intervention group have higher rates of death from cancer and of death from accidents, violence, trauma, or suicide, generally referred to as *violent* death (Muldoon, Manuck, & Matthews, 1990; Davey Smith, Song, & Sheldon, 1992).

It is not clear whether this increase is caused by the low absolute concentration of cholesterol or whether it is due to side effects of the cholesterol-lowering therapy. To explain the elevated risk of violent death, it was hypothesized that a sudden lowering of cholesterol may change personality characteristics, predisposing to aggressive and suicidal behavior. One of the physiological mechanisms that is suggested is that a drop in serum cholesterol may contribute to a depletion of brain serotonin, resulting in a poorer suppression of aggressive behavior (Engelberg, 1992). Morgan, Palinkas, Barrett-Connor, and Wingard (1993) found that depression was three times more common in elderly men with low cholesterol levels than in men with higher levels. Also, Gallerani et al. (1995) and Modai, Valesvki, Dror, and Weizman (1994) observed lower cholesterol levels in people who committed parasuicide than in controls.

The acute lowering of serum cholesterol in trials may have a more profound biological effect than innately low levels. So far, only a few observational studies have reported on the association between low cholesterol and violent death. Lindberg, Råstam, Gullberg, and Eklund (1992) observed an increase in violent death in men (but not women) age 45 to 74, during a 7-year follow-up. The association disappeared with increasing duration of follow-up. In prospective studies among British male civil servants age 40 to 64 (18 years of follow-up) and Finnish men age 40 to 59 years (20.5 years of follow-up) low serum cholesterol was not associated with risk of violent death (Davey Smith, Shipley, Marmot, & Rose, 1992; Pekkanen, Nissinen, Punsar, & Karvonen, 1989).

The Dutch Civil Servants Study was a longitudinal study with a follow-up period of 28 years. Of nearly 3,000 middle-aged men and women, baseline serum cholesterol was measured, and of 98% of the population, survival status and, if deceased, cause of death were determined. This study provides a possibility to further explore the long-term effect of low serum cholesterol on mortality from violent causes, the results of which are reported here. The chapter also compares the results of this study with other observational studies, followed by a discussion of biological mechanisms.

Design and Procedure of the Dutch Civil Servants Study

In 1953–1954, a health survey was conducted among civil servants of the city of Amsterdam and their spouses. All 11,700 Amsterdam civil servants on active duty age 40 years and over, and their spouses, were invited to be examined. Of the eligible civil servants, 54% volunteered, with or without their spouses. From these volunteers, an age- and sex-stratified random sample was taken, to obtain approximately equal numbers in each 5-year age and sex category. This way, a cohort of 3,091 persons were examined: 1,583 men, 9 of whom were husbands of female civil servants, and 1,508 women, 1,074 of whom were wives of male civil servants.

The baseline examination consisted of a detailed medical history, a physical examination, a chest radiograph, an electrocardiogram, and some laboratory measurements. Nonfasting serum total cholesterol levels were determined in units of 10 mg/dl according to the modified Liebermann Burchard method described by Saifer and Kammerer (1946). In 1981, a mortality follow-up of 99.9% of the population was added to the original data of the health survey. In 1989, the primary cause of death was assessed for those who had died by 1981, by linking the original data to the causes of death recorded by the Dutch Central Bureau of Statistics. Causes of death were classified according to the International Classification of Diseases (ICD), eighth and ninth revision. The death certificates from 1969 and earlier, which had been coded according to the sixth and seventh revisions of the ICD, were recoded according to the ninth revision by officers of the Central Bureau of Statistics, using the original notification forms. The ICD codes for mortality from violent causes are 800–999.

Causes of death were obtained for 98.0% of the deceased men and 98.1% of the deceased women. Information on survival status or cause of death was not available for 19 men and 12 women, and information on serum total cholesterol was missing for 88 men and 27 women, leaving a study population of 1,476 men and 1,469 women.

Method

To obtain a description of the characteristics of the men and women of the study population, mean levels of age, serum total cholesterol, body mass index, and systolic blood pressure were calculated. Subsequently, mean concentration of serum total cholesterol of men and women who died from accidents or suicide were compared with the rest of the population.

Participants were classified in tertiles of serum cholesterol, men and women combined. Cutpoints were 240 mg/dl and 280 mg/dl. The risk of violent death in participants in the lower cholesterol groups was compared with that of participants in the high-cholesterol group, by means of Cox's (1972) proportional hazards regression. The predictive value of serum total cholesterol for death from a violent cause was calculated over periods of 15 and 28 years. Potential confounders were also stratified in categories: gender (men or women); age in years (<50, 50–57, or >57, based on tertiles); smoking (yes or no); and alcohol consumption (yes or no). Categories of cholesterol and potential confounders were included in the model as indicator variables.

Results

Table 1 shows mean levels of serum total cholesterol, age, body mass index, systolic blood pressure, and the proportion of smokers and alcohol users in the total study population at the start of the study. Women had significantly higher serum total cholesterol concentration than did men: 274.8 mg/dl versus 258.4 mg/dl, respectively. Also, the women were younger (mean age = 51.8 years vs. 53.1 years), had a higher level of systolic blood pressure (M = 147.5 mmHg vs. 140.0 mmHg), and had a higher body mass index (M = 26.5 vs. 24.6). There were fewer smokers and alcohol users among women than among men.

During the 28-year follow-up period, 42 participants (21 men and 21 women) died from violent deaths, 11 (7 men and 4 women) of whom during the first 15 years of follow-up. Of the total violent deaths, 79% were ac-

Table 1. Characteristics of the Dutch Civil Servant Population at Baseline

Measure	Men		Women	
	M	SD	M	SD
n	1,476		1,469	
Age	53.1	7.3	51.8	7.2
Total cholesterol	258.4	49.9	274.8	55.4
Systolic blood pressure	140.0	18.6	147.5	23.2
Body mass index	24.7	2.7	26.5	3.8
Alcohol drinkers	62		42	
Smokers	71		37	
No. cigarettes smoked per week among smokers	72	52	22	30

Note: Age was measured in years, cholesterol was measured in milligrams per deciliter, systolic blood pressure was measured in millimeters of mercury, body mass index was measured in kilograms per meter, and entries for alcohol drinkers and smokers are percentages.

Table 2. Mean Total Cholesterol Concentration at Baseline of Deaths During Follow-Up Period for the Dutch Civil Servants Study

Deaths	Men			Women		
	n	*M*	*SD*	*n*	*M*	*SD*
At 15 years						
Accidents and suicide	7	260.0	57.4	4	247.5	41.9
Coronary heart disease	101	270.4	48.6	21	306.2	57.3
Cancer	112	248.4	44.0	53	276.2	50.4
At 15–28 years						
Accidents and suicide	14	242.9	44.8	17	269.4	56.3
Coronary heart disease	125	265.8	42.9	73	288.6	57.0
Cancer	149	260.8	51.3	93	282.5	51.5

cidents. All others (21%) were suicidal deaths. In Table 2, mean concentration of total cholesterol is presented among participants who died from accidents or suicide, coronary heart disease, and cancer after 15 years and between 15 to 28 years of follow-up. The average serum cholesterol concentration of men who died violently during the first 15 years was 260.0 mg/dl; however, exclusion of 1 outlier (cholesterol concentration of 380 mg/dl) resulted in a mean concentration of 240.0 mg/dl. The rest of the male population, including the survivors, had an average of 258.4 mg/dl. In women, the average serum cholesterol concentration of those who died from violent causes was 247.5 mg/dl, compared with 274.9 mg/dl for the rest of the women, including the survivors (p = .3). The average cholesterol concentration of participants who died violently in the period between 15 and 28 years of follow-up was 242.9 mg/dl for men and 269.4 mg/dl for women (exclusion of 2 outliers with cholesterol concentration of 360 mg/dl and 400 mg/dl resulted in a mean of 245.7 mg/dl). These levels were below the serum cholesterol levels of the total deceased in that period, but not significantly (p = .2 for men and .7 for women).

In Figure 1, the estimated survival probability of violent death among participants divided in tertiles of total cholesterol is presented for the follow-up period of 28 years. Men and women in the lowest tertile (M = 216.2, SD = 21.3 mg/dl) had a continuously higher risk, compared with the other tertiles (M = 328.2, SD = 40.4 mg/dl).

The results of the proportional hazards analysis are shown in Table 3. Participants with low serum cholesterol had a threefold risk of violent death during the first 15 years of follow-up, compared with participants with the highest concentration, not significantly, however, probably due to the low numbers of cases. After 28 years, the association between low cholesterol and violent death persisted and even became significant. The age and gender adjusted-rate ratio of participants with the lowest compared with the highest total cholesterol was 2.4 (95% confidence interval

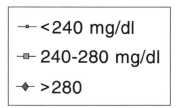

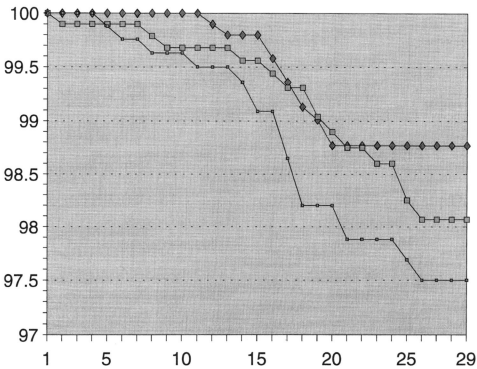

Figure 1. Estimated survival probability of violent death by tertiles of cholesterol.

= 1.0–5.4). Additional correction for smoking and alcohol consumption did not markedly affect the rate ratio. We also performed separate analyses for men and women, using tertiles based on the gender-specific distribution of serum cholesterol. In both men and women, we found similar associations, although not significant, again likely to be attributable to the low numbers.

To study the possibility that the observed association was due to prevalent (subclinical) disease, we performed additional analyses, in which participants who died during the first 5 years of follow-up were excluded. Only two cases of violent death occurred during that period. The resulting age- and gender-adjusted relative rates in the low-cholesterol category were 2.2, for the 6- to 15-year period, and 2.1, for the 6- to 28-year period.

Table 3. Relative Risk of Violent Death After 15 and 28 Years of Follow-Up for the Dutch Civil Servants Study

Adjustment	Low cholesterol		Mid cholesterol		High cholesterol
	RR	95% CI	RR	95% CI	RR
At 15 years					
Gender	3.0	0.6–14.6	1.0	0.1–7.2	1
Gender and age	3.3	0.7–18.8	1.0	0.1–7.0	1
Multivariate	3.2	0.7–18.5	1.0	0.1–4.7	1
At 28 years					
Gender	2.1	0.9–4.8	1.7	0.7–4.2	1
Gender and age	2.4	1.0–5.4	1.8	0.7–4.2	1
Multivariate	2.4	1.0–5.4	1.8	0.8–4.2	1

Note: The low-cholesterol group had less than 240 mg/dl of serum total cholesterol concentration, the mid-cholesterol group had 240–280 mg/dl of serum total cholesterol concentration, and the high-cholesterol group had greater than 280 mg/dl of serum total cholesterol concentration. RR = rate ratio (calculated by Cox's proportional hazards regression analysis), CI = confidence interval. Multivariate adjustment was adjusted for age, gender, smoking, and alcohol consumption.

Discussion

In this study, we observed an increased risk of death from accidents and suicide in persons with the lowest serum total cholesterol levels. The association was most profound in the first 15 years of follow-up but persisted after 28 years of follow-up.

Serum total cholesterol was measured only once. Because of the intraindividual variation, a single measurement can misclassify a participant's habitual concentration. Because this misclassification is presumably unrelated to mortality, it will generally result in a bias of the relative risk towards one. Because in this population, we found the expected relationship between high serum total cholesterol levels and cardiovascular disease, we believe that this single measurement has sufficient predictive power. Moreover, our study population consisted of middle-aged civil servants not very likely to change their lifestyle radically. Therefore, it may be assumed that their position in the distribution of serum cholesterol did not change to a great extent during the follow-up period.

Another possible source of bias may be misclassification in cause of death. The most likely possibility would be misclassification of suicides, which would have diluted the association. It is unlikely that misclassification would be related to baseline cholesterol, because all deaths occurred before 1981, and certifying physicians at that time were not aware of a possible association between serum total cholesterol and violent death, because this had not yet been reported. Misclassification is therefore random and would probably underestimate the relative risk.

The Lieberman Burchard method is known to somewhat overestimate cholesterol concentration. This would not affect the classification of participants relative to each other, but it could account for the overall high levels of cholesterol, and, consequently, for the concentration of 216.2 mg/dl (SD = 21.3) among participants in the lowest tertile, which is not very low. The increased risk of violent death among participants in the middle tertile after 28 years, although not significant, is suggestive of a dose-dependent relationship between cholesterol and violent death over the whole range of cholesterol values. This is at variance with the hypothesis of a threshold below which the risk is increased.

Confounders

Whether the association of low serum total cholesterol and violent death is a causal one remains unclear. In our study, we corrected for age, gender, smoking, and alcohol consumption. Other characteristics that may be associated both with low serum cholesterol and higher mortality from violence are lower employment grade, being unmarried, unexplained weight loss, respiratory symptoms, and low body mass index (Davey Smith, Shipley, et al., 1992; Lewis & Tikkanen, 1994; Manolio et al., 1993). Owing both to lack of information and low numbers of cases, we could not perform analyses in which we controlled for these confounders.

It may be argued that people with fatal disease (and low cholesterol as a consequence) are more prone to commit suicide or have fatal accidents because of use of medication or depression. Those participants are expected to die during the 1st years of follow-up. In a 23-year follow-up study among Japanese American men, with a total of 1,954 deaths, it was shown that correction for confounders and exclusion of the first 5 years of follow-up from the analysis reduced the excess risk of all-cause mortality in the lowest total cholesterol group by 56%, from 1.32 to 1.10 (Iribarren, Reed, Burchfiel, & Dwyer, 1995). We repeated the analysis, after exclusion of people who died during the first 5 years of follow-up. This did not affect the observed association. Furthermore, at the time the blood samples were taken in this study (the early 1950s), the theory about high cholesterol and cardiovascular disease risk was unknown. Therefore, participants in the low-cholesterol category could not have been on cholesterol-lowering diets or have used cholesterol-lowering drugs because of a prevalent disease. Cholesterol levels are thus likely to reflect habitual values.

Other Observational Studies

Until now, only a few studies have been published on the long-term exposure of cholesterol and risk of violent death. From the Whitehall Study among London civil servants (18 years of follow-up), no significant association was reported between low cholesterol and death from accidents, violence, or suicide (Davey Smith, Shipley, et al., 1992). Also in the Finnish cohort of the Seven Countries Study, there was no association between serum cholesterol and death rates from accidents, violence, or suicide, in a 25-year follow-up (Pekkanen et al., 1989). In fact, in one of the two cohorts, a positive relationship was observed. Kromhout, Katan, Menotti, and Keys (1992) presented relative risks from the total population of the Seven Countries Study. Again, no significant association was reported.

Lindberg et al. (1992) presented a significant association between low serum cholesterol and death from injuries in Swedish men during the first 7 years of follow-up. The relative risk of men in the lowest quartile of cholesterol distribution ($M = 5.3$ mmol/L) was 2.8 (95%; confidence interval $= 1.5-5.0$), compared with the highest quartile ($M = 7.6$ mmol/L). Men in the lowest quartile had especially high risk of suicide. In women, no significant association was found. In this large cohort, 515 participants (376 men and 139 women) died from injuries in 20.5 years of follow-up, compared with 21 men and 21 women in the Dutch cohort. In our cohort, it was, therefore, not possible to distinguish the separate violent causes (e.g., suicide). The mean concentration of total cholesterol of the lowest quartile in the Swedish study was similar to the mean concentration of the lowest tertile in our study. In concordance with our study, the association in the Swedish cohort diminished after a while. But unlike the Swedish cohort, the association in our population was significant after 28 years. Lindberg et al. assumed that the increased risk in the first 7 years of follow-up was caused by a cholesterol concentration below a participant's habitual value. This would be in keeping with the hypothesis of an increased risk of participants lowering their cholesterol concentration by diet or drugs or because of prevalent disease. As mentioned before, this was not plausible in our cohort in the early 1950s. The declining rate ratio with long duration of follow-up is, however, in keeping with a restricted predictive power of the single baseline measurement, as well as with a survivor effect.

In 1992, Jacobs et al., on behalf of a National Heart, Lung, and Blood Conference, conducted a summary analysis of cholesterol and mortality on data from 19 large-cohort studies among middle-aged people. This included studies from the United States, Southern Europe, Israel, Great Britain, Scandinavia, and Japan, with follow-up periods ranging from 9 to 30 years. Of a total of 68,406 deaths, 6% died of ICD 800–900. The results of multivariate survival analysis, with exclusion of the first 5 years of follow-up, showed that men and women with cholesterol levels of less than 160 mg/dl had a relative risk of about 1.3, compared with participants with levels of 160–199 mg/dl (not significant for women). Participants with higher levels did not have a lower risk of death from violent causes. In the individual studies, elevated risk in the low-cholesterol category was observed in 13 out of 15 studies among men and in 4 out of 6 among women. In our study, only 11 participants had cholesterol levels of less than 160 mg/dl, and their relative risk was 7.6 (0.8–74), compared with people with cholesterol levels of 160–199 mg/dl.

Biological Mechanisms

Most papers relating to the issue of cholesterol and mortality from accidents, violence, and suicide discuss the diet and drug intervention trials. In the first paper published (Muldoon et al., 1990), a meta-analysis was presented on the effects of cholesterol lowering in primary prevention trials. Although mortality from coronary heart disease tended to be lower in the intervention groups, a significant increase in deaths not related to illness was observed. Muldoon et al. recommended a more cautious approach to population-based intervention for the control of lipids. The subsequent papers on this issue discussed the benefits of drug intervention trials in the total population.

Because especially in intervention trials, an association between low cholesterol and violent death is observed, it was speculated that the effects of lowered cholesterol levels may differ from those of innately low levels. Cells may become dependent on the high cholesterol levels of Western populations, and a sudden depletion may disturb proper cell function.

Although only specifically reported in two studies, participants with innately low levels may have higher risk of death from violence. Perhaps also long-term exposure to low blood cholesterol may affect cell membrane function. Engelberg (1992) hypothesized that low serum cholesterol affected the fluidity and other functional properties of the membranes of brain cells. This could cause a diminished uptake of serotonin in the cells. The fall in serotonin uptake may lead to a lower impulse control, which may manifest itself either as suicidal, aggressive, or accident-prone behavior. Recently, Steegman et al. (1996) reported lower plasma serotonin levels in middle-aged men with persistently low serum cholesterol levels (4.5 mmol/L or lower), compared with men with a cholesterol level between 6 and 7 mmol/L, adjusted for age and socioeconomic background, which indicated that serotonin metabolism might be implicated in the association between serum cholesterol and violent death. Three studies are in line with the hypothesis of Engelberg. Gallerani et al. (1995) reported low cholesterol levels in 331 parasuicidal participants, compared with controls (M = 192 mg/dl, SD = 45 vs. M = 210 mg/dl, SD = 50). Furthermore, the cholesterol levels at hospital admission at other occasions, available for 109 of these cases, were comparable to the levels of the controls. Modai et al. (1994) investigated the relationship between serum cholesterol and suicide in psychiatric inpatients. This study reports a significantly lower serum cholesterol level ($p < 0.01$) for inpatients who had attempted suicide, compared with nonsuicidal inpatients. The association of cholesterol with suicide was limited to patients with depression. Morgan et al. (1993) investigated risk of developing depressive symptoms during 10–15 years of follow-up, according to initial cholesterol level, in 1,020 men, age 50–89 years. Men of 70 years or older and with cholesterol less than 160 mg/dl had threefold higher risk of developing depressive symptoms than men with levels of 160 mg/dl or more. This was not due to differences in age, health status, number of chronic illnesses, number of medicines, exercise, measured weight loss, or change of cholesterol during follow-up. The association was not observed in younger men, but depression was very rare in that age category. Still, Engelberg's hypothesis was very speculative, and more work needs to be done to elucidate the association among serum cholesterol, serotonin, and violent death.

Implications

The discussion about the benefit of cholesterol-lowering intervention programs as a national health objective is still going on. It has been shown that cholesterol-lowering intervention is beneficial in people with very high risk of coronary heart disease (Davey Smith, Song, & Sheldon, 1992). However, in addition to a possible elevated risk of violent death, participants with a low serum total cholesterol concentration also seem to have an increased risk of mortality from some cancers, hemorrhagic stroke, and some noncancer/noncardiovascular diseases (Iribarren et al., 1995; Jacobs & Blackburn, 1993; Schuit, van Dijk, Dekker, Schouten, & Kok, 1993). Still, it is too premature to draw conclusions regarding the dangers of cholesterol-lowering intervention. More information is needed on the mechanism behind the association between low cholesterol and violent death.

Conclusion

In a middle-aged population in the early 1950s, we found an inverse association between low serum cholesterol and death caused by accidents or suicide. The association persisted during a follow-up of 28 years. Note that the low number of cases limited the possibility to adjust for possible confounders. The question of whether the association was causal has not yet been definitively answered. Experimental research may be the most appropriate way to elucidate the nature of the link between low cholesterol and violent death.

References

Cox, D. R. (1972). Regression models and life tables (with discussions). *Journal of the Royal Statistical Society, B34*, 187–220.

Davey Smith, G., Shipley, M. J., Marmot, M. G., & Rose, G. (1992). Plasma cholesterol concentration and mortality: The Whitehall Study. *Journal of the American Medical Association, 267*, 70–76.

Davey Smith, G., Song, F., & Sheldon, T. A. (1992). Cholesterol lowering and mortality: The importance of considering initial level of risk. *British Medical Journal, 306*, 1367–1373.

Engelberg, H. (1992). Low serum cholesterol and suicide. *The Lancet, 339*, 727–729.

Gallerani, M., Manfredini, R., Caracciolo, S., Scapoli, C., Molinari, S., & Fersini, C. (1995). Serum cholesterol concentrations in parasuicide. *British Medical Journal, 310*, 1632–1636.

Iribarren, C., Reed, D. M., Burchfiel, C. M., & Dwyer, J. H. (1995). Serum total cholesterol and mortality: Confounding factors and risk modification in Japanese-American men. *Journal of the American Medical Association, 273,* 1926–1932.

Jacobs, D. R., & Blackburn, H. (1993). Models of effects of low blood cholesterol on the public health: Implications for practice and policy. *Circulation, 87,* 1033–1036.

Jacobs, D., Blackburn, H., Higgins, M., Reed, D., Iso, H., McMillan, G., Neaton, J., Nelson, J., Potter, J., Rifkind, B., Rossouw, J., Shekelle, R., & Yusuf, S. (1992). Report of the conference on low blood cholesterol: Mortality associations. *Circulation, 86,* 1046–1060.

Kromhout, D., Katan, M. B., Menotti, A., & Keys, A. (1992). Serum cholesterol and long-term death rates from suicide, accidents, or violence. *The Lancet, 340,* 317.

Lewis, B., & Tikkanen, M. J. (1994). Low blood total cholesterol and mortality: Causality, consequence and confounders. *American Journal of Cardiology, 73,* 80–85.

Lindberg, G., Råstam, L., Gullberg, B., & Eklund, G. A. (1992). Low serum cholesterol concentration and short term mortality from injuries in men and women. *British Medical Journal, 305,* 277–279.

Manolio, T. A., Ettinger, W. H., Tracy, R. P., Kuller, L. H., Borhani, N. O., Lynch, J. C., & Fried, L. P., for the CHS Collaborative Research Group. (1993). Epidemiology of low cholesterol in older adults: The Cardiovascular Health Study. *Circulation, 87,* 728–737.

Modai, I., Valesvki, A., Dror, S., & Weizman, A. (1994). Serum cholesterol levels and suicidal tendencies in psychiatric inpatients. *Journal of Clinical Psychiatry, 55,* 252–254.

Morgan, R. E., Palinkas, L. A., Barrett-Connor, E. L., & Wingard, D. L. (1993). Plasma cholesterol and depressive symptoms in older men. *The Lancet, 341,* 75–79.

Muldoon, M. F., Manuck, S. B., & Matthews, K. A. (1990). Lowering cholesterol concentrations and mortality: A quantitative review of primary prevention trials. *British Medical Journal, 301,* 309–314.

Pekkanen, J., Nissinen, A., Punsar, S., & Karvonen, M. J. (1989). Serum cholesterol and risk of accidental or violent death in a 25-year follow-up: The Finnish cohorts of the Seven Countries Study. *Archives of Internal Medicine, 149,* 1589–1591.

Saifer, A., & Kammerer, O. J. (1946). Photometric determination of total cholesterol in plasma or serum by a modified Liebermann Burchard reaction. *Journal of Biologic Chemistry, 164,* 657–677.

Schuit, A. J., van Dijk, L. C. M. J., Dekker, J. M., Schouten, E. G., & Kok, F. J. (1993). Inverse association between total serum cholesterol and 28-year cancer mortality in Dutch civil servants. *American Journal of Epidemiology, 137,* 966–976.

Steegmans, P. H., Fekkes, D., Hoes, A. W., Bak, A. A., Van der Does, E., & Grobbee, D. E. (1996). Low serum cholesterol concentration and serotonin metabolism in men. *British Medical Journal, 312,* 221.

16

Cholesterol Lowering, Low Cholesterol, and Noncardiovascular Disease

John C. LaRosa

Over the last 2 decades, it has been unequivocally demonstrated that lowering of circulating cholesterol levels can prevent, arrest, and even reverse coronary atherosclerosis. This has been shown in participants both with and without clinically apparent cardiovascular disease (CVD; Davies, Krikler, & Katz, 1991; Holme, 1993). Most of these studies were done on middle-aged men. Limited, but useful, data indicate that similar findings can be demonstrated as well in women (Group of Physicians of the Newcastle upon Tyne Region, 1971; Kane et al., 1990; Miettinen, Karvonen, Turpeinen, Elosuo, & Paavilainen, 1972; Research Committee of the Scottish Society of Physicians, 1971).

During the same period of time, observational studies of a variety of populations have indicated that total cholesterol, low density lipoprotein (LDL) cholesterol, and high density lipoprotein (HDL) cholesterol are strong predictors of coronary risk in both sexes over a wide age spectrum (LaRosa et al., 1990; Tyroler, 1987).

As a result, advisory bodies in most of the Western world—including the United States, through the National Cholesterol Education Program (NCEP; Expert Panel on Detection, Evaluation, and Treatment of High Blood Cholesterol in Adults, 1993) and the European community, through the European Atherosclerosis Society (Pyorala et al., 1994)—have issued guidelines for the detection, evaluation, and treatment of high blood cholesterol and related lipoprotein disorders. The guidelines have been widely disseminated, widely discussed, and widely accepted in clinical practice (Schucker et al., 1991).

A good deal is known about how lipoproteins promote atherogenesis in the coronary arteries and how that process can be prevented or at least retarded. A brief review of lipoprotein metabolism is necessary to put that information in perspective.

Normal Lipid Metabolism

Lipoprotein metabolism may be viewed as a process whereby large, triglyceride-carrying particles from the intestine and liver are broken down into smaller cholesterol-enriched lipoprotein particles. In the process, triglyceride is transported from the intestine and liver to adipose and other storage tissues.

Triglyceride-transporting lipoproteins from the intestine, which transport dietary fat, are called *chylomicrons*. With the help of *lipoprotein lipase* (LPL), a lipolytic enzyme found primarily in adipose tissue, chylomicrons deposit dietary triglyceride in storage sites in adipose and other tissues. The remaining smaller lipoprotein that is then formed is cholesterol enriched. It is called a *chylomicron remnant*. These remnants are transported to the liver, where they are taken up by specific remnant receptors and the contents are catabolized.

Triglyceride-transporting lipoproteins formed in the liver from circulating glucose and free fatty acids are called *very low density lipoproteins* (VLDLs). They also undergo lipolysis in adipose tissue. After their triglyceride has been largely removed, a smaller cholesterol-enriched remnant, called by convention *intermediate-density lipoprotein* (IDL), is formed and taken to the liver. In the liver, IDL may be removed or, through the removal of additional triglyceride (probably with the help of an enzyme called *hepatic triglyceride lipase* [HTGL]), converted to a more cholesterol-enriched particle, LDL.

As a result of the breakdown of these large particles, redundant surface material composed of protein, phospholipid, and free cholesterol (but no triglyceride) is also produced. It joins the HDL fraction. High density lipoprotein is a small lipoprotein with relatively little cholesterol or triglyceride but with the ability to accept both unesterified cholesterol and triglyceride for transport. High density lipoprotein can, therefore, function as a means to remove cholesterol from cells and transport it to the liver or transfer it to other lipoproteins. Hepatic triglyceride lipase can act on a subclass of HDL, termed HDL_2, which is thought to be particularly important in this reverse cholesterol transport process, and convert HDL_2 to a denser, lipid-poor form of HDL, termed HDL_3.

Lipoproteins and Atherogenesis

Cholesterol-rich products of chylomicron and VLDL catabolism, chylomicron remnants, IDL, and LDL are all thought to be atherogenic, that is, they can be taken up (perhaps after oxidation by endothelial cells) by macrophages in the subintimal spaces. These macrophages cannot catabolize cholesteryl ester. As they accumulate it in their cytoplasm, macrophages are converted to foam cells. Foam cells are thought to form the nidus of the atherosclerotic plaque (O'Brien & Chait, 1994).

High density lipoprotein has the ability to reverse this process of foam cell formation, stimulating foam cells to deesterify their cytoplasmic cholesterol and transfer it to HDL particles, where it is reesterified and transported to the liver or transferred to other lipoproteins. Thus, excess chylomicron remnants (the result of high-fat diets), IDL, and LDL promote foam cell formation and atherogenesis, whereas HDL (perhaps particularly HDL_2) inhibits the process.

Primary and Secondary Prevention of Cardiovascular Disease

Interventions to prevent or retard the initial appearance of clinical cardiovascular disease are termed *primary* prevention. Interventions taken after the onset of clinical disease are termed *secondary* prevention.

Primary prevention aims to identify risk factors that predict the cause of CVD and intervene on those risk factors to prevent its initial occurrence. Primary prevention intervention must, of necessity, be applied to many people who are not destined to develop clinical coronary disease. The safety of such interventions, therefore, is of particular importance. For this reason, the emphasis in primary prevention is usually on hygienic, that is, on nonpharmacologic interventions, including diet, exercise, and weight loss. Even so, in selected individuals, pharmacologic interventions may be indicated.

The focus of secondary prevention is more precise. Here, the interventions are directed to patients who already have clinical manifestations of atherosclerosis. Without intervention, approximately 80% of individuals with clinical CVD are destined to die of it. As a result, it is easier to demonstrate the benefits of risk-factor interventions in patients with established disease.

Secondary Prevention Trials

Early trials of cholesterol lowering were primarily done in those with CVD. They succeeded in lowering total cholesterol only 5% to 15% (LaRosa & Cleeman, 1992). These trials were relatively short, from 2 to 4 years, and generally provided little or no data on LDL, HDL, or triglyceride levels. Nevertheless, when viewed in meta-analysis, they demonstrated borderline effects on total mortality, statistically significant benefits on CVD morbidity and mortality (Rossouw, Lewis, & Rifkind, 1990) and no increase in mortality from noncardiovascular causes (Holme, 1993; Rossouw et al., 1990).

Indeed, even individual studies, including long-term follow-up of the niacin group in the Coronary Drug Project (Canner et al., 1986) and the Stockholm Ischaemic Heart Disease Secondary Prevention Study (Carlson & Rosenhamer, 1988), using a combination of niacin and clofibrate, demonstrated statistically significant declines in total mortality.

Even so, the mixed results of these early secondary prevention studies were confusing, particularly before the availability of meta-analysis. As a result, attention turned to studies in which the end points were clinical events to studies of serial coronary angiogram. Although many of the pioneering studies were completed before the widespread availability of the 3-hydroxy-3 methylglutaryl Coenzyme A (HMG-CoA) reductase-inhibiting drugs (hereafter called *statins*), substantially more LDL lowering was achieved than had been the case in earlier secondary prevention trials. In the Cholesterol Lowering Atherosclerosis Study, LDL levels fell 43%, and HDL levels rose 37.6%, as a result of a combination of niacin and colestipol (Blankenhorn et al., 1987). A study done in familial hypercholesterolemics, using multiple drugs, achieved a 38% lowering of LDL and a 21% increase in HDL (Kane et al., 1990). The Program on the Surgical Control of the Hyperlipidemias study, using partial ileal bypass surgery, achieved a 34% reduction in LDL (Buchwald et al., 1990). The Lifestyle Heart Trial used rigorous diet and exercise and achieved a 37% decline in LDL (Ornish et al., 1990). The Familial Atherosclerosis Treatment Study, which was the first angiographic study to use colestipol, niacin, and lovastatin in the drug regimen, produced a 46% decline in LDL and 15% increase in HDL (Brown et al., 1990).

In many of these early regression studies, there were numerous examples of dramatic improvement in individual coronary segments. In the aggregate, however, the angiographic outcome was not very dramatic. In a summary analysis of eight of these studies, Brown, Zhao, Sacco, and Albers (1993) noted that in control participants there was about a 3% increase in average segmental stenosis, whereas in treated participants, there was about a 1.4% decrease. Even allowing for the relative insensitivity of either visual or computerized quantitative measures of lesions, these results, although in the right direction, seemed marginal. What was not appreciated initially, however, was the dramatic reduction in coronary events, ranging from 26% to 89% in individual studies in those treated versus those in the placebo group (Brown et al., 1993). This decline, moreover, occurred in a relatively short time, because most of these studies were conducted only over a 2-to-4-year period. In fact, a recent study with pravastatin demonstrated significant reduction in coronary events after only 6 months (Pravastatin Multinational Study Group for Cardiac Risk Patients, 1993).

Newer regression studies using statin monotherapy and achieving 20% to 40% LDL reductions have generally confirmed these results with benefit of arrest of atherosclerosis both in the coronary and carotid beds (see Table 1). In addition, events are consistently lower in the treated group in these studies, as was true in earlier regression studies (Blankenhorn et al., 1993; Crouse et al., 1995; Furberg et al., 1994; Jukema et al., 1995; MAAS investigators, 1994; Pitt, Mancini, Ellis, Rosman, & McGovern, 1994; Waters et al., 1994). A recent study with simvastatin, the Scandinavian Simvastatin Survival Study Group (1994), moreover, demonstrated a 35% decline in coronary mortality and a 40% decline in total mortality, with no increase in noncardiovascular mortality, dispelling the notion that LDL cholesterol lowering does not lower total mortality.

Table 1. Vascular Changes in Statin Regression Studies

Study	N	Duration of study	Drug and dose	Vascular bed	Vascular parameter	Vascular changes	CVD events (RX/control)	Comment
PLAC I[a]	408	3	20 mg PRA	Coronary	QCA	Report pending[b]	7/18	
PLAC II[b]	151	3	20–40 mg LOV	Carotid	B-mode US	12% less carotid with medial thickening	4/10	
CCAIT[c]	331	2	40–80 mg LOV	Coronary	QCA	Mean diameter: −6.0% PC; −3.2% LOV[i]	14/18	LOV: decrease progression, new lesions; increased regression
MAAS[d]	381	4	20 mg SIM	Coronary	QCA	Mean diameter: −2.8% PC; −0.7% SIM[h]	53/74	SIM: decreased new lesions, total occlusions
REGRESS[e]	885	2	40 mg PRA	Coronary	QCA	Mean diameter: −3.6% PC; −2.4% PRA	59/93	PRA: decreased progression in focal lesions
ACAPS[f]	919	3	20–40 mg LOV	Carotid	B-mode US	Carotid medial thickening: 1.8% PC; −1.8% LOV	5/14	LOV: decreased progression
MARS[g]	270	2	80 mg LOV	Coronary	QCA	Mean diameter: −2.2% PC; −1.6% LOV[h]	22/31	
Total							164/258	35% decrease in treated groups

Note: Duration of study is in years. PLAC I = Pravastatin Limitation of Atherosclerosis in the Coronary Arteries, PLAC II = Pravastatin, Lipids, and Atherosclerosis in the Carotids, CCAIT = Canadian Coronary Atherosclerosis Intervention Trial, MAAS = Multicentre Anti-Antheroma Study, REGRESS = Regression of Growth Evaluation Statin Study, ACAPS = Asymptomatic Carotid Artery Progression Study, MARS = Monitored Atherosclerosis Regression Study, PC = placebo, PRA = pravastatin, LOV = lovastatin, SIM = simvastatin, QCA = quantitative coronary angiography, US = ultrasonography, Rx = treated group.

[a]From "Pravastatin Limitation of Atherosclerosis in the Coronary Arteries (PLAC I)," by B. Pitt et al., 1994, *Journal of American College of Cardiology*, 484A, p. 131A. Copyright 1994 by Elsevier Science Inc. Reprinted with permission. [b]From "Pravastatin, Lipids, and Atherosclerosis in the Carotid Arteries (PLAC II)," by J. R. Crouse III et al., 1995, *American Journal of Cardiology*, 75, 455–459. Copyright 1995 by Excerpta Medica. Adapted with permission. [c]From "Effects of Monotherapy With an HMG-CoA Reductase Inhibitor on the Progression of Coronary Atherosclerosis as Assessed by Serial Quantitative Arteriography," by D. Waters et al., 1994, *Circulation*, 89, 959–968. Copyright 1994 by the American Heart Association. Reprinted with permission. [d]From "Effect of Simvastatin on Coronary Atheroma: The Multicentre Anti-Antheroma Study (MAAS)," by MAAS investigators, 1994, *Lancet*, 344, 633–638. Copyright 1994 by The Lancet Ltd. Reprinted with permission. [e]From "Effect of Lipid Lowering by Pravastatin on Progression and Regression of Coronary Artery Disease in Symptomatic Men With Normal to Moderately Elevated Serum Cholesterol Levels," by J. W. Jukema et al., 1995, *Circulation*, 91, 2528–2540. Copyright 1994 by the American Heart Association. Reprinted with permission. [f]From "Effect of Lovastatin on Early Carotid Atherosclerosis and Cardiovascular Events," by C. D. Furberg et al., 1994, *Circulation*, 90, 1679–1687. Copyright 1994 by the American Heart Association. Reprinted with permission. [g]From "Coronary Angiographic Changes with Lovastatin Therapy," by D. H. Blankenhorn et al., 1993, *Annals of Internal Medicine*, 119, 969–976. Copyright 1993 by American College of Physicians. Reprinted with permission. [h]Greater benefit in lesions ≥ 50% occluded. [i]Greater benefit in lesions < 50 occluded.

Primary Prevention Trials

As noted, *primary prevention* refers to cholesterol lowering in patients who do not yet have clinically manifest disease. This is not the same as saying that such patients do not have coronary atherosclerosis. Autopsy studies of casualties in both the Korean and Vietnam wars demonstrated that even young men in their late teens and early 20s have evidence of coronary atherosclerosis (Strong, 1986). Studies in young adults indicate that the extent of aortic atherosclerotic lesions can be correlated to lipoprotein levels (Pathobiological Determinants of Atherosclerosis in Youth [PDAY] Research Group, 1990). Primary prevention trials, then, are performed in patients earlier in the course of their atherosclerosis, before they have clinical symptoms, and when they are less likely to die of their disease.

Patients who volunteer for such clinical trials are more health conscious and less likely to succumb to morbid and mortal events than those with the same entry characteristics who do not volunteer (Hulley, Gove, Browner, & Cummings, 1988). Clinical trials, moreover, deliberately exclude those with other diseases in order not to confuse the results. For example, patients with diabetes mellitus have been excluded from most clinical trials. (As a result, there are no definitive trials of lipid lowering and CVD in diabetic patients.) Thus, both because of the early nature of the disease and because of the health of the patients, mortality rates in primary prevention trials are generally low. Primary prevention trials are conducted over a relatively short period of time, from 5 to 9 years. Given the initial good health of the patients, they are unlikely to accumulate significant numbers of mortal events during the period of observation. Meta-analyses cannot address this shortcoming because they can effectively increase the number of patients studied but not the duration of the studies.

Both individual analyses and meta-analyses of primary prevention studies have been reported (Committee of Principal Investigators, 1978; Dayton, Pearce, Hashimoto, Dixon, & Tomiyasu, 1969; Dorr, Gundersen, Schneider, Spencer, & Martin, 1978; Frantz et al., 1989; Frick et al., 1987; Lipid Research Clinics Program, 1984; Muldoon, Manuck, & Matthews, 1990). Taken both individually and collectively, these studies have demonstrated favorable effects in preventing myocardial infarction but have not demonstrated favorable effects on total mortality (Muldoon et al., 1990). Except in the World Health Organization study (Committee of Principal Investigators, 1978; 1984), which demonstrated an excess mortality from gastrointestinal cancer, they did not show statistically significant increases in specific causes of mortality.

In meta-analyses of these studies, benefits on all-cause mortality cannot be demonstrated (see Figure 1). The slight decline demonstrable in coronary mortality is offset by increased mortality from noncardiovascular causes, including deaths from accidents, suicides, and homicides (Muldoon et al., 1990). These findings have led to speculation that either cholesterol lowering itself or the drugs used in these studies may, in and of themselves, be promoters of traumatic mortal events, either because of intrinsic

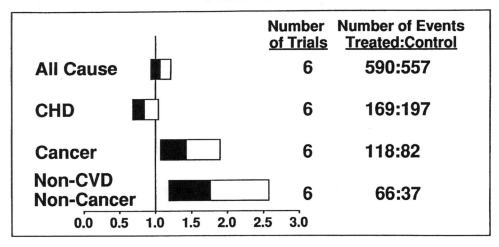

Figure 1. Mortality in primary prevention trials. Relative risk of mortality from various causes is displayed by the horizontal bars. Increased mortality from noncardiovascular (non-CVD; e.g., accidents, violence, trauma, and suicide) causes is seen in primary prevention studies. Overall mortality was not significantly reduced. CHD = coronary heart disease. Data from "Lowering Cholesterol Concentrations and Mortality: A Quantitative Review of Primary Prevention Trials," by M. F. Muldoon et al., 1990, *British Medical Journal, 301,* 309–314. Copyright 1990 by *British Medical Journal.* Reprinted with permission.

toxicity or through their cholesterol-lowering properties (Oliver, 1992). The relation of these mortal events to cholesterol lowering, however, is dubious. In a case-by-case audit of cases of violent death in the Lipid Research Clinic Coronary Primary Prevention Trial and the Helsinki study, no relation between the degree of cholesterol lowering and violent death could be demonstrated, that is, there was no dose–response relation (see Table 2; Wysowski & Gross, 1990). Indeed, most suicide victims were not taking the prescribed medication at the time of their demise. One patient had not taken medication for 4 months; another had not taken medication for 4 years.

In another analysis, Jacobs et al. (1992) and Yusuf, Wittes, and Friedman (1988) attempted to relate noncardiovascular, non-cancer-related mortality in intervention studies to the strength of the intervention (strength equaled the degree of cholesterol lowering multiplied by the duration). No dose–response relation could be demonstrated. A recent meta-analysis by Gould, Rossouw, Santanello, Heyse, and Furberg (1995) demonstrated no relationship between the extent of cholesterol lowering and noncardiovascular mortality but did demonstrate that the use of either fibric acid derivatives (particularly clofibrate) or high-dose estrogens (in men only) were associated with increased noncardiovascular mortality, correlated to cholesterol lowering.

Table 2. Case Audits of Violent Deaths in LRC-CPPT and Helsinki Studies

Type of death	Taking drugs	Not taking drugs
Suicides	3	5[a]
Accidents	8[b]	2
Homicides	1	1
Total	12	8

Note: LRC-CPPT = Lipid Research Clinics Coronary Primary Prevention Trial. From "Deaths Due to Accidents and Violence in Two Recent Trials of Cholesterol-Lowering Drugs," by D. K. Wysowski and T. P. Gross, 1990, *Archives of Internal Medicine, 150*, pp. 2169–2172.
[a]One had taken no drugs for 4 months. One had taken no drugs for 4 years.   [b]Four with less than 50% adherence. Five with elevated blood alcohol.

An argument could be made that there is no logical reason to add together deaths from accidents, suicides, and homicides. They have little in common aside from the fact that the mode of death is usually violent. The justification for adding them together comes from the fact that they vary together in longitudinal population studies (Holinger & Klemen, 1982). These studies, however, also indicate that they appear to increase when economic conditions become more adverse. This is not a surprising observation, nor is it one that requires a metabolic- or cholesterol-related explanation.

Epidemiologic principles require that before a relationship can be considered to be of a cause-and-effect nature, certain criteria must be met. These criteria include that (a) the disease that is alleged to be caused by a risk factor be preceded by the appearance of the risk factor, (b) the risk factor be strongly related statistically to the disease, (c) the risk factor be consistently related to the disease in multiple studies, (d) there be a dose–response relation between the risk factor and the disease, (e) the risk factor be related specifically to the disease and not to a number of disparate conditions, and (f) there be biologic plausibility to the relation (Friedman, 1980).

How does the relationship of violent death to cholesterol lowering in clinical trials fit these criteria? In clinical trials, case audits indicate that cholesterol lowering may not precede the mortal event (see previous explanation) or even its presumed antecedent (some change in mood or mental status). The relation between assignment to the treated group and traumatic mortality in clinical trials, moreover, is statistically weak and inconsistent, that is, not seen in most cholesterol-lowering trials. As previously noted, there is no dose–response relation. Many of those dying violently were not, in fact, receiving cholesterol-lowering treatment.

What about biologic plausibility? There is evidence that primates given low-cholesterol diets exhibit more aggressive behavior (Kaplan, Manuck, & Shively, 1991). In contrast, a recent report in 305 men and women indicated that a cholesterol-lowering diet resulted in both lower cholesterol levels and reductions in depression and aggressive hostility (Weidner, Connor, Hollis, & Connor, 1992). The same result has been shown in use of cholesterol-lowering drugs, including both lovastatin and pravastatin (Strandberg et al., 1994).

It has been hypothesized that low cholesterol levels are associated, through a complex mechanism involving changes in membrane cholesterol, with low levels of brain serotonin and, therefore, with changes in mood (Engelberg, 1992). There is no direct evidence, however, linking such biochemical changes to behavioral abnormalities in humans. A recent review of basic science literature, moreover, concluded that low circulating cholesterol levels favorably affect most aspects of cellular function (Sullivan, 1994). Until the relation between cholesterol reduction, spontaneously low cholesterol (at levels not generally achieved in cholesterol-lowering trials), and violent deaths is clarified, the biologic significance of these scattered clinical trial findings is, at best, uncertain.

Uses of Meta-Analysis

Much of the concern about the effect of cholesterol lowering arises from meta-analyses of disparate clinical trials. Obviously, meta-analyses give different results depending on the studies selected for inclusion. On the other hand, attempts to do meta-analyses with minimal exclusion criteria result in mixing studies of such heterogeneity in quality of research, design, and interventions that the results may be meaningless. One such analysis, in an attempt to be inclusive (and, therefore, in the author's mind, to avoid bias), mixed studies of diet, drug, and even hormonal intervention in men and women with and without CVD with only minimal attention to study design (Ravnskov, 1992). Because it has now been demonstrated that fibrates and estrogen (in men) may have adverse effects on noncardiovascular mortality independent of their cholesterol-lowering effect, the danger of combining studies of all drugs in one meta-analysis is clear (Gould et al., 1995). Finally, it is important to remember that the large primary prevention trials of the 1970s and 1980s were done because of concerns about the quality of earlier studies. To include those early studies of poor quality in such analyses defeats the purpose of doing large, better-quality experiments. Without careful attention to the design and quality of studies included, meta-analyses can obscure rather than clarify clinical questions.

Relationships of Spontaneously Occurring Low Cholesterol Levels

In some observational studies (not clinical trials), persons who are prone to suicide, violence, or homicidal behavior (as perpetrator, not as victim) have been observed to have lower than average cholesterol levels (Glueck et al., 1994; Iribarren, Reed, Wergowske, Burchfiel, & Dwyer, 1995; Virkkunen, 1979, 1983; Virkkunen, DeJong, Bartko, & Linnoila, 1989). Some population studies indicate that, particularly in men, the curve relating

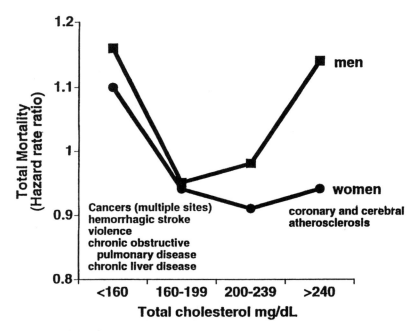

Figure 2. Total cholesterol and total mortality. Relative risk of total mortality is plotted against total cholesterol. In these pooled populations, total mortality is increased with increasing cholesterol in men only. Coronary mortality, as well as all-cause mortality, in women, however, has been shown in other studies to be directly related to total and low density lipoprotein cholesterol and inversely to high density lipoprotein cholesterol. Data are from "Report of the Conference on Low Blood Cholesterol: Mortality Associations," by D. Jacobs et al., 1992, *Circulation, 86,* 1046–1060. Copyright 1992 by the American Heart Association. Reprinted with permission.

cholesterol to mortality is U shaped, with higher mortality rates at both ends of the cholesterol distribution (see Figure 2; Jacobs et al., 1992). The right side of the curve—the relation of rising cholesterols to increasing mortality—is overwhelmingly the result of two causes of death: atherosclerotic coronary heart disease and stroke resulting from vascular occlusion. There is a clear-cut, unequivocal cause-and-effect relation between high cholesterol levels, atherogenesis, and clinical coronary and occlusive cerebrovascular disease.

The left side of the curve is different. A number of apparently disparate diseases are associated with increasingly low cholesterol levels. These range from violent deaths to a variety of cancer deaths (including hematologic cancers), as well as deaths from hemorrhagic stroke, chronic obstructive pulmonary disease, and benign cirrhotic liver disease.

In population studies, low cholesterol precedes the event by as much as 5 to 10 years. It has been suggested that this lends credence to the hypothesis that it may be a cause, rather than a result, of the associated disease (Jacobs et al., 1992). On the other hand, infection with hepatitis B virus, long before clinical hepatitis or liver failure is apparent, is asso-

Table 3. Relative Risk of Mortality with Low Cholesterol (<4.0 mmol/liter or <160 mg/dl)

Gender	Age	RR	CI
Men	35–59	1.2	(0.8–2.0)
Men	70–74	1.9	(1.3–2.7)
Women	35–59	1.0	(0.6–1.8)
Women	70–74	2.1	(1.2–3.7)

Note: RR = relative risk, CI = confidence interval. From "The Low Cholesterol–Mortality Association in a National Cohort," by T. Harris et al., 1992, *Journal of Clinical Epidemiology, 45,* pp. 595–601. Copyright 1992 by Elsevier Science Inc. Reprinted with permission.

ciated with low cholesterol (Chen et al., 1993), indicating that long-term effect–cause relations are quite possible.

It is difficult to imagine, in fact, that low cholesterol causes all of these diseases. On the contrary, there is considerable evidence that these diseases themselves often result in a low cholesterol level (an effect–cause relation). This is particularly true in hematologic cancers (Budd & Ginsberg, 1986), cirrhosis of the liver, and chronic hepatitis (Chen, Keech, et al., 1993; Chen, Peto, et al., 1991). A recent review of 10 of the largest cohort studies, 2 international studies, and 28 clinical trials indicated that only hemorrhagic stroke could not be attributed to an effect–cause relationship (Law, Thompson, & Wald, 1994).

The possibility that low cholesterol–mortality relationships are of the effect–cause variety is further buttressed by observations that in a study of a statistically representative sample of the U.S. population, low cholesterol was most strongly associated with noncardiovascular mortality in people age over 70 years (Harris et al., 1992; see Table 3). Other studies have indicated that the relation is stronger among people of low socioeconomic status and among those with other evidence of declining health (i.e., weight loss, lack of exercise, alcohol or tobacco use; Harris et al., 1992; Smith, Shipley, Marmot, & Rose, 1992). Thus, a large portion of this relation occurs in older persons in declining health whose disease results in, rather than is caused by, low cholesterol.

It is also possible (although by no means proven) that many of these associations are a result of confounding variables. For example, it is a plausible hypothesis that in the Japanese, whose cholesterols are low and whose rates of hemorrhagic stroke are high (Goto & Moriguchi, 1990), the real culprit is a diet low in saturated fat but high in salt and fish, resulting in low cholesterol, hypertension, decreased platelet adhesiveness, and increased cerebral hemorrhage. Under such circumstances, both low cholesterol and hemorrhagic stroke would result from common confounding dietary antecedents.

Another observation that has received little attention is that the lowest cholesterol quartile in population studies is quite different from one population to another. In studies of Scandinavian populations, for example, the lowest quartile is actually about at the median for the U.S. population (Lindberg, Rastam, Gullberg, & Eklund, 1992). Therefore, relations between lower cholesterol levels and increasing noncardiovascular mortality must be seen as relations between relative, not absolute, cholesterol levels. This diminishes the argument that low cholesterol is related to disease and increases the likelihood that the observations being made are the result of effect–cause, not cause–effect.

Finally, it is important not to equate observations made in prevention trials, where high initial cholesterol levels have, in general, been lowered only 5% to 15%, to spontaneously occurring, much lower cholesterol levels in population studies. Cholesterols of 160 mg/dl (4.1 mmol/l) seen in the lowest quartile of populations have not been achieved in large clinical trials.

Current U.S. Guidelines for Detecting and Treating High Cholesterol

As a result of the biologic, population, and clinical trial data linking elevated blood cholesterol to atherogenesis, atherosclerosis, and clinical coronary disease, the U.S. National Cholesterol Education Program (NCEP) has developed clinical guidelines for the detection and treatment of high blood cholesterol. These guidelines recommend that all individuals over age 20, male and female, have measurements of total cholesterol and HDL cholesterol, to screen for individuals who may be at increased risk of coronary atherosclerosis as a result of dyslipoproteinemia. (The NCEP also recommends total cholesterol screening in children with family histories of CVD or hypertriglyceridemia or with other coronary-risk factors, such as diabetes, obesity, or hypertension.)

Those adults with cholesterols >240 mg/dl (6.2 mmol/l) or >200 mg/dl (5.2 mmol/l), if two or more risk factors are present, are considered candidates for a full lipoprotein profile, consisting of total cholesterol, total triglyceride, HDL cholesterol, and LDL cholesterol (the last estimated by the formula LDL cholesterol equals total cholesterol minus the sum of HDL cholesterol plus triglyceride, divided by 5). The risk factors that the NCEP considers important are summarized in the Appendix (Expert Panel, 1993).

The guidelines recommend that all patients with elevated cholesterol ought to be treated with hygienic interventions. These include changes in dietary composition to lower saturated fat and cholesterol content, low calorie diets to lower body weight, and exercise to aid in weight loss or the prevention of weight gain, as well as to gain the benefits of regular exercise in retarding the onset of atherosclerosis.

The value of cholesterol-lowering drugs, however, although clearly apparent in patients with established coronary disease, and probably indicated in all patients with high LDL cholesterols (>160 mg/dl [4.1 mmol/l]), when such individuals also have other risk factors such as diabetes or hypertension, is less apparent in those without clinical CVD and with no other risk factors. Guidelines for drug use for such individuals are very conservative.

Implications of These Controversies to
Public Health Interventions

It has been argued that if low cholesterol is causally associated with non-cardiovascular mortality, population strategies to lower the mean cholesterol in the population by diet change may increase the risk of non-cardiovascular mortality. Indeed, even the most vocal champions of cholesterol lowering do not claim that it will provide immortality. On the other hand, the current decline in cardiovascular mortality in the United States, about one third of which is quite likely attributable to lower cholesterol levels (Goldman & Cook, 1984), has been associated with a decline, not an increase, in noncardiovascular mortality (Trends in Coronary Heart Disease Mortality, 1988).

It is certain that persons who do not die of coronary atherosclerosis will die of some other cause. It is also possible that some of the dietary changes that result in low cholesterol may result in other unfavorable metabolic changes that predispose persons to other diseases.

There is great danger, however, in applying poorly understood observations to public health policy. For example, in the Whitehall study, a 10-year controlled trial of antismoking advice, a 53% net decline in smoking was associated with a statistically insignificant decline in total CVD and lung cancer deaths and a statistically significant increase in non–lung cancer deaths (Rose, Hamilton, Colwell, & Shipley, 1982). These findings did not (and should not) result in outcries to change antismoking public health policies. The investigators pointed out that the excess cancer deaths showed no site specificity and were not correlated with changes in smoking habits (i.e., no dose–response relation), exactly analogous to the situation with cholesterol lowering and noncardiovascular disease mortality.

Data from the Multiple Risk Factor Intervention Trial indicate that the cholesterol level associated with the lowest risk of death is 122 mg/dl (3.1 mmol/l); Neaton et al., 1992). Below this level, the incidence of non-cardiovascular mortalities begins to increase. Even if a cause–effect relationship between low cholesterol levels and mortality were to be established (and it has not), this is a level not likely to be achieved in most of the American population in the foreseeable future and, in fact, not achieved in most human populations in the world.

As we go about sorting out these relations, note that the Japanese smoke more cigarettes per capita than are consumed in the United States, have higher average blood pressures, and just as much diabetes. They still, however, have lower cholesterol levels, lower mortality rates, and a longer life expectancy (Goto & Moriguchi, 1990). Theoretical concerns about the potential dangers of exposing a population to lower animal fat diets should be tempered by remembering the adverse effects of our current diet, providing high morbidity and mortality rates from obesity-related disorders, coronary atherosclerosis (still the leading cause of death in Western countries), and perhaps increasing the risk of common cancers (Koop, 1988).

We should better understand the relation, if any, between cholesterol lowering, spontaneously low cholesterol levels, and noncardiovascular disease and what cholesterol level is ideal. More research is most certainly warranted, but for the time being, changes in current public health recommendations are not.

References

Blankenhorn, D. H., Azen, S. P., Kramsch, D. M., Mack, W. J., Cashin-Hemphill, L., Hodis, H. N., DeBoer, L. W. V., Mahrer, P. R., Masteller, M. J., Vailas, L. I., Alaupovic, P., Hirsch, L. J., & the MARS Research Group. (1993). Coronary angiographic changes with lovastatin therapy. *Annals of Internal Medicine, 119*, 969–976.

Blankenhorn, D. H., Nessim, S. A., Johnson, R. L., Sanmarco, M. E., Azen, S. P., & Cashin-Hemphill, L. (1987). Beneficial effects of combined colestipol–niacin therapy on coronary atherosclerosis and coronary venous bypass grafts. *Journal of the American Medical Association, 257*, 3233–3240.

Brown, G., Zhao, X.-Q., Sacco, D. E., & Albers, J. J. (1993). Arteriographic view of treatment to achieve regression of coronary atherosclerosis and to prevent plaque disruption and clinical cardiovascular events. *British Heart Journal, 69*(Suppl.), S48–S53.

Brown, G., Albers, J. J., Fisher, L. D., Schaffer, S. M., Lin, J. T., Kaplan, C., Zhao, X. Q., Bisson, B. D., Fitzpatrick, V. F., & Dodge, H. T. (1990). Regression of coronary artery disease as a result of intensive lipid-lowering therapy in men with high levels of apolipoprotein B. *New England Journal of Medicine, 323*, 1289–1298.

Buchwald, H., Varco, R. L., Matts, J. P., Long, J. M., Fitch, L. L., Campbell, G. S., Pearce, M. B., Yellin, A. E., Edmiston, W. A., Smink, R. D., Jr., Sawin, H. S., Jr., Campos, C. T., Hansen, B. J., Tuna, N., Karnegis, J. N., Sanmarco, M. E., Amplatz, K., Castaneda-Zuniga, W. R., Hunter, D. W., Bissett, J. K., Weber, F. J., Stevenson, J. W., Leon, A. S., Chalmers, T. C., & the POSCH Group. (1990). Effect of partial ileal bypass surgery on mortality and morbidity from coronary heart disease in patients with hypercholesterolemia. *New England Journal of Medicine, 323*, 946–955.

Budd, D., & Ginsberg, H. (1986). Hypocholesterolemia and acute myelogenous leukemia: Association between disease activity and plasma low-density lipoprotein cholesterol concentrations. *Cancer, 58*, 1361–1365.

Canner, P. L., Berge, K. G., Wenger, N. K., Stamler, J., Friedman, L., Prineas, R. J., & Friedewald, W. (1986). Fifteen year mortality in coronary drug project patients: Long-term benefit with niacin. *Journal of the American College of Cardiology, 8*, 1245–1255.

Carlson, L. A., & Rosenhamer, G. (1988). Reduction of mortality in the Stockholm Ischaemic Heart Disease Secondary Prevention Study by combined treatment with clofibrate and nicotinic acid. *Acta Medica Scandinavica, 223*, 405–418.

Chen, Z., Keech, A., Collins, R., Slavin, B., Chen, J., Campbell, T. C., & Peto, R. (1993). Prolonged infection with hepatitis B virus and association between low blood cholesterol concentration and liver cancer. *British Medical Journal, 306*, 890–894.

Chen, Z., Peto, R., Collins, R., MacMahon, S., Lu, J., & Li, W. (1991). Serum cholesterol and coronary heart disease in population with low cholesterol concentrations. *British Medical Journal, 303*, 276–282.

Committee of Principal Investigators. (1978). A co-operative trial in the primary prevention of ischaemic heart disease using clofibrate. *British Heart Journal, 40*, 1069–1118.

Committee of Principal Investigators. (1984). WHO cooperative trial on primary prevention of ischaemic heart disease with clofibrate to lower serum cholesterol: Final mortality follow-up. *The Lancet, 2*, 600–604.

Crouse, J. R., III, Byington, R. P., Bond, M. G., Espeland, M. A., Craven, T. E., Sprinkle, J. W., McGovern, M. E., & Furberg, C. D. (1995). Pravastatin, lipids, and atherosclerosis in the carotid arteries (PLAC-II). *American Journal of Cardiology, 75*, 455–459.

Davies, M. J., Krikler, D. M., & Katz, D. (1991). Atherosclerosis: Inhibition or regression as therapeutic possibilities. *British Heart Journal, 65*, 302–310.

Dayton, S., Pearce, M. L., Hashimoto, S., Dixon, W. J., & Tomiyasu, U. (1969). A controlled clinical trial of a diet high in unsaturated fat in preventing complications of atherosclerosis. *Circulation, 40*(Suppl. II), II-1–II-63.

Dorr, A. E., Gundersen, K., Schneider, J. C., Spencer, T. W., & Martin, W. B. (1978). Colestipol hydrochloride in hypercholesterolaemic patients: Effect on serum cholesterol and mortality. *Journal of Chronic Diseases, 31*, 5–14.

Engelberg, H. (1992). Low serum cholesterol and suicide. *The Lancet, 339*, 727–729.

Expert Panel on Detection, Evaluation, and Treatment of High Blood Cholesterol in Adults. (1993). Summary of the second report of the National Cholesterol Education Program (NCEP) expert panel on detection, evaluation, and treatment of high blood cholesterol in adults (Adult Treatment Panel II). *Journal of the American Medical Association, 269*, 3015–3023.

Frantz, I. D., Jr., Dawson, E. A., Ashman, P. L., Gatewood, L. C., Bartsch, G. E., Kuba, K., & Brewer, E. R. (1989). Test of effect of lipid lowering by diet on cardiovascular risk. *Arteriosclerosis, 9*, 129–135.

Frick, M. H., Elo, O., Haapa, K., Heinonen, O. P., Heinsalmi, P., Helo, P., Huttunen, J. K., Kaitaniemi, P., Koskinen, P., Manninen, V., Maenpaa, H., Malkonen, M., Manttari, M., Norolo, S., Pasternack, A., Pikkarainen, J., Romo, M., Sjoblom, T., & Nikkila, E. A. (1987). Helsinki Heart Study: Primary-prevention trial with gemfibrozil in middle-aged men with dyslipidemia: Safety of treatment, changes in risk factors, and incidence of coronary heart disease. *New England Journal of Medicine, 317*, 1237–1245.

Friedman, G. D. (1980). Making sense out of statistical associations. In Friedman, G. D. (Ed.), *Primer of epidemiology* (pp. 173–195). New York: McGraw-Hill.

Furberg, C. D., Adams, H. P., Jr., Applegate, W. B., Byington, R. P., Espeland, M. A., Hartwell, T., Hunninghake, D. B., Lefkowitz, D. S., Probstfield, J., Riley, W. A., & Young, B., for the Asymptomatic Carotid Artery Progression Study (ACAPS) Research Group. (1994). Effect of lovastatin on early carotid atherosclerosis and cardiovascular events. *Circulation, 90*, 1679–1687.

Glueck, C. J., Tieger, M., Kunkel, R., Hamer, T., Tracy, T., & Speirs, J. (1994) Hypocholesterolemia and affective disorders. *American Journal of the Medical Sciences, 308*, 218–225.

Goldman, L., & Cook, E. F. (1984). The decline in ischemic heart disease mortality rates: An analysis of the comparative effects of medical interventions and changes in lifestyle. *Annals of Internal Medicine, 101*, 825–836.

Goto, Y., & Moriguchi, E. H. (1990). Diet and ischemic heart disease in Japan. *Atherosclerosis Review, 21*, 21–33.

Gould, A. L., Rossouw, J. E., Santanello, N. C., Heyse, J. F., & Furberg, C. D. (1995). Cholesterol reduction yields clinical benefit: A new look at old data. *Circulation, 91*, 2274–2282.

Group of Physicians of the Newcastle Upon Tyne Region. (1971). Trial of clofibrate in the treatment of ischaemic heart disease. *British Medical Journal, 4*, 767–775.

Harris, T., Feldman, J. J., Kleinman, J. C., Ettinger, W. H., Jr., Makuc, D. M., & Schatzkin, A. G. (1992). The low cholesterol–mortality association in a national cohort. *Journal of Clinical Epidemiology, 45*, 595–601.

Holinger, P. C., & Klemen, E. H. (1982). Violent deaths in the United States—1900–1975: Relationships between suicide, homicide and accidental death. *Social Science and Medicine, 16*, 1929–1938.

Holme, I. (1993). Relation of coronary heart disease incidence and total mortality to plasma cholesterol reduction in randomised trials: Use of meta-analysis. *British Heart Journal, 69*(Suppl.), S42–S47.

Hulley, S. B., Gove, S., Browner, W. S., & Cummings, S. R. (1988). Choosing the study subjects: Specification and sampling. In S. B. Hulley & S. R. Cummings (Eds.), *Designing clinical research: An epidemiological approach* (pp. 18–30). Baltimore: Williams & Wilkins.

Iribarren, C., Reed, D. M., Wergowske, G., Burchfiel, C. M., & Dwyer, J. H. (1995). Serum cholesterol level and mortality due to suicide and trauma in the Honolulu Heart Program. *Archives of Internal Medicine, 155*, 695–700.

Jacobs, D., Blackburn, H., Higgins, M., Reed, D., Iso, H., McMillan, G., Neaton, J., Nelson, J., Potter, J., Rifkind, B., Rossouw, J., Shekelle, R., & Yusuf, S. (1992). Report of the Conference on Low Blood Cholesterol: Mortality associations. *Circulation, 86,* 1046–1060.

Jukema, J. W., Bruschke, A. V. G., van Boven, A. J., Reiber, J. H. C., Bal, E. T., Zwinderman, A. H., Jansen, H., Boerma, G. J. M., van Rappard, F. M., & Lie, K. I., on behalf of the REGRESS Study Group. (1995). Effects of lipid lowering by pravastatin on progression and regression of coronary artery disease in symptomatic men with normal to moderately elevated serum cholesterol levels: The Regression Growth Evaluation Statin Study (REGRESS). *Circulation, 91,* 2528–2540.

Kane, J. P., Malloy, M. J., Ports, T. A., Phillips, N. R., Diehl, J. C., & Havel, R. J. (1990). Regression of coronary atherosclerosis during treatment of familial hypercholesterolemia with combined drug regimens. *Journal of the American Medical Association, 264,* 3007–3012.

Kaplan, J. R., Manuck, S. B., & Shively, C. (1991). The effects of fat and cholesterol on social behavior in monkeys. *Psychosomatic Medicine, 53,* 634–642.

Koop, C. E. (1988). The surgeon general's report on nutrition and health. (DHHS Publication No. 88-50210). Washington, DC: U.S. Government Printing Office.

LaRosa, J. C., & Cleeman, J. I. (1992). Cholesterol lowering as a treatment for established coronary heart disease. *Circulation, 85,* 1229–1235.

LaRosa, J. C., Hunninghake, D., Bush, D., Criqui, M. H., Getz, G. S., Gotto, A. M., Jr., Grundy, S. M., Rakita, L., Robertson, R. M., Weisfeldt, M. L., & Cleeman, J. L. (1990). The cholesterol facts: A summary of the evidence relating dietary fats, serum cholesterol, and coronary heart disease. A joint statement by the American Heart Association and the National Heart, Lung, and Blood Institute. *Circulation, 81,* 1721–1733.

Law, M. R., Thompson, S. G., & Wald, N. J. (1994). Assessing possible hazards of reducing serum cholesterol. *British Medical Journal, 308,* 373–379.

Lindberg, G., Rastam, L., Gullberg, B., & Eklund, G. A. (1992). Low serum cholesterol concentration and short term mortality from injuries in men and women. *British Medical Journal, 305,* 277–279.

Lipid Research Clinics Program. (1984). The Lipid Research Clinics Coronary Primary Prevention Trial results. *Journal of the American Medical Association, 251,* 351–374.

MAAS investigators. (1994). Effect of simvastatin on coronary atheroma: The Multicentre Anti-Atheroma Study (MAAS). *The Lancet, 344,* 633–638.

Miettinen, M., Karvonen, M. J., Turpeinen, O., Elosuo, R., & Paavilainen, E. (1972). Effect of cholesterol-lowering diet on mortality from coronary heart disease and other causes. *The Lancet, 2,* 835–838.

Muldoon, M. F., Manuck, S. B., & Matthews, K. A. (1990). Lowering cholesterol concentrations and mortality: A quantitative review of primary prevention trials. *British Medical Journal, 301,* 309–314.

Neaton, J. D., Blackburn, H., Jacobs, D., Kuller, L., Lee, D.-J., Sherwin, J., Shih, J., Stamler, J., & Wentworth, D. (1992). Serum cholesterol level and mortality findings for men screened in the Multiple Risk Factor Intervention Trial. *Archives of Internal Medicine, 152,* 1490–1500.

O'Brien, K. D., & Chait, A. (1994). The biology of the artery wall in atherogenesis. *Medical Clinics of North America, 78,* 41–67.

Oliver, M. F. (1992). Cholesterol and coronary disease: Outstanding questions. *Cardiovascular Drugs and Therapy, 6,* 131–136.

Ornish, D., Brown, S. E., Scherwitz, L. W., Billings, J. H., Armstrong, W. T., Ports, T. A., McLanahan, S. M., Kirkeeide, R. L., Brand, R. J., & Gould, K. L. (1990). Can lifestyle changes reverse coronary heart disease? The Lifestyle Heart Trial. *The Lancet, 336,* 129–133.

Pathobiological Determinants of Atherosclerosis in Youth (PDAY) Research Group. (1990). Relationship of atherosclerosis in young men to serum lipoprotein cholesterol concentrations and smoking: A preliminary report. *Journal of the American Medical Association, 264,* 3018–3024.

Pitt, B., Mancini, J., Ellis, S. G., Rosman, H. S., & McGovern, M. E., for the PLAC I investigators. (1994). Pravastatin limitation of atherosclerosis in the coronary arteries (PLAC I) [Abstract No. 739-2]. *Journal of the American College of Cardiology, 484A*, 131A.

Pravastatin Multinational Study Group for Cardiac Risk Patients. (1993). Effects of pravastatin in patients with serum total cholesterol levels from 5.2 to 7.8 mmol/liter (200 to 300 mg/dl) plus two additional atherosclerotic risk factors. *American Journal of Cardiology, 72*, 1031–1037.

Pyorala, K., De Backer, G., Graham, I., Poole-Wilson, P., & Wood, D., on behalf of the Task Force. (1994). Prevention of coronary heart disease in clinical practice: Recommendations of the Task Force of the European Society of Cardiology, European Atherosclerosis Society and European Society of Hypertension. *Atherosclerosis, 110*, 121–161.

Ravnskov, U. (1992). Cholesterol lowering trials in coronary heart disease: Frequency of citation and outcome. *British Medical Journal, 305*, 15–19.

Research Committee of the Scottish Society of Physicians. (1971). Ischaemic heart disease: A secondary prevention trial using clofibrate. *British Medical Journal, 4*, 775–784.

Rose, G., Hamilton, P. J. S., Colwell, L., & Shipley, M. J. (1982). A randomised controlled trial of anti-smoking advice: 10-year results. *Journal of Epidemiology and Community Health, 36*, 102–108.

Rossouw, J. E., Lewis, B., & Rifkind, B. M. (1990). The value of lowering cholesterol after myocardial infarction. *New England Journal of Medicine, 323*, 1112–1119.

Scandinavian Simvastatin Survival Study Group. (1994). Randomised trial of cholesterol lowering in 4444 patients with coronary heart disease: The Scandinavian Simvastatin Survival Study (4S). *The Lancet, 344*, 1383–1389.

Schucker, B., Wittes, J. T., Santanello, N. C., Weber, S. J., McGoldrick, D., Donato, K., Levy, A., & Rifkind, B. M. (1991). Change in cholesterol awareness and action. *Archives of Internal Medicine, 151*, 666–673.

Smith, G. D., Shipley, M. J., Marmot, M. G., & Rose, G. (1992). Plasma cholesterol concentration and mortality: The Whitehall Study. *Journal of the American Medical Association, 267*, 70–76.

Strandberg, T. E., Raikkonen, K., Partinen, M., Pihl, S., Vanhanen, H., & Miettinen, T. A. (1994). Associations of cholesterol lowering by statins with anger and hostility in hypercholesterolemic men. *Biological Psychiatry, 35*, 575–577.

Strong, J. P. (1986). Coronary atherosclerosis in soldiers: A clue to the natural history of atherosclerosis in the young. *Journal of the American Medical Association, 256*, 2863–2866.

Sullivan, D. (1994). Cholesterol and non-cardiovascular disease: Basic science. *Australian and New Zealand Journal of Medicine, 24*, 92–97.

Trends in coronary heart disease mortality [Preface]. (1988). In M. W. Higgins & R. V. Luepker (Eds.), *The influence of medical care* (pp. vii–x). New York: Oxford University Press.

Tyroler, H. A. (1987). Review of lipid-lowering clinical trials in relation to observational epidemiologic studies. *Circulation, 76*, 515–522.

Virkkunen, M. (1979). Serum cholesterol in antisocial personality. *Neuropsychobiology, 5*, 27–30.

Virkkunen, M. (1983). Serum cholesterol levels in homicidal offenders. *Neuropsychobiology, 10*, 65–69.

Virkkunen, M., DeJong, J., Bartko, J., & Linnoila, M. (1989). Psychobiological concomitants of history of suicide attempts among violent offenders and impulsive fire setters. *Archives of General Psychiatry, 46*, 604–606.

Waters, D., Higginson, L., Gladstone, P., Kimball, B., Le May, M., Boccuzzi, S. J., & Lesperance, J., for the Canadian Coronary Atherosclerosis Intervention Trial (CCAIT) Study Group. (1994). Effects of monotherapy with an HMG-CoA reductase inhibitor on the progression of coronary atherosclerosis as assessed by serial quantitative arteriography. *Circulation, 89*, 959–968.

Weidner, G., Connor, S. L., Hollis, J. F., & Connor, W. E. (1992). Improvements in hostility and depression in relation to dietary change and cholesterol lowering: The Family Heart Study. *Annals of Internal Medicine, 117*, 820–823.

Wysowski, D. K., & Gross, T. P. (1990). Deaths due to accidents and violence in two recent trials of cholesterol-lowering drugs. *Archives of Internal Medicine, 150,* 2169–2172.

Yusuf, S., Wittes, J., & Friedman, L. (1988). Overview of results of randomized clinical trials in heart disease: II. Unstable angina, heart failure, primary prevention with aspirin, and risk factor modification. *Journal of the American Medical Association, 260,* 2259–2263.

Appendix

Risk Status Based on Presence of CVD Risk Factors Other Than LDL Cholesterol

Positive risk factors
   Age
      Men: $\geq$ 45 years
      Women: $\geq$ 55 years or premature menopause without ERT
   Family history of premature CVD (definite myocardial infarction or sudden death before 55 years of age in father or other male first-degree relative or before 65 years of age in mother or other female first-degree relative)
   Current cigarette smoking
   Hypertension ($\geq$140/90 mm Hg[a] or on antihypertensive medication)
   Low HDL cholesterol (<35 mg/dl[a])
   Diabetes mellitus
Negative risk factors[b]
   High HDL cholesterol ($\geq$60 mg/dl)

Note: CVD = cardiovascular disease, LDL = low density lipoprotein, ERT = estrogen replacement therapy, HDL = high density lipoprotein. High risk, defined as a net of two or more CVD risk factors, leads to more vigorous intervention. Age (defined differently for men and for women) is treated as a risk factor because rates of CVD are higher in the elderly than in the young and in men than in women of the same age. Obesity is not listed as a risk factor because it operates through other risk factors that are included (hypertension, hyperlipidemia, decreased HDL cholesterol, and diabetes mellitus), but it should be considered a target for intervention. Physical inactivity similarly is not listed as a risk factor, but it too should be considered a target for intervention, and physical activity is recommended as desirable for everyone. From "Summary of the Second Report of the National Cholesterol Education Program (NCEP) Expert Panel on Detection, Evaluation, and Treatment of High Blood Pressure Cholesterol in Adults," 1993, *Journal of the American Medical Association*, *269*, pp. 3015–3023.
[a]Confirmed by measurement on several occasions. [b]If the HDL cholesterol level is $\geq$60 mg/dl, subtract one risk factor (because high HDL cholesterol levels decrease CVD risk).

Concluding Issues

17

Public Health Issues and Directions for Future Research

Reuben T. Spitz and Marc Hillbrand

Cholesterol Lowering and Public Health

As preceding chapters have shown, increased mortality from suicide, accidents, and homicide has been shown to be associated with low cholesterol in randomized trials of cholesterol-lowering studies and in cohort studies. There is no scientific consensus on how to interpret this phenomenon, and two viewpoints have emerged on this issue (Jacobs, Muldoon, & Rastam, 1995).

One viewpoint, exemplified in this text by LaRosa (chapter 16), suggests that the connection between lowered cholesterol and non-illness-related mortality is artifactual. Three main arguments have been put forth to buttress this position. First, the biological plausibility of a low cholesterol—non-illness-related mortality connection is questionable. The connection between low cholesterol and non-illness-related mortality may in fact be a case of reverse causality (i.e., an unknown disease process may cause lowered cholesterol and later death) or may be mediated through factors such as age, smoking, alcohol use, or socioeconomic status. Second, no dose—response relation between degree of cholesterol lowering and non-illness-related mortality has been established in clinical trials or in the meta-analysis by Muldoon, Manuck, and Matthews (1990). Third, antilipidemic drugs per se may have adverse effects (e.g., toxicity) that contribute to non-illness-related mortality.

In summary, LaRosa (1993) argues that major changes in current public health policy to lower cholesterol are not warranted from the evidence presented. In terms of either primary or secondary prevention, he believes that cholesterol reduction is good policy for most of the population, regardless of gender or age. From his perspective, evidence linking high blood cholesterol to cardiovascular disease (CVD) and cholesterol lowering to its prevention is "broad-based and definitive" (p. 776). LaRosa asserts that studies relating behavioral disturbance to low cholesterol (<160 mg/dl) are full of uncertainty, and he suggests that increased noncardiac mortality associated with low serum total cholesterol (TC) is unlikely to occur in most human populations.

Many researchers, however, do not view the low cholesterol—non-illness-related mortality link as artifactual. That position, illustrated by Kaplan and colleagues in chapter 9, is supported by three main arguments. First, there is strong experimental evidence in nonhuman primates relating dietary reductions in cholesterol and aggressive behavior. Results of the studies conducted by Kaplan and his colleagues have led them to propose a model linking cholesterol, serotonin, and aggression that has not only biological but also evolutionary plausibility. Second, non-illness-related mortality has been linked to lowered cholesterol in clinical trials using pharmacological interventions as well as trials using dietary interventions. Increased non-illness-related mortality may thus not be solely attributed to the toxicity of antilipidemic agents. Third, the lack of a dose–response relation between degree of cholesterol lowering and nonillness-related mortality may simply be a function of insufficient statistical power, itself a consequence of the small variability in cholesterol reduction.

Further support for a more cautious approach to cholesterol reduction comes from Hulley, Walsh, and Newman (1992), who reviewed the findings of a 1990 National Heart, Lung, and Blood Institute Conference presenting an overview of 68,406 deaths. For males with serum TC below 160 mg/dl, there was a 20% higher age-adjusted rate of cancer deaths than in males with TC between 160 and 199 mg/dl. There was also a 40% higher rate of non-CVD, non-cancer deaths. The latter included increased rates of injury (35%), respiratory system deaths (15%), digestive system deaths (50%), and other causes (70%). The same general results were found for females, with the exception that cancer mortality was 5% lower in females than in males. Overall, in terms of health policy to date, the authors present three conclusions: (a) Evidence suggests that there is no statistically significant association between high TC and CVD death in women, (b) in individuals with no manifestations of CVD, results of intervention programs have revealed an increase in non-CVD deaths that is similar in magnitude to the decrease in CVD death rates, and (c) in view of the demonstrated association between low cholesterol and non-CVD deaths in men and women, "it may be time to review national policies aimed at shifting the entire population distribution of blood cholesterol to the left" (Hulley et al., 1992, p. 1029).

The public health implications of these findings have been recently noted by Newman and Hulley (1996). They point out that the past decade has seen a greater than tenfold increase in prescriptions for lipid-lowering drugs, with more than 26 million prescriptions written in 1992 in the United States. However, the hazards associated with cholesterol reduction are not fully understood. In response to cholesterol-screening guidelines created by the National Cholesterol Education Program, the American College of Physicians (ACP) has recently argued for a downsizing in widespread testing (Zoler, 1996). A theme pervading the ACP guidelines is that a lack of clearly safe and effective cholesterol treatment makes screening of low-risk individuals questionable. Clearly, the need for continued investigation of all cholesterol-related health risks is called for.

Directions for Future Research

The next generation of studies examining the link between lipids and behavior will quite likely be characterized by greater methodological sophistication. Nearly half a century ago, the first generation of such studies typically examined total serum cholesterol and stress or the Type A personality pattern, both in the field and in the lab. Recent studies have tended to be more precise. For instance, they have examined lipid subfractions (i.e., high density lipoprotein, low density lipoprotein, very low density lipoprotein, triglycerides, and even the apolipoproteins) rather than simply examining total serum cholesterol. They have also looked at specific behaviors, such as hostility, depression, or anxiety, in contrast to global concepts such as Type A personality pattern.

Measurement Error

Some of the inconsistency in the literature (as pointed out in chapter 5, by van Doornen) may be a function of measurement error. Instruments purported to measure the same construct (e.g., hostility) often demonstrate low correlations among themselves. A researcher using such an instrument is actually dealing with variance related to the construct of interest and variance uniquely related to the instrument, the latter contributing to error variance. The simple but often ignored answer to this problem is to use several measures of the construct and to examine their shared variance.

Physiology of Lipids

In addition to these general methodological improvements, future studies will need to be enlightened by a better understanding of the physiology of lipids and aimed toward a better understanding of the mechanisms that link lipids and behavior. For instance, Stoney and West (chapter 3) emphasize the fact that plasma-volume changes alter concentrations of blood constituents. They also point out the need to study insulin resistance, adipose beta receptors, and lipase activity when studying the link between behavioral stress and stress hormones. Potential confounders abound in the link between lipids and psychological variables. It is often crucial to control for some (e.g., age and socioeconomic status), but as van Doornen judiciously points out, canceling the influence of a confounder may result in a detrimental loss of information.

Inter- and Intraindividual Lipid Variability

Two early studies reported hourly variation in total cholesterol in a group of medical students (Peterson, Keith, & Wilcox, 1962; Peterson, Wilcox, Haley, & Keith, 1960). In these studies, two groups of students were selected because of stability or lability of serum TC levels, as determined by observation over a 2-year period. Each group was subjected to a regimen of cold stress, psychological tests involving the reciting of proverbs, and epinephrine infusion. In a 24-hr period, for the labile group, changes from a nonstress to a stress condition resulted in TC changes ranging from 30% to 70%. For the stable group, similar conditions elicited average changes of approximately 20%–30%. Whereas these studies demonstrated substantial changes in serum TC on an hourly basis, others noted significant change over a number of days or weeks (Friedman, Rosenman, & Carroll, 1958). There have been few published attempts to follow up or replicate the handful of studies showing fluctuations in serum lipids over a short period of time.

Low Versus Lowered Cholesterol

Individuals with inherently low cholesterol (<160 mg/dl) probably differ biologically from hypercholesterolemic individuals whose cholesterol has been lowered (usually by 5% to 15%) by drugs. Most studies involving lipids and behavior do not report analyses according to baseline cholesterol values. The polemic about the link between low or lowered cholesterol and non-illness-related mortality cannot be empirically resolved at this time. Future studies should clarify this issue. It is likely that more will be learned from cohort studies than from clinical trials. Large-scale studies are required to secure adequate statistical power in comparisons involving subsets of the sample, for instance, to examine the low cholesterol–non-illness-related mortality link in the elderly as a function of socioeconomic status. Additionally, more needs to be learned about individuals with low cholesterol. Jacobs et al. (1995) speculated that there may be two types of individuals with low cholesterol, healthy and ill, with unemployed and low socioeconomic status individuals overrepresented among the latter. As Mason and colleagues pointed out in chapter 8, little is known about the link between circulating cholesterol and cellular cholesterol. Similarly, little is known about whether the ability to synthesize cholesterol may be a protective factor against certain (noncardiovascular) illnesses.

Sex Differences

As is true of many other health issues, much less is known about the relationships between lipids and behavior in women than men. Is the relationship between low cholesterol and non-illness-related mortality comparable in men and women? The answer to this question is not clear yet. In their review, Jacobs and colleagues (1995) reported equivocal findings regarding sex differences. Furthermore, certain demographic variables may be predictive of increased CVD risk. Kushnir and Kristal-Boneh (1995), for example, reported serum lipid elevations in formerly married women as compared with married women. Finally, Kaplan and colleagues (chapter 9) reported no sex difference in a group of cynomolgus macaques fed diets either high or low in cholesterol. However, that sample was small ($n = 17$), and the monkeys were sexually immature. Clearly, more data on lipid fluctuations in women is needed.

Serum Lipids Versus Brain Lipids

As Kaplan and colleagues point out in chapter 9, there is, to date, no evidence that alterations in TC result in functionally significant changes in serotonin activity. Similarly, there is no evidence that TC may not be simply altering tryptophan crossing the blood–brain barrier, as opposed to altering cell membrane characteristics. Much further investigation is needed to understand the relationship between lipids and neurochemistry. Studies such as those of Kaplan and colleagues are an invaluable bridge to theories of human lipid–behavior associations.

The Role of Alcohol

Although the popular press has devoted much attention to the beneficial impact of moderate alcohol consumption on lipid levels (Thomas, 1994), little is known about the interrelationship among alcohol, lipids, and behavior. The role of alcohol as a mediating factor between low TC and violent death has not been adequately explored. Preliminary findings suggest an abnormal lipid metabolism in violent offenders with a history of alcohol abuse (Virkkunen, Horrobin, Jenkins, & Manku, 1987). Whereas Kaplan and colleagues have hypothesized a cholesterol–serotonin–aggression link, Linnoila and Virkunnen have described an alcohol–serotonin–aggression link, raising the question of the interrelationship among lipids, serotonin, alcohol, and aggression (Linnoila & Virkunnen, 1992).

Closing Remarks

The study of serum lipids and human behavior is a complex and rapidly expanding area of investigation. As demonstrated throughout this book, understanding of this biobehavioral connection necessarily involves a multidisciplinary approach. Due to the necessity for such a perspective, it is of particular importance that the parameters of investigation for each variable domain be clearly delineated. For example, as lipid analysis has gradually evolved from TC to a wide range of subfractions, so must behavioral measurement continue to increase in empirical sophistication. Inconsistencies in findings across studies using comparable psychological constructs indicate a need for continued examination and refinement of these variables.

The chapters in this book are offered as a progress report on select areas of investigation concerning the interrelationship of lipids, health, and behavior. In this fertile area of investigation, research directions are expanding as rapidly as is our horizon of understanding. The considerable diversity of perspectives represented here has raised more questions than positions presented. In closing, we must echo the sentiment of David Jacobs, that almost all remains to be discovered in this emerging field of biobehavioral study.

References

Friedman, M., Rosenman, R. H., & Carroll, V. (1958). Changes in serum cholesterol and blood clotting time in men subjected to variation of occupational stress. *Circulation, 17,* 852–861.

Hulley, S. B., Walsh, J. M. B., & Newman, T. B. (1992). Health policy on blood cholesterol: Time to change directions. *Circulation, 86,* 1026–1029.

Jacobs, D. R., Muldoon, M. F., & Rastam, L. (1995). Invited commentary: Low blood cholesterol, nonillness mortality, and other nonatherosclerotic disease mortality. A search for cause and confounders. *American Journal of Epidemiology, 141,* 518–522.

Kushnir, T., & Kristal-Boneh, E. (1995). Blood lipids and lipoproteins in married and formerly married women. *Psychosomatic Medicine, 57,* 116–120.

LaRosa, J. C. (1993). Cholesterol lowering, low cholesterol, and mortality. *American Journal of Cardiology, 72,* 776–786.

Linnoila, M., & Virkkunen, M. E. (1992). Aggression, suicidality, and serotonin. *Journal of Clinical Psychiatry, 53,* 46–51.

Muldoon, M. F., Manuck, S. B., & Matthews, K. A. (1990). Lowering cholesterol concentrations and mortality: A quantitative review of primary prevention trials. *British Medical Journal, 301,* 309–314.

Newman, T. B., & Hulley, S. B. (1996). Carcinogenicity of lipid-lowering drugs. *Journal of the American Medical Association, 275,* 55–60.

Peterson, J. E., Keith, R. A., & Wilcox, A. A. (1962). Hourly changes in serum cholesterol concentration. *Circulation, 25,* 798–803.

Peterson, J. E., Wilcox, A. A., Haley, M. I., & Keith, R. A. (1960). Hourly variation in total serum cholesterol. *Circulation, 22,* 247–253.

Thomas, P. (1994, March). A toast to the heart. *Harvard Health Letter, 19,* 4–5.

Virkkunen, M. E., Horrobin, D. F., Jenkins, D. K., & Manku, M. S. (1987). Plasma phospholipid essential fatty acids and prostaglandins in alcoholic, habitually violent, and impulsive offenders. *Biological Psychiatry, 22,* 1087–1096.

Zoler, M. L. (1996, April). ACP downsizes cholesterol testing. *Internal Medicine News, 29,* 1–2.

Author Index

Numbers in italics refer to listings in reference sections.

Subject Index

About the Editors

Marc Hillbrand was born and raised in France. He received undergraduate degrees from the Université de Paris and State University of New York College at Buffalo, and a PhD in clinical psychology from Kent State University. He is Assistant Clinical Professor of Psychiatry at Yale University School of Medicine. Since 1988, he has been Director of Psychological Research at the Whiting Forensic Institute in Middletown, Connecticut. His research on aggression has focused on two major areas of inquiry: the relationship between interpersonal violence and self-destructive behavior, and the interplay of biological and psychological factors in the etiology and treatment of aggressive behavior. In this context, he has investigated the role of lipids in aggression. With Nathaniel Pallone, he edited *The Psychobiology of Aggression* (1994). He has published numerous scientific articles, including "Aggression Against Self and Aggression Against Others in Violent Psychiatric Patients" in the *Journal of Consulting and Clinical Psychology* (1995) and (with R. T. Spitz) "Lipids and Aggression" in *Aggression and Violent Behavior* (in press). He also maintains a private practice in clinical psychology in Wallingford, Connecticut, specializing in the treatment of marital conflicts.

Reuben T. Spitz was educated at Harvard University and Connecticut College. He is currently completing the PhD program in clinical health psychology at Ferkauf Graduate School of Psychology and Albert Einstein College of Medicine at Yeshiva University in New York City. Since 1992, he has been a research associate at the Whiting Forensic Institute. He has also lectured in psychology at Central Connecticut State University and has recently become a clinical associate at the Center for Clinical Health Psychology in Waterford, Connecticut. Primary research interests have focused on the relationship between neurobiological factors and various behavior disorders, with particular emphasis on depression, aggression, and schizophrenia. He is the coauthor (with H. G. Foster) of "Biochemistry and Aggression: A Psychohematological Model" in *The Psychobiology of Aggression* (edited by M. Hillbrand and N. J. Pallone, 1994) and (with M. Hillbrand and H. G. Foster) of "Serum Cholesterol and Aggression in Hospitalized Male Forensic Patients" in the *Journal of Behavioral Medicine* (1995). In addition, he is currently conducting a research project investigating the association of diagnostic, personality, and behavioral characteristics with medication compliance among psychiatric inpatients.